Soft Algebra C-E

Problem-Solving Adventure

*The EzraMath™ Introduction to Algebra**

Victoria Kofman, Ph.D.

Stella Academy

Illustrated by Boris Klissourski

---

* *Soft Algebra* has five parts. Each part has a supplementary workbook. There is also a teacher's manual with detailed solutions for all practice-problems. *Soft Algebra PLUS* contains enrichment topics.

Soft Algebra C-E

Problem-Solving Adventure

The EzraMath™ Introduction to Algebra

VKPublishing

Illustrator: Boris Klissourski

VKPublishing Wheeling, IL

EzraMath.com

Preface by the Author

If you want to learn how to solve sophisticated problems, study *Soft Algebra*!

This book was designed to be a course which prepares students for the STEM careers of their dreams. With that being said, *Soft Algebra* helps any student to build a solid foundation in problem solving for life—that includes students with non-STEM career plans, and those who feel lost when math involves letters. *Soft Algebra* softens the barriers between arithmetic, problem-solving, and algebra by teaching algebraic concepts on an intuitive level.

Soft Algebra students learn dozens of problem-solving strategies—they organize information and design models, solve problems with ratios and rates of change, work with radicals and geometric shapes, deal with proportions and percentages. Throughout all these topics, students use conceptual understanding to solve problems, rather than a set of memorized "rules of math".

Only at the end of the book, Part E, do students start using number properties and equality properties (a.k.a "Algebra") formally. When students are finally prompted to apply formal rules, these rules merely summarize ideas which *Soft Algebra* students have already internalized and befriended. *Soft Algebra* prepares students to solve challenging problems, including word problems which involve systems of equations, as well as bizarre problems they've never seen before.

The course prepares students for solving challenging problems in class and on math contests too. Many *Soft Algebra* students participate in AMC, MATHCOUNTS, and other math competitions.

Soft Algebra is part of EzraMath™, a math program which I originally created for students of my learning center, Stella Academy (Wheeling, IL, USA). I created the program after decades of applying mathematics to scientific research[*] and six years teaching in public schools.

EzraMath™ integrates mathematics education with developing intelligent thinking through active problem solving[†]. The program starts from counting and then continues through mental math, basic word problems, and fractions. After those courses, students begin *Soft Algebra,* most commonly between 5th and 8th grade, since it roughly matches the material of a 7th grade math curriculum in the United States. Of course, *Soft Algebra* is appropriate for ages 5-125 and every student's journey is unique! The most advanced students supplement their studies using *Soft Algebra PLUS*.

---

[*] Dr. Kofman earned her B.S. and M.S. in Pedagogy of Physics from Moscow State Educational University (former USSR) and her Ph.D. in Physical Chemistry from Weizmann Institute of Sciences (Rehovot, Israel). She spent years performing research in physical chemistry and physics. In 2000, Dr. Kofman began teaching mathematics in a Chicago public school and, in 2006, earned her second masters degree, an M.S. in Secondary Education from DePaul University (Chicago, IL, USA).

[†] Elements of Dr. Kofman's program have been presented at the Joint Mathematics Meeting, the MAA Math Festival, the Annual Conference of the North American Chapter of the International Group for the Psychology of Mathematical Education, and the NCTM Innov8 Meeting. EzraMath continues to be refined using internationally recognized pedagogical principles and current research findings as well as through input from the brilliant students of Stella Academy.

CONTENTS

After completing all five parts of *Soft Algebra*, some students further improve their problem-solving skills by studying *Soft Algebra PLUS*.

Soft Algebra Plus continues working on problem-solving skills training.

Part A+, *Creativity and Problem Solving* deepens students' knowledge regarding creative problem-solving (Chapters 2 and 4) and briefly delves into multidimensional problems, which are quite important for Physics and Geometry. Part B+, *x-y Vision*, helps students to explore graphs. Special attention is devoted to function transformations.

At the end of *Soft Algebra PLUS*, readers will find a few dozen review problems. Some of the problems are highly challenging.

For an art project, Gail, Graham, and Gilbert had to bring blue and green marbles. Gail brought 28 green marbles, and Graham brought one-fourth of that number. Gilbert brought 180 blue marbles. He also brought 80 green marbles. Graham brought a dozen blue marbles more than the number of green marbles Gail brought. How many marbles did all the children bring if Gail brought twice as many green marbles as blue?

Part A

Point M revolves along the circumference of a circle with a radius 1 and center at the origin. We call it a unit-circle. M begins to move at (1,0) and continues counterclockwise. After we draw a radius from the center of the circle to M, we see how the angle of rotation, *alpha*, changes when M revolves. The angle of rotation *alpha* is defined as an angle between the radius and the *x*-axis. Point M begins moving when *alpha*=0 degrees. We define a function *Sine* as the *y*-coordinate of M, M_y. The *Sine* function depends on *alpha*. Draw a large unit-circle. Use the unit-circle to complete an M_y-*alpha* chart. Finally, draw a graph for *Sine*.

Part B

INTRODUCTION

$$\begin{cases} \dfrac{x - 3y}{5} = -2 \\ \dfrac{7x - 4y}{x} = 5 \end{cases}$$

Part E

A client left a $36 tip, which was quite a high tip—40% of the check. What part of the total payment was the tip? Present your answer in percentage form rounded to the nearest tenth.

Part D

A machine was digging a 2-foot-deep rectangular (4 by 6 feet) trench for a pond, moving on average 1 cubic foot of dirt in 5 minutes. If the machine works at the same speed, how much time it will take the machine to dig the trench for a second pond with dimensions of 8 by 6 feet and a depth of 2.5 feet?

Part C

Find the sum of all negative three-digit numbers divisible by 2.

Soft Algebra PLUS

What is *Soft Algebra*?

The core *Soft Algebra* course combines teaching math with teaching problem solving[*]. The sole requirement to begin is students' proficiency with integers and fractions.

Introductory Algebra Course = Visualized Math + Problem Solving
Prerequisites = Arithmetic + Desire to Become Smarter

Soft Algebra teaches the basics of problem solving. Students mine important information from challenging word problems and present the data using mathematical (algebraic) language and visual models. In addition, the book introduces the concept of substitution and the idea of analogous problems, teaches how to solve problems with radicals, and discusses problem with constraints.

Parts A and B = Comprehension + Visualization + Math Language + Intro to Creative Models

Soft Algebra also teaches students about measurable attributes, units of measurement, and how to solve problems involving rates of change, fractional parts, percentages, and ratios. It also shows how to draw velocity(time) and distance(time) graphs and work with derived units of measure. Finally, the book covers simple geometry and visual algebra problems. The problems help students to better understand problem-solving techniques and the role of auxiliary elements in problem solving.

Parts C, D, and E = Rate of Change + Fractions + Percents + Ratios + Geometry + Visual Algebra

After students complete *Soft Algebra*, they are ready for Algebra. However, advanced students are advised to supplement their studies with the *Soft Algebra PLUS* enrichment book. The *PLUS* book teaches how to solve equations with parameters and transform graphs, deepens students' understanding of problem solving, and has plenty of challenging and super-challenging problems.

In addition to the *Soft Algebra*, and *Soft Algebra PLUS*, readers can find workbooks and teacher's manuals, sold separately. The workbooks supplement each part of the program; they offer scaffolding and space for solutions. The manuals present detailed solutions for all problems.

EzraMath Introductory Algebra = Soft Algebra + Workbooks + Soft Algebra PLUS + Teacher's Manuals

Soft Algebra is written in dialogue form, so read the dialogues with a partner for extra fun. For some problems, you will need to apply your common sense and the Internet. Also, use the Internet to check answers for consistency.
A study at Berlin's Academy of Music showed that, by age 20, star violinists had spent 10,000 hours practicing the violin. While *Soft Algebra* will not take this long, you will only improve your problem-solving skills, prepare for algebra, and develop your creativity if you practice a lot, too. To complete the course, solve all—or at least most—of the problems.

Read the theory and solve the problems. Just reading or only solving problems will not do the trick.

Solving the tricky problems from this course will make your ability to overcome challenges second nature.

Good luck with problem solving.

---

[*] The Introduction for Soft Algebra Parts A-B includes more details on the methodology of this textbook.

Dedicated to those who have a passion for intellectual challenge.

The idea that the harder you work, the better you're going to be is just garbage.
The greatest improvement is made by the man or woman who works most intelligently.

— Bill Bowerman, co-founder of Nike

Welcome to the second book of *Soft Algebra* with its 514 problems and exercises.

Don't look at the clock. Make a Prep and a couple of models.

Theory Overview

for Mining and Logic

Look at challenging problems from a different angle.

The trickiest problems demand the trickiest approaches.

1

Chapter 13
Digest for Chapters 1 through 12

 Chapter 13 is a theory digest for Parts A and B. Students are expected to briskly skim this chapter to see how much they have learned from MINING and LOGIC.

Stella, I remember all I learned in *Soft Algebra* course: exponents, graphs, substitution, and mining. I also remember how to mine change-problems.

 Good for you, Ezra. At the end of Chapter 13, there are four quintessential problems. They will help you examen the depth of your knowledge.

Mr. Refiner, Chapter 13 is like a 13th floor in a multistory building! You know, many tall buildings stand without 13th floor. So, I hope I will survive too... without reading the unlucky chapter.
I will start from solving your *quintessential*, whatever it means, problems and will read this unlucky-number chapter only if I forget something. Can I start from the "quintess" problems?

 Sure, you can, Ezra. But your choice must depend on your learning style rather than on your superstition or laziness!
By the way, *quintessential problems* means that the problems *concentrate the essence* of what you have learned in MINING and LOGIC.

Some students will benefit from reviewing theory; others—from trying to solve the problems at first.
Now, students must choose reading or problem solving and start working.

Section 13.1 All About Mining

 Simplifying word problems involves five stages: *extracting* useful data, *chunking* sentences, *detailing*, *refining* problems' text, and finally *organizing*. Below, I will briefly describe each stage.

To *extract data* from a problem, remove the waste and underline the question of the problem. Also, write numbers as numerals.

To *chunk sentences*, break them into smaller sentences and write each sentence on a new row. Use only *independent sentences*. You can transform *dependent sentences* into independent ones by substituting pronouns and other unclear words with *clarifying (specific) words*.

To perform *detailing* and create a *Prep*, abbreviate key words. If possible, extract some waste and perform additional chunking.

To *refine* math-related sentences, introduce parameters and translate the Prep into *mathematical (algebraic) language*.

To *organize* an outline into an *Algebraic Organizer*, arrange the information in a logical order. Group all *givens* together and draw a line to separate the question from the givens. Rewrite the questions under the givens and the line. Apply the *constraints bookkeeping* method when needed.

Ezra, you presented a brilliant digest for mining mathematical problems. I only want to add that detailing and refining are not needed for logic problems.

 Also, students must remember that *Soft Algebra* has strict requirements for problems' presentations. As a *solution to a problem*, students must define parameters and create an Algebraic Organizer before displaying step-by-step computations and the answer to the problem. If needed, students add extra outlines.

In *half-problems*, the problems that ask students to find a number, presenting parameters is not necessary. We use N to mark the word *number*. N_1 marks *the first number* and N_2 marks *the second number*.

Folders Problem: Lina has 5 blue and 7 brown folders. How many blue and brown folders does Lina have in all?

Parameters	Bl	*The number of blue folders.*
	Br	*The number of brown folders.*

Algebraic Organizer	**Solution**
$Bl = 5\ folders$	$Bl + Br = 5 + 7 = 12, [folders]$
$Br = 7\ folders$	*Above exemplifies the lazy format for writing measuring units.*
$Bl + Br = ?\ folders$	

Answer: Lina has 12 blue and brown folders in all.

Section 13.2 Math Language Review

Math language is comprised of numbers, letters, and mathematical operations; many mathematical sentences are *equations*, *inequalities*, and *sets*.

To define a set, we can use an *element-list* presentation or *descriptive format*. For the set with the elements 2, 4, and 6, the *element-list* presentation is $\{2, 4, 6\}$. The sentence $2 \in \{2, 4, 6\}$ means "2 belongs ($\in$) to the set, $\{2, 4, 6\}$."

{SET}

Symbols in equations are called *parameters*. *Soft Algebra* uses one- or two-letter uppercase parameters. The parameters remind students of key words and the values they represent.

If a parameter denotes an unknown value, it is called an *unknown*. If a parameter does not change, it is a *constant*. When a parameter denotes a value that varies, it is a *variable*.

Do not use colloquial phrases such as "A number is 3 <u>times larger than</u> 6" since the phrase can have two meanings. Instead, say 3 <u>*times as large*</u> as 6. Also, do not use the phrase "A number is 3 <u>times smaller than</u> 6" since this phrase is grammatically incorrect. You may say <u>*one-third of*</u> 6 or *a number is* <u>*the quotient of*</u> 6 *and* 3.

Also remember, to avoid ambiguity, *Soft Algebra* uses the word *difference* only in the following meaning: the *difference* between two numbers is the distance between the numbers on a number line. It is always non-negative.

It can be tricky to create an Algebraic Organizer for a problem with *consecutive numbers*, whether *ascending* (each number is greater than the previous) or *descending* (each number is less than the previous). So, on the right-hand side, I made an example of how to chunk a list of ascending consecutive numbers.

$$N_1$$
$$N_2 = N_1 + 1$$
$$N_3 = N_2 + 1$$
$$N_4 = N_3 + 1$$
$$...$$

Ezra, I want to add that we always must follow *math etiquette*. We place the *coefficient* first when presenting products. We write non-numerical factors in alphabetical order. We order the *terms* starting from the higher power to the lower. In addition, we use a restricted set of the letters to denote integer numbers: i, j, k, l, m, and n.

And don't forget how to make sense of *formulas*. For example, to clarify the meaning of the number properties' formulas presented below, *substitute* the variables a, b, and c with small positive integers.

Number Properties

Commutative properties: $a + b = b + a$ and $a \cdot b = b \cdot a$.

Distributive property: $a \cdot (b + c) = a \cdot b + a \cdot c$.

Associative properties: $a + (b + c) = (a + b) + c$ and $a \cdot (b \cdot c) = (a \cdot b) \cdot c$.

Identity properties: $a + 0 = 0 + a = a$ and $a \cdot 1 = 1 \cdot 1 = a$.

Section 13.3 Grammar Review

Sometimes we do not understand a word problem because we cannot parse the meaning of a pronoun. So, we apply the following rules.

A. If there are two sentences, and the subject in the second sentence is a *pronoun* (*it*, *he*, *she*, or *they*), the pronoun carries the meaning of the subject from the first sentence. When chunking, use the subject from the first sentence instead of a pronoun.

K is less than M. It is not even.

1. K is less than M.
2. K is not even.

B. The pronoun *it* can carry the meaning of the entire sentence.

K is greater than M. It means, K is not the same as M.

1. K is greater than M.
2. K is not the same as M.
3. *The second sentence follows from the first.*

C. When a sentence combines two simple sentences connected with conjunctions, the *subject-pronouns it*, *he*, *she*, or *they* substitute for the subject of the first simple sentence.

N_1 is greater than N_2, but it is less than N_3.

1. N_1 is greater than N_2.
2. N_1 is less than N_3.

D. In two sentences connected with the pronouns *that*, *which*, *who*, or *whom*, the pronoun substitutes for the word or phrase that goes immediately before the pronoun.

Karina has a sister who has a cat.

1. Karina has a sister.
2. Karina's sister has a cat.

Sometimes, difficulties relate to the constructions *that of*, *as much as*, or *in turn*.

The initial value of the first number is 3, and that of the second number is 8.

1. The initial value of N_1 is 3.
2. The initial value of N_2 is 8.

The second number was increased as much as the first number was decreased.

1. N_1 was decreased by $\underline{D}$.
2. N_2 was increased by $\underline{D}$.

The third number is 3 more than the second number. In turn, the second number is 5 more than the first number.

1. N_3 is 3 more than N_2.
2. N_2 is 5 more than N_1.

Knowing how to read word problems' text significantly increases your ability to solve the problems.

Section 13.4 Exponents Review

Some math problems involve exponents such as 5^2, N^3, or $(-3)^2$.

When exponents have a base with a negative sign, draw an arrow to determine if the base is negative and then perform factorization.

$$-3^2$$
$$(-3)^2$$

Some exponents are applied backwards. We call them roots or radicals. In general, the opposite of $a = b^3$ is the equation $b = \sqrt[3]{a}$. We read it as *b is the third root of a* or *b is the cubic root of a*.

The root of a positive number is always positive. The equation $x^2 = 25$ has two solutions: 5 and -5. However, the square root of 25 is positive by definition: $\sqrt{25} = 5$. The square root of a negative number cannot be found on a number line, so the problem $\sqrt{-4}$ has no solution.

To multiply and divide radicals, we *combine* radicals with the same indices and *break* radicals into several parts when needed: $\sqrt[n]{a} \cdot \sqrt[n]{b} = \sqrt[n]{a \cdot b}$ and $\frac{\sqrt[n]{c}}{\sqrt[n]{d}} = \sqrt[n]{\frac{c}{d}}$. Also, we can use $\left(\sqrt[n]{a}\right)^m = \sqrt[n]{a^m}$.

To visualize radicals, use a *factor-box picture*. The picture on the right demonstrates how to change a *double radical* ($\sqrt{\sqrt{}}$) into a normal radical: $\sqrt[3]{\sqrt{64}} = \sqrt[6]{64}$.

When we make a single radical from a double radical, the resulting index is the product of the two indices in the double radical: $\sqrt[k]{\sqrt[m]{N}} = \sqrt[km]{N}$.

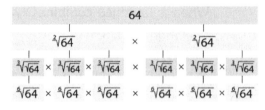

We can combine any radicals after changing the indices. To change the index of a radical, we use the *apply-compensate-simplify* strategy. Below, the strategy helps us transform $\sqrt[3]{2}$ into $\sqrt[6]{4}$:

1) Apply the root: $\sqrt[3]{2} \to \sqrt[2]{\sqrt[3]{2}}$. 2) Compensate: $\sqrt[2]{\sqrt[3]{2}} \to \sqrt[2]{\sqrt[3]{2}^2}$. 3) Simplify: $\sqrt[2]{\sqrt[3]{2}^2} = \sqrt[6]{4}$.

Students must **always present roots that cannot be calculated exactly in their simplest form.**

1) Irrational roots must be simplified to the lowest terms:

a) $\sqrt{90} = \sqrt{9 \cdot 10} = \sqrt{9} \cdot \sqrt{10} = 3 \cdot \sqrt{10}$ or $3\sqrt{10}$. b) $\sqrt[4]{25} = \sqrt[2]{\sqrt[2]{25}} = \sqrt{5}$.

2) According to math etiquette, radicals must be removed from a denominator: $\frac{1}{\sqrt{5}} = \frac{1 \cdot \sqrt{5}}{\sqrt{5} \cdot \sqrt{5}} = \frac{\sqrt{5}}{5}$.

Some problems require students to **approximate irrational numbers by the nearest rational numbers.** If so, students must apply the correct strategies.

To *approximate* (estimate) an *irrational root*,

1. Find the rational numbers that represent the boundaries of the range where the root can be.
2. Find the number exactly in the *middle of the range*.
3. Compare the middle-of-range number (MOR) with the root.
   - If the root is less than the MOR, the approximate answer equals the lower boundary.
   - If the root is greater than the MOR, the approximate answer equals the upper boundary.

Section 13.5 Techniques and Skills Review

Logical conversion, mapping, and alien eye are three strategies that involve special ways of looking at problems and solving them.

To perform *logical conversion*, we look at a logical statement backwards to transform a data-entry. For example, *the first number is 4 less than the second* must be converted into the phrase *the second number is 4 more than the first*. For super-challenging problems, *Soft Algebra* recommends applying logical conversion blindly, even if you do not yet know if the *blind logical conversion* will prove useful.

To perform *mapping*, we look at a whole problem from the opposite direction. We analyze the problem starting from what is unknown. The *map model* for the *Lego Blocks Problem* exemplifies the strategy.

$$B_y + B_r = 4(T_y + T_r)$$
$$B_y = T_r + 17\ bl.$$
$$P_r = 171\ bl.$$
$$P_y = 71\ bl.$$
$$T_y = 17\ bl.$$
$$T_r = 0\ bl.$$

$$T_y + P_y + B_y = ?\ bl.$$

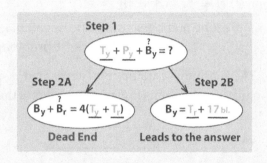

To perform the *alien eye* technique, we look at a problem through the eyes of an alien. Students must slow down and add extra steps to the solution to reduce the number of careless mistakes. Also, students must create a list of known techniques and check off the techniques they already applied. The second requirement helps students control mistakes in the problem-solving procedure.

Students must always apply logical conversion, mapping, and alien eye when they cannot solve a problem and expand the list to include all new techniques they learn. In addition, students must strive to maintain *goal awareness*, the ability to concentrate on a primary goal.

Goal awareness is a *problem-solving skill*.
Unlike *problem-solving techniques*, which students can memorize and use immediately, skills cannot be taught on the spot. Problems and exercises in *Soft Algebra* help students improve their goal awareness, neatness, attention to detail, and other problem-solving skills.

Section 13.6 Visual Models Review

Modeling means finding the important features of the initial problems and then designing simplified copies that carry these features. Discrete and Continuous Visual Representations are the models most frequently used in mathematics.

Simple discrete models are diagrams with separated dots, sticks, lines, etc. An example of a popular discrete representation, the Bug Model, is presented on the right.

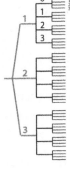

How many 3-digit positive numbers can you make using the digits 0, 1, 2, and 3?

After the 3-digit numbers are organized in a chart, the data can be presented in a form of a *Bug Model*. In the representation on the right-hand side, the quantity of bug's feet, N, shows how many 3-digit numbers can be made from the digits 0, 1, 2, and 3. $N = 3 \cdot 4 \cdot 4 = 48$.

Continuous visual models present numbers using line-segments or boxes. The *Three Lines* Problem illustrates how a simple *Line-Segment Model* can benefit problem solving.

Three Lines Problem: There are three numbers. The second is 16 more than the first number, and the third is 30 more than the first number. How much greater is the third number than the second?

N_1
$N_2 \quad = \quad N_1 \quad + \quad 16$
$N_3 = N_1 + 30$
_____
$N_3 - N_2 = ?$

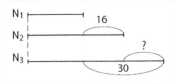

The visual model helped to solve this problem and find the answer, 14.

In addition to Line-Segment Models, Area-Box Models, and Length-Box Models, there are many other visual representations, most of which use coordinates. A number line is the simplest visual model with coordinates.

On a schematic illustration, we indicate *the number is* 3 by placing a *filled circle* on the mark that denotes the number 3. So the first picture on the left means $N = 3$.

We indicate *the number is not* 3 by placing a *hollow circle* around the grid that marks the number 3. The second picture means $N \neq 3$.

To indicate *the number is strictly greater than* 3, we draw a *thick solid line* starting

from the hollow circle at point 3 and extend it to the right. The third picture means $N > 3$ or $N \in (3; \infty)$. To show an interval that does not include the boundaries, we use parentheses. By convention, *infinity* and *negative infinity* are never included. *Intervals with brackets*—for example, $[2; 6]$—mean the border numbers are included in the ranges of solutions.

In addition to visual models, in math we frequently use creative models in the form of *analogous problems*—simplified versions of real problems. Creating these models can involve approximation, up-scaling, down-scaling, and constructing singletons.

Section 13.7 Descartes Coordinates Review

The *Descartes coordinate* plane has two axes. The intersection of X- and Y-axes is called the *origin*.

I will demonstrate how to draw a graph by analyzing a simple graph, $y = 2 \cdot x$.
For a given relationship between variables x and y, we can construct a graph in five steps:

1. Calculate y for several x-es starting from zero.

$y(0) = 2 \cdot 0 = 0;$ $y(2) = 2 \cdot 2 = 4;$ $y(4) = 2 \cdot 4 = 8;$ $y(-2) = 2 \cdot (-2) = -4;$

$y(1) = 2 \cdot 1 = 2;$ $y(3) = 2 \cdot 3 = 6;$ $y(-1) = 2 \cdot (-1) = -2;$ $y(-3) = 2 \cdot (-3) = -6.$

2. Organize the data in an x-y chart.

x	0	1	2	3	4	-1	-2	-3	-4
y	0	2	4	6	8	-2	-4	-6	-8

3. Plot points from the chart on a coordinate plane.   4. Approximate the remaining points.

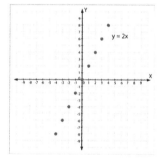 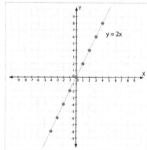

5. Add more points if needed. But for many graphs, we skip this step.

Sure, Ezra, for the graph $y = 2 \cdot x$, we can ignore step 5, but for complex graphs, all five steps are needed.

The graph $y = \frac{2}{x}$ looks unclear (see below on the left) after the first 3 steps. Adding several points in uncertain regions allows us to return to step 4 and draw a finalized graph (see below on the right).

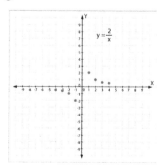 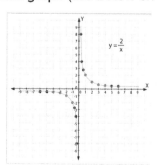

The graphs $y = 2x$ and $y = \frac{2}{x}$ are functions. A *function* is a relationship between a set of inputs where each input (x) results in exactly one output (y). Not all equations are functions.

Section 13.8 Change-Problems Review

Soft Algebra calls problems where values change over the course of the problem *change-problems*.

The *House* Problem will demonstrate how to create parameters and models for change-problems.

> *House* **Problem:** A couple lived in a house for several decades. When the price of their house tripled, they thought the house would bring them a lot of money for their retirement. However, during the last few years, the price fell by 60,000 dollars. In the end, they sold the house for $150,000. What was the initial price of the house?

In the *House* Problem, *time coordinates* (times before, between, and after described changes) are not given explicitly. Therefore, we introduce three *artificial time-coordinates*: *Time A* is the time the house was purchased; *Time B* is the time after the price tripled; and *Time C* is the time after the price fell. Using these time coordinates, we can create the *Time & Change Organizer*.

Time A:	P_A (the initial price at time A) - ?
Change 1:	P_A is tripled and becomes P_B.
Time B:	P_B (the price after it tripled).
Change 2:	P_B is reduced by $60,000 and becomes P_C.
Time C:	P_C is $150,000 (the price at the end).

In addition, the time coordinates help us create a *Time Line* and a *Time Plane*.

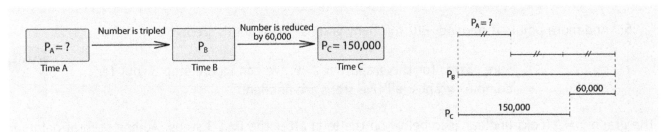

While the Time Line describes the times and changes in general, the Time Plane helps us visualize these changes in a detailed way.

$$P_A$$
$$P_B = 3 \cdot P_A$$
$$P_C = P_B - 60,000 \, d.$$
$$P_C = 150,000 \, d.$$

$$P_A = ? \, d.$$

Finally, artificially fabricated time indices for the *House* Problem allow us to represent the changes and create an Algebraic Model.

> For challenging change-problems, we use multiple representations (Time & Change Organizer, a Time Line, a Time Plane, and an Algebraic Model with artificial time-coordinates) to look at the problems from different angles and find an elegant solution.

Quintessential Problems

AB1   Use substitution to find the exact answer if $a = -18, b = 81, c = -729$, and $d = 7$.

$$\frac{a\sqrt[6]{b}}{\frac{a}{\sqrt[3]{c+726}}} - \sqrt[3]{c} \cdot \sqrt[2]{d} - \frac{1}{3} \cdot \sqrt[3]{b} + \sqrt[4]{b} - \sqrt[2]{bd}.$$

AB2   *For the following problem, start by creating a Prep and defining parameters. Then, present your visual model as a Time Plane. Create an Algebraic Organizer. Finally, explain each step of your solution.*

By September first, a one-pound grey squirrel collected 135 more nuts than a red squirrel, which weighed three-fifths of a pound, and 528 less nuts than a fox squirrel, which weighed five-thirds of a pound. Then, a quarter of the fox squirrel's nuts and 76 of the grey squirrel's nuts were transferred into the red squirrel's stockpile. After 3 hours, some nuts from the red squirrel's stockpile were transferred into the grey squirrel's stockpile so, at the end, all squirrels had the same number of nuts. How many nuts did the grey squirrel have initially?

AB3   In the division problem below, each digit is represented by a different letter. Decode the problem.

```
                                          M   S   I   T   N
    S   P   O   R   T  |  P   R   O   M   O   T   I   O   N
                          S   P   O   R   T
                        _____
                          O   R   M   S   T
                          E   O   E   M   R
                        _____
                          S   S   O   M   T   I
                          S   M   P   P   E   T
                        _____
                          M   P   N   M   E   O
                          M   M   N   T   S   T
                        _____
                          M   I   W   S   S   N
                          M   N   I   W   E   R
                        _____
                          W   T   N   N
```

0	1	2	3	4	5	6	7	8	9

AB4   Find where the two graphs, $y = -x$ and $x = -0.25y^2 + 10$, intersect. Approximate your answer to the nearest ½*. In addition, analyze whether the graphs are functions.

Congratulations, you have completed the quintessential review problems for parts A and B. You ready to start Part C!

---

* To approximate a number to the nearest ½ means to substitute the number by the nearest 0.5 or -0.5, 1 or -1, 1.5 or -1.5, 2 or -2, 2.5 or -2.5, 3 or -3, 3.5 or -3.5, and so on.

Part C

math and physics connected

PHYSICS-LAND

Physics-Land...Stella, is it the Physical Education field? You will teach me PE! Can we start with archery?

Ezra, Physics-Land means the Land of Physics. This part will teach you bits and pieces of physics. Physics is the science that studies the laws governing our universe.

Part C will teach you how to solve problems involving several types of units.

But Stell, I already studied measuring units in Part A.

Ezra, starting from Part C, besides "normal" measuring units, you will work with units like *students per group*, *miles per hour*, *km/s*, and *mi/gal*. We will solve problems involving time, weight, speed, distance, volume, proportion, and values which change with a constant rate.

A lot of motion! It is healthier than sitting still.

You will learn a couple of approaches needed for solving *motion* and *proportion* problems.

To succeed, Ezra, you must be fluent with concepts introduced in the previous chapters. You will need to perform chunking and organizing, make Preps and Algebraic Organizers, format problems' presentations, and draw visual models.

Prerequisites for Part C

Algebraic Model or Algebraic Organizer (AM or AO) A problem presented in the most concise and organized form using algebraic language.

Visual Model The result of translating a problem's data into visual language and creating visual representation. This involves Line-Segment Models, the simplest Box Models, and graphs.

Analogous Problem A problem that serves as a creative model. It is easier than the original problem but carries features of the original problem.

Logical Conversion The action of inverting a statement. For example, "Tom is older than Nick" can be logically converted to "Nick is younger than Tom."

Mapping Reordering a problem's data by starting with the question and working backwards.

Alien Eye Looking at the process of problem solving through the eyes of an alien and trying to control mistakes.

Time-Line and **Time-Plane Models** Visual models that summarize information regarding changes happening in change-problems.

Graphs Visual models that use number lines or Descartes coordinate planes.

Chapter 14
Quantitative Observations

Most math problems involve measured values or measuring. Such problems require understanding *properties of matter*. Examples of the properties include temperature, length, distance, width, color, odor, weight, time, and texture.

I see. Some properties can be described in words, but many other properties must be measured or calculated.

The latter frequently leads to challenges in word problems.

The latter?

When you discuss two topics, the word *latter* points to the second of them. Similarly, *former* points to the first topic. I meant; difficulties arise because properties in word problems are frequently not stated directly.

When the names of the properties are not in the text, you must identify the properties based on the meaning of other words. For example, in the sentence *Ezra rode a horse for* 2 *hours*, the word *time* is not mentioned. However, the sentence means the *time* of riding was 2 hours.

I've never rode a horse in my life. But I'd love to.

It was just an example, Ezra. In Chapter 14, we will discuss international and customary units, scientific notation for numbers and parameters, and a new method for unit conversion. Overall, it will prepare you for solving new types of problems in Chapters 15 and 16.

However, before working with the main topics of Part C, you must expand your scientific vocabulary. So, start by reading about properties of matter.

Section 14.1 Properties of Matter

 Physics calls everything you can see or touch *matter*. Matter has features. We call these features *properties of matter*.

Mathematicians call the properties *attributes*. Some properties we describe without measurements and others, with.

 Non-measurable properties are also known as qualitative properties. These properties can be described using *qualitative observations*. We can qualitatively describe color, odor, and texture in words or by using pictures.

Stella, I bet the mushroom in this picture has a strong earthy odor.

 That is a good example of qualitative observation. However, the properties in math problems are described *quantitatively*—with measurements!
Before talking about quantitative observations, let's define what measuring is:

Measuring is a comparison of a value with a unit of measure.
When a property is measured, it is represented by a <u>number</u>, a <u>measuring unit</u>, and a measurable attribute—the name of the measurable property.

Stella, what's a quantitative observation? Is it a measurement?

 Almost. *Quantitative observation* is the result of measuring. It includes the same components: a number, a measuring unit, and a measurable attribute.

So, in your example of me riding a horse for 2 hours...

 The implicit measurable attribute is <u>time</u>, the number is <u>2</u>, and the measuring unit is <u>hour</u>.
Other examples of measurable attributes are weight, length, distance, area, volume, mileage, speed, and temperature (to name a few).

Technically, *how many* is a measurable attribute, too. Finding *how many* legs a frog has is a result of measurement: counting legs. Therefore, when we say 4 *legs*, we present a measurable attribute: the *quantity of a frog's legs*.

Below, I will list *qualitative* and *quantitative observations* with an example of a wood frog. I found the data for a typical wood frog on the Internet.

Wood Frog: The Results of Observations

1. The number of the frog's legs (**quantity**) is 4.

2. The frog **consists mostly of** muscles, skin, and bones.

3. The **shape** (when it is sitting) is egg-like.

4. The **length** of the frog is 3.25 *centimeters*.

5. The **diameter** of the frog is approximately 16 *mm*.

6. The **color** of the frog's back is brown.

7. The **color** of the frog's belly is tan.

8. The **weight** of the frog is 3.1 *grams*.

Sentences #2, 3, 6, and 7 do not contain numerals. They represent the results of qualitative observations.

Wood Frog: Results of Qualitative Observations

Materials – muscles, skin, and bones   Colors – brown and tan   Shape – egg-like

The remaining sentences have numbers. They talk about number of legs, weight, length, and diameter.

Below, I present the results of quantitative observations as a chart. Here, each entry has three elements: a measurable attribute, number, and unit of measure.

Wood Frog: Results of Quantitative Observations

Measurable Attribute	Number	Unit
Quantity	4	Legs
Length	3.25	Centimeters
Diameter	16	Millimeters
Weight	3.1	Grams

A measurable attribute (or property), number, and unit of measure are three features that characterize any quantitative observation.
In word problems, you should always pay attention to these three features.

Summary

Quantitative observations: number, unit, and measurable attribute. Qualitative observations — words & pictures.

Use the following sentences to answer the questions below.

Tom can ride his green bicycle with a speed of 25 miles per hour. Although his red bicycle has lighter wheels, Tom cannot ride it faster than 22 miles in one hour.

(1) What are the results of qualitative and quantitative observations in the sentences above?

(2) What are the number-value, measurable attribute, and the unit that characterize each value?

(3) What is the difference between qualitative and quantitative observations?

1   For quantitative properties (*measurable attributes*) from List A, find matching measuring units from List B. Many entries have more than one match. Circle the word which expresses a qualitative characteristic.

List A: Height, weight, expenses, width, shape, time, depth, age, salary, length.

List B: Miles, dollars, seconds, millimeters, kilometers, yens, rubles, cents, years, kilograms.

2   Use qualitative and quantitative observations to describe the properties of your chair. For the quantitative observations, provide results from measurements—exact or estimated. *Describe the material and shape of each component. Characterize the height, function, color(s), and weight of the chair.*

3   List some results of qualitative and quantitative observations of a book. For quantitative observations, provide estimated values.

4   List four values that characterize a particular car. For each value, besides a number, specify a measurable attribute and a unit. Use online resources. Specify the car you are describing and the Internet link you are using.

Section 14.2 Measurable Attributes

Ezra, do you remember what an indirect description of a property is?

It is...presenting a number and forgetting to name a property.

It is not *forgetting*. Regular English sentences frequently sound better without naming properties of matter.
When properties are not clearly stated, reading the problems is like trying to see a butterfly through a pupa. The most important things are hidden.

Oh, now I understand why the butterflies are there.

As the pupa becomes a beautiful butterfly, unclear sentences can be changed to text, where each detail is clearly stated. Just transform the sentences into a *math-focused* format.

Wait, wait, Stella. I remember. Math-focused sentences must have the words "set" and "belongs." I made sentences like that when learning about sets.

That's for sets! Talking about quantitative properties has different requirements.
Math-focused sentences must clearly state three characteristics:
a measurable attribute, a unit of measure, and a numeral!
Below, I translated a few sentences into the math-focused format.

Translating Math-Related Sentences into a Math-Focused Format: Examples

Robert is <u>four feet</u> tall.	Robert's <u>height</u> is 4 *feet*.
<u>How many pencils</u> does Kate have?	Find the <u>quantity (number)</u> of Kate's pencils.
Sam is <u>30 years</u> old.	Sam's <u>age</u> is 30 *years*.
A trip took <u>a dozen hours</u>. During the trip, a car covered <u>500 miles</u>.	A car covered the <u>distance</u> of 500 *miles*. The <u>time</u> duration (time-length) for this trip was 12 *hours*.

I see. The sentence *Robert is four feet tall* leaves out the word *height*. But you added it. Also, in the sentence about Sam, you added a measurable attribute, *age*.

After we have math-focused sentences, identifying the three main characteristics for each quantity is fairly simple.

Quantitative Characteristics for Each Value: Property, Number, and Unit

Sentence	Property	Number	Unit
Robert's <u>height</u> is 4 *feet*.	Height	4	foot
Find the <u>quantity (number)</u> of Kate's pencils.	Quantity	?	pencil
Sam's <u>age</u> is 30 *years*.	Age	30	year
A car covered the <u>distance</u> of 500 *miles*.	Distance	500	mile
The <u>time</u> duration for this trip was 12 *hours*.	Time	12	hour

I will use math-focused sentences in Preps. It will simplify the translation into algebraic language. Math-focused sentences are easier to translate into equations and inequalities because all the necessary key words are present.

Good idea. When making Preps and Algebraic Organizers, use these rules:
A. For Preps, use math-focused language and abbreviate the measurable attributes when possible.
B. For Algebraic Organizers, use the parameters that reflect the measurable attributes they represent. When possible, use standard abbreviations.

Look at this chart of examples. Then I will explain the *standard abbreviations* that lead to creating standard parameters.

Math-Focused Language: Preps and Algebraic Organizers

The *H* of *R* is 4 *feet*.	$H_R = 4\ feet$
Find the number of *K*'s pencils.	$K = ?\ pencils$
Age of *S* is 30 *years*.	$Age_S = 30\ yeas$
t of the trip is 5 *hous*.	$t = 5\ hours$
d covered by a car is 300 *miles*.	$d = 300\ miles$

There are numerous *standard parameters* in science. We will use some of them in the *Soft Algebra,* too.
Scientists usually use a parameter H or h to mark height, L or l to mark length, V to mark volume, and lowercase t, d, and v to mark time, distance, and speed (or *velocity*). The capital T and D frequently mark temperature and density.

Density? What density?

The simplest way to understand the word density would be to define it as the weight of a cubic centimeter of a material. For example, water density is 1 since the cubic centimeter of water weighs 1 gram.

Thanks for your dense explanation about density. So, Stella, you used the parameters H_R, t, and d according to the standards you explained. However, you did not tell me about a standard abbreviation for age.

The word age has no standard abbreviation. Therefore, as a parameter, I used the word *age* with subscript, Age_S, to denote the age of Sam.

And the parameter K? Is it a standard?

I used K to denote *the quantity of pencils that Kate has.*

Why not a parameter like Q_K?

For the case of counting objects, usually a key word or letter is sufficient. When dealing with length, distance, width, speed, time, or similar, it is customary to use parameters reflecting measurable attributes.

During your practice, Ezra, you will identify measurable attributes and units of measurement. You will also create math-focused sentences. The practice will help you become skillful in creating Preps and Algebraic Organizers even for challenging problems.

Summary

Math-focused sentences: state property (measurable attribute), measuring unit, and number value. Use standard parameters to abbreviate the words that name the properties.

---

(1) Define the measurable attributes and the units in the following sentences: Fred walked from his home to the library. He covered 2 miles in 50 minutes.

(2) Present the following text in a math-focused format: In three hours a car drove 240 mi.

---

5   For the sentences below, define the measurable attribute and units connected with each value. Use the provided lists of properties and units. Find the sentence that provides insufficient information and can be understood two different ways.

     <u>Properties</u>: *age, depth, distance, height, length, quantity, time-period, weight, temperature, time, salary, and width.*

     <u>Units</u>: *centimeters, feet, hat, hours, inches, pounds, miles, degrees, US dollars, years, and days.*

     (a) A book is 1.5 inches wide.   *(b)* Sophia has 2 hats.

     (c) How long is a day?   *(d)* Micah is 5 years old.

     (e) The car covered 600 miles in 1 day.   *(f)* Aiden weighs 53 pounds.

     (g) Lila's dog has a 5-cm tail.   *(h)* In its deepest place, the lake is 10 feet deep.

     (i) The elephant was 12 feet tall.   *(j)* Today is 20 degrees below zero.

     (k) For my work, I am receiving $3,000 per month.

6   Use the sentences from problem **7** to create math-focused sentences. Underline the words naming measurable attributes. Translate the sentences into algebraic language.

     Hint: When the word length has the meaning of time length, use the word <u>time-length</u> in math-focused sentences. Another option is placing time in parentheses: <u>length (time)</u>.

7   *This is a reasoning problem. Therefore, an Algebraic Organizer is unnecessary. Solve the problem and explain your solution. For this problem, you will need to use data from the Internet.*

     The day before yesterday, Eva went to the zoo, which was 70 miles from her house. Yesterday, Eva had her birthday. It was the second time in her life when her birthday was on a Sunday, so all her sisters and brothers could come on the actual day of her birthday instead of another day of the week. She was so happy that tomorrow, Valentine's Day, will probably be one of the happiest days in her life. She always dreams that her birthday will fall on Sunday. Once before, it did, but it was so long ago she does not remember it. And it was not even during this century! She thinks it is so rare because she was born on a Monday. What was the exact date of the trip to the zoo described in the problem?

8-9   *In the following problems, make Preps and define all parameters before solving the problem. In the Preps, specify and abbreviate each attribute when possible.*

8   Alan will not be able to start his project for another week, although the due date is in 15 days. How much time will Alan spend completing his project?

9   Mia spent 3 and a half hours completing her homework on Monday. Tuesday, it took her twice more time than Monday. Then, on Wednesday, it took her as much time as for Monday and Tuesday combined. How much time did Mia's homework take during the first three days of the week?

Section 14.3 Quantitative Reasoning

Before seeking the true value of things, you must first define its true meaning.

Adele Mandez

Math-focused sentences from this section will help you improve your quantitative reasoning.

Great, Stella. But what is quantitative reasoning?

Quantitative reasoning means understanding and presenting the relationships between values in a form of equations, inequalities, or sets. To emphasize quantitative relationships between the values, you must create *math-focused sentences*, which include words that clearly describe math operations.

A sum can be presented with the words *in all*, *together*, or similar, but it is clearer to use the word **total**. Similarly, use **difference** instead of *how many more*, *how many fewer*, *how much older*, etc.

For a product, use the word **product** or clauses such as *one-half of a number*, 5 *times as many*, or 6 *times as long* to show comparison. If a problem involves division, use the word **quotient** if feasible.

Finding common factors or multiples is frequently required in problems that involve fitting tile or other shaped objects into a given space. So, for such problems, use the words **common factor** and **multiple**.

Below are a few examples of math-focused sentences: all measurable attributes are named while each math operation is clearly described.

Math-Focused Sentences: Mathematical Operations and Procedures

Original Sentence	Math-Focused Sentence
Together, Amal and Nya weigh 110 pounds.	The <u>total weight</u> of Amal and Nya is 110 pounds.
Martin is twice as old as David.	The <u>age</u> of Martin is <u>2 times</u> the <u>age</u> of David.
How many times does the age of Rosa go into the age of Steve?	What is the <u>quotient</u> of the <u>ages</u> of Steve and Rosa?
What size border would fit both types of tile without cutting? The green tile has dimensions 3 by 3 inches, and the brown tile is 4 by 4 inches.	Find the length of a border in inches. The length is a <u>common multiple</u> of 3 and 4 expressed in inches.
How much older is Victor than Tom?	Find the <u>difference</u> between the <u>ages</u> of Victor and Tom. Victor is older than Tom.

Stella, look. In the last math-focused sentence, the word "difference" does not say who is older. However, this information is implied in the original sentence. It is why Mr. Refiner added the sentence "Victor is older than Tom."

Correct, Ezra. Math-focused language can be quite long, but it prepares problems for translation into algebraic language.

Algebraic Language: Examples

The <u>total weight</u> of Amal and Nya is 110 pounds.	$W_A + W_N = 110\,Lbs$
The <u>age</u> of Martin is <u>2 times</u> the <u>age</u> of David.	$Age_M = 2Age_D$
What is the <u>quotient</u> between the ages of Steve and Rosa?	$Age_S \div Age_R = ?$
Find the length of a border in inches. The length is a <u>common multiple</u> of 3 and 4, expressed in inches.	$CM(3,4) = ?, [in]$
Find the <u>difference</u> between the <u>ages</u> of Victor and Tom. Victor is older than Tom.	$Age_V - Age_T = ?\,years$

To summarize, in a math-focused Prep, you must state the measurable attributes and emphasize mathematical relationships. Also, after each number, you must write the units of measure.

After some training, you will be able to form math-focused sentences mentally and translate even unclear texts into algebraic equations in one step.

Summary

When writing math-focused sentences, use key words that emphasize math operations.

Create math-focused sentences from the three sentences below:
(1) How much will 3 pounds of apples and 4 pounds of pears weigh altogether?
(2) How much heavier are pears than apples? (3) Tanya is 5 years older than Ben.

10 Gabriel walked from home to the library for an entire hour. When Michael walked from his home to the same library, it took him 40 minutes. How much more time did it take Gabriel to arrive at the library than Michael? *In the Prep, underline the word that shows what math operation is needed.*

11 There is a 110-foot-long building, and cars are permitted to park next to it. If each car needs 4 feet of parking space, what is the greatest number of cars that can be parked along the building? *In the Prep, use the word that shows what math operation is needed.*

12 Aviva bought three strings. Each was 3 inches longer than the previous string. The medium string was 22 inches long. The three strings were glued together to make the string as long as possible. What was the length of the resulting string?

13 Without cutting, identical square-shaped tiles need to fit into a 36 by 24-inch space. The length of the tile's side is an integer when a measuring unit is an inch. What is the greatest tile size possible?

Section 14.4 International System of Units: Basics

Property	Unit name
Mass, M	Kilogram, kg
Length, L	Meter, m
Time, T	Second, s

The *International System of Units* (abbreviated *SI*) is the most popular system of measurement. Basic units in SI are meter, kilogram, and second.

Stella, these units can't be the most popular in the world! All of the people I know use inches, feet, and pounds.

Ezra, the USA is not "the world." It is a part of the world. So, back to the topic: the size of one meter, one kilogram, and one second.

One *kilogram* is the mass of the International Prototype Kilogram, which is a standard block weighing exactly 1 *kilogram*.
A *kilogram* is approximately the weight of 3 mid-sized oranges or the weight of a one-liter water bottle. Also, 1 *gram* makes one thousandth of a kilogram.

Now, I will introduce a *meter*. One *meter* is the distance travelled by light in a vacuum in $\frac{1}{299792458}$ of a second.

How can anyone measure a time with such high precision?

You will learn the details in Physics. Later. Now we are discussing the units.

A *meter* equals the approximate distance from the left shoulder to the end of a right hand, and 1 *centimeter* makes one hundredth of a meter.

Finally, we will discuss time. As you know, Ezra, a clock has a thin hand showing seconds.

Stella, I know what a second is. One *second* is a bit longer than the time between my heartbeats.

To help you even better understand units of time, Ezra, I presented the relationship between seconds, minutes, and hours:

Popular Units of Time

60 s = 1 min   *60 min = 1 hr, so 1hr = 360 s*

Hours and minutes are not considered SI units. They are mentioned here to allow you better estimate the duration of one second.

What is SI?

SI stands for *System International*. *SI* units are frequently abbreviated to symbols shorten the amount of writing. The abbreviation follows a convention that everyone must respect: SI symbols do not have a period at the end.

Most of the SI measuring units are shortened to one or two letters, *second → s, meter → m, kilogram → kg, kilometer → km*, and *gram → g*, which is highly convenient.

Also, as a rule, international units are case sensitive.

Stella! How can UNITS sense anything?

They cannot. *Case sensitive* means you must use lowercase letters or uppercase letters, depending on the unit. It is not arbitrary.

Arbitrary? *Arbitrage* is a word Uncle Dino uses talking about stock market...

Arbitrary means doing whatever you want. So, you cannot abbreviate grams with a capital G, only with a lowercase g. It is not an arbitrary choice.

Now, back to the measuring units. Minutes and hours are not *SI* units. Therefore, their abbreviations can be followed with a period (*min.*, *hr.*, or *h.*) or not (*min*, *hr*, or *h*), depending on the book or journal. Although the abbreviation might be quite arbitrary, I abbreviate hours to *hr* and this is the abbreviation I expect to see in your work, too.

First, you say writing *hr* or *h* is arbitrary. Then you want me to write *hr*.

Ezra, it's important to know what people in the world use. But I want you to use *Soft Algebra's* conventions.
Now, it is your choice whether or not to use a period in *min* and *hr*. However, following current tendencies, *Soft Algebra* does not use the period.

Summary

International System of Units (SI): kilograms (kg), meters (m), and seconds (s). No period in these abbreviations.

(1) Estimate the length of a table in meters and its weight in kilograms. (2) Estimate the weight of a full school backpack, also in kilograms.
(3) What international units have you already used? (4) What international units from this section are new to you?

14   Bella hiked 4,700 meters. Steve hiked 6,300 meters, and the distance that Peter hiked was twice the combined hikes of Bella and Steve. What is the total distance the three friends hiked? *Define the parameters, make an Algebraic Organizer, and solve the problem.*

15   *Perform measurements. Use the International System of Units to present the results of your measurements.* Find the length and the width of the room you live in. Measure how much time it takes for you to get to your school. Find your height and the height of a celling in your room. Determine the volume of your bathtub and the volume of your teapot in liters.

16   Rami's height is about 2 ___. Lila's weight is 25 ___. Monica is 1,000 ___ heavier than Kate. The width of Donovan's father's nail is 1.2 ___. A school had windows, which were 180 ___ wide. A school was 12 ___ high. The screen was 40 ___ wide.
Lila bought 3 apples; their total weight was 1 ___. Lessons in the school were 35 ___. A trip took 12 ___. The duration for a single heartbeat is less than 1 ___. The volume of a toilet sink is 450 ___. The duration of 1 hour is 3,600 ___. The Earth makes one rotation every 24 ___. A tree was old and still was only 12 ___ tall. 1 meter is 99 ___ longer than 1 ___.
(a) Complete the blanks using the given units: m, cm, s, min, hr, g, or kg. (b) What sentence had more than one answer? Why? (c) What sentence had no answer? Explain.

Section 14.5 International System of Units in Depth

I know meters, kilograms, and seconds. What can be deeper than this?

Using three *fundamental international units*—meter, kilogram, and second—to derive other *SI* units. The easiest way of making a new unit is adding a prefix.

Pre-fix? Fix what?

Prefixes are parts that can be attached from the left-hand side to a main word to add a new meaning. Below are the most popular prefixes used in *SI*:

SI Units of Measure: Prefixes

Prefix	Meaning	Examples	
micro-	$\frac{1}{1,000,000}$	**Micro**liter	$1\mu L = 0.000001\,m$; $1\,m = 1,000,000\,\mu L$
milli-	$\frac{1}{1,000}$	**Milli**liter	$1mL = 0.001\,L$; $1\,L = 1,000\,mL$
centi-	$\frac{1}{100}$	**Centi**meter	$1\,cm = 0.01\,m$; $1\,m = 100\,cm$
deci-	$\frac{1}{10}$	**Deci**meter	$1\,dm = 0.1\,m$; $1\,m = 10\,dm$
kilo-	$1,000$	**Kilo**gram	$1\,kg = 1,000g$; $1\,g = 0.001\,kg$
Mega-	10^6	**Mega**byte	$1\,MB = 1,000,000\,B$
Giga-	10^9	**Giga**byte	$1\,GB = 1,000,000,000\,B$

To avoid mistakes, when a problem involves measuring units, indicate them in Algebraic Organizer. Also, convert units into a *homogeneous* form.

SI Units of Measure: A Word Problem

Find the perimeter of a rectangle if the length is 33 *cm* and the width is 2 *dm*.

$W = 2\,dm = 20\,cm$
$L = 33\,cm$

$P = ?\,cm$

$P = 2 \cdot (20\,cm + 33\,cm) = 106\,cm$

Answer: $P = 106\,cm.$

I see your example, but I still don't know where a *homogeneous* stuff in your organizer is.

Look, Ezra. The Algebraic Organizer presents the width of a rectangle in decimeters and the length in centimeters. Within the organizer, I converted decimeters into centimeters. After I converted decimeters into centimeters, all units of length have a *homogeneous* (same) format.

Ezra, to help you memorize prefixes, you may use the following song.

😊 Kilo means one thousand,
one thousand,
one thousand.
And one divided by one thousand
equals m, i, l, l, i.

😊 *means that one group of students sings*
😊😊😊😊 *- four groups sing together*

😊😊 Mega means one million,
one million,
one million.
And one divided by one million
equals m, i, c, r, o.

😊😊😊 Giga is one billion,
one billion,
one billion.
And one divided by one hundred
equals c, e, n, t, i.

😊😊😊😊 Deci is one over ten,
one over ten,
one over ten.
And deca always will be ten,
deca will be ten!

Summary

Memorize SI prefixes. For calculations, use grams with grams, millimeters with millimeters, and cents with cents.

(1) *Place the values in ascending order: 35 cm, 3 dm, and 349 mm.*
(2) *Draw a line segment 5 cm long.*
(3) *Draw a line segment 5 in. long.*

17   Finish writing the presented identities. Show your calculations.

      (1) 58 cm = ___ m   *(2)* 250 ml = ___ l   *(3)* 0.02 dm = ___ m

      (4) 28.4 mm = ___ m   *(5)* 1,960 g = ___ kg   *(6)* 1,030 kg = ___ g

      (7) 120 s = ___ min   *(8)* 1.2 hr = ___ min   *(9)* 5 km 150 m = ___ m

      (10) $4\frac{1}{3}$ hr = ___ min   *(11)* 17,000 mg = ___ g   *(12)* 700,000 µg = ___ g

      (13) 30.4 dm = ___ m   *(14)* 5.06 kY = ___ Y, where Y is an unknown unit.

18   Complete the blanks. As units, use one of the following: *km, m, cm, or mm.*
Her finger was 4 ___ long. The living area of his house was 100 square ___. The table was 65 ___ long. Lila's mom's height was about 1.5 ___. His bedroom was 3 ___ wide. Peter's teacher's foot length was exactly 12 ___. Her book was very thin; the width was 3 ___. The distance between two cities was about 50 ___.

19   *Complete the blanks. As units, use one of the following: kg or g.*
The watermelon weighed 2 ___ . A pencil weighed 12 ___. 10 erasers weighed 50 ___. A boy weighed 30 ___. The book weighed 1 ___. An apple weighed 600 ___ . The telephone was heavy; it weighed 200 ___.

20   *Complete the blanks. Use the following: s, min, hours, years, or centuries.*
Samuel said he is 3 ___ old. Monica's age was 20. Levi was a good runner; he was running 100 meters in 15 ___ . During a marathon, runners usually run for several ___ . I can hold my breath for almost 1 ___. A heart makes about a beat per ___. The first car was designed about 1 ___ ago.

21   *Complete the blanks. Use the metric system. The last two blanks are the same.*
It took Leona 8 ___ to walk from school to her home, 400 ___ from her school. Dana was 22 ___ when she wrote her first article. Logan had a 2 ___ long fishing pole. The fishing pole weighed 700 ___. Without proper equipment, a human usually cannot stay under water for more than 50 ___. During lunch, Paulina took the plate with a radius of 50 ___.
One ___ shoes! It was too much for my poor feet! Peter weighed 15 ___ more than his dog, but 100,000 ___ less than his dad. *In the last sentence, the units are the same in both places.*

22   Sebastian is as tall as Carter, who is 1 m and 24 centimeters high. Liana and Sara have a 10-gram difference in their weight and are only one-half as tall as the boys. When 620 divides the total height for all four children, measured in millimeters, the quotient has the same value as the weight of Sara in kilograms. What is the weight of Liana in grams?

Section 14.6 Magic-One Approach to Unit Conversion

After you know the meaning of all the *SI* prefixes, you can start moving from one unit to the next. However, you might experience difficulties until you learn *multiplication by a magic one*.

Multiplication by one cannot change anything!

The Magic-One Approach is based on a property of one in mathematics.

I remember the property. $3 \cdot 1 = 3$, $17 \cdot 1 = 17$, $b \cdot 1 = b$, and so on.

Correct, Ezra. *To convert a unit, you must multiply the value by one.* The trick is to find a *magic one*—the one which helps to change the unit. The examples below will help you understand how the magic one spell works.

Unit Conversion Using the Magic-One Approach: Converting m into dm

Convert 50 m into decimeters.

1. Create a magic 1. $deci = \frac{1}{10}$, *therefore* $1 = 10\ deci$

2. Use the magic 1. $50\ m = 50\ m \cdot 1 = 50\ m \cdot 10\ deci = 500\ decimeter = 500\ dm$

Answer: $50\ m = 500\ dm$.

The spell is simple: create a *magic one* and use the *magic one* to convert the units. Here is one more example:

Unit Conversion Using the Magic-One Approach: Converting min into hr

Convert 45 min into hours.

1. Create a magic 1. $1\ hour = 60\ min$, therefore $1 = \frac{1\ hr}{60\ min}$

2. Use the magic 1. $45\ mi = 45\ min \cdot 1 = 45\ min \cdot \frac{\mathbf{1\ hr}}{\mathbf{60\ min}} = \frac{45}{60}\ hr = \frac{3}{4}\ hr = 0.75\ hr$

Answer: $45\ min = 0.75\ hr$.

Stell, from the equation $1\,hr = 60\,min$, it follows $1 = \frac{1\,hr}{60\,min}$ and $1 = \frac{60\,min}{1\,hr}$. How did you know which formula to use?

To convert minutes into hours, we divide minutes by minutes and then multiply by hours.

I see. In your example, to divide by minutes, you used $1 = \frac{1\,hr}{60\,min}$. Now, I understand how to pick the correct *magic one*.

Below, I will convert 400 micrometers into centimeters starting by converting micrometers into standard units, meters:

Unit Conversion Using the Magic-One Approach: Converting μm into cm

Convert $400\ \mu m$ into cm.

1. Transform μm into a standard unit. $400\ \mu m = \frac{1}{1,000,000} \cdot 400\ m = 0.0004\ m$

2. Create a magic 1. $centi = \frac{1}{100}$, therefore $\mathbf{1} = 100\ centi$

3. Use the magic 1. $0.0004\ m = 0.0004\ m \cdot \mathbf{1} = 0.0004\ m \cdot 100\ centi = 0.04\ cm$

Answer: $400\ \mu m = 0.04\ cm$.

I understand, Stella. For complex units, you add a transformation into a standard unit. Then, you create a *magic one*.

You see, Ezra, after a *magic one* is found, the conversion goes effortlessly. Therefore, I highly recommend using the Magic-One Approach when converting various kinds of units.

Summary

For unit conversion, create a magic one—the one which will help you with the conversion.

(1) Create a <u>magic one</u> for the following prefixes: micro-, deca-, milli-, mega-.

(2) Use Magic-One Approach to perform conversion:

   $3m =$ _____ Mm $0.2g =$ _____μg $5cm =$ _____dm $600g =$ _____kg

23   Create two alternative *magic ones* for each equation below:

Example: If $1m = 100cm$, then $1 = 100\frac{cm}{m}$ and $1 = \frac{1}{100}\frac{m}{cm}$.

(a) $1\,kilo = 1,000$

(b) $micro = \frac{1}{1,000,000}$

(c) $\mu g = \frac{g}{1,000,000}$

(d) $mL = 0.001L$

(e) $Gsec = 1,000,000,000sec$

(f) $1min = 60sec$

(g) $Mega = 1,000,000$

(h) $1hr = 3,600sec$

(i) $2a = b \ (a \neq 0 \text{ and } b \neq 0)$

(j) $m = 2$

24   Finish writing the presented identities. Show your calculations. Apply the Magic-One Approach. When needed, before using the Magic-One Approach, transform complex units into a simple form. When using the Magic-One Approach, follow the example below.

$$54\,mm = \frac{1}{1,000} \cdot 54\,m = 0.054m \cdot [100centi] = 5.4\,cm.$$

(a) $6\,mg = \underline{\hspace{0.5cm}}\mu g$

(b) $450\,ml = \underline{\hspace{0.5cm}}kl$

(c) $0.004\,km = \underline{\hspace{0.5cm}}dm$

(d) $254\,mm = \underline{\hspace{0.5cm}}dm$

(e) $1,964\,g = \underline{\hspace{0.5cm}}kg$

(f) $6,000,000\,kg = \underline{\hspace{0.5cm}}Gg$

(g) $180\,s = \underline{\hspace{0.5cm}}min$

(h) $2.2\,hr = \underline{\hspace{0.5cm}}min$

(i) $3\,km\,4\,m = \underline{\hspace{0.5cm}}cm$

(j) $220\,min = \underline{\hspace{0.5cm}}hr$

(k) $870,000\,mg = \underline{\hspace{0.5cm}}kg$

(l) $500,000\,\mu g = \underline{\hspace{0.5cm}}kg$

(m) $0.04\,kQ = \underline{\hspace{0.5cm}}mQ$

25   Some hot air balloon travelers found they needed to soar higher to fly over the mountains. They calculated that removing 60 kg should be enough. However, they did not have a scale to weigh the items they had in their possession. They only knew the precise weight of their ballast bags.

So, when they came close to the mountains, they became scared and started throwing overboard whatever came to their hands. Particularly, the travelers threw away the following objects: 11 ballast bags (each weighed 5.3 kg); 3 notebooks, each weighing 16 g; a sand-clock, which weighed 23g; three pairs of gloves (one weighed 45 g, another weighed 23 g, and the third weighed 16 g); a clock that weighed 117 grams; an iPad (0.73 kg), and a bag with 29 coins, where the weight of each coin was 40 g, and the bag weighed 40g.

Did they succeed in flying over the mountains?

Section 14.7 Scientific Notation

Section 14.7 discusses a convention connected with writing numbers.

Scientific notation means representing a number in the form of a product of a single-digit nonzero integer followed by a decimal fraction and an exponent of 10.

It means, instead of writing 3,876,876,876, scientists choose to write $3.876876876 \cdot 10^9$. A *number* times an *exponent*.

Why, Mr. Refiner? Why would people write this way? I mean scientists.

Scientists are also people. Scientists deal with numbers of different sizes and want to know the size of each number at the first glance.

In scientific notation, the exponent of 10 tells the size of each number. The first factor only adds precision. Here is an example of scientific notation: $52,000,000 = 5.2 \cdot 10^7$.

In this number, $Size \approx 10^7$, and the precision is defined by a factor, 5.2.

Here is another example, $45 = 4.5 \cdot 10$. Hm. For small numbers, I think non-scientific notation is better.

Also, I cannot figure out scientific notation for 0.023. Applying scientific notation, I must write $0.023 = 2.3 \cdot 10^{power}$. But whatever power I apply, I will never obtain $\frac{1}{100}$.

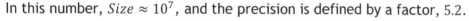

Here, you are incorrect. Ten to the power -2 is 0.01. A *negative exponent* means the following: $a^{-n} = \frac{1}{a^n}$.

With negative exponents, it is possible to represent any number using scientific notation. For example, $10^{-2} = \frac{1}{10^2} = 0.01$,

$0.00023 = 2.3 \cdot \frac{1}{10^4} = 2.3 \cdot 10^{-4}$, and $-0.23 = -2.3 \cdot 10^{-1}$.

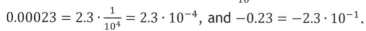

I will add two more examples. First, an approximate distance from Earth to the sun is 149,600,000,000 *meters* or, in scientific notation, $1.496 \cdot 10^{11}$ *m*. Second, let me show you a very special number, the number of atoms in 13 grams of carbon: $R = 602,214,129,270,000,000,000,000 \frac{Atoms}{Mole}$. In scientific notation, $R = 6.0221412927 \cdot 10^{23} \frac{Atoms}{Mole}$.

These are cool numbers, Mr. Refiner. Do negative exponents work only with base ten?

Negative exponents can be used with any base. Look, $(-3)^{-4} = \frac{1}{(-3)^4} = \frac{1}{81}$ or $2^{-3} = \frac{1}{2^3} = \frac{1}{8} = 0.125$.

So, the exponent can be positive or negative. It would be interesting if an exponent can be a fraction, too.

Ah, fractional exponents...you will see them at the end of this book. Now, Ezra, you must develop fluency with scientific notation and integer exponents, both positive and negative.

Summary

Negative Power: $a^{-n} = \frac{1}{a^n}$. Scientific notation: $NonzeroDigit \cdot moredigits \cdot 10^{power}$.

Present the following numbers using scientific notation: 35.2 and $0.02 \cdot 10^{-2}$.

26   Represent the following numbers in scientific notation:
(a) 127.3; (b) 0.00004578; (c) 920,000,000,000,000; (d) 0.000000076.
Transform these numbers into a non-exponential format: (e) $4.5708 \cdot 10^{-3}$ and (f) $3.67891 \cdot 10^7$.

27   Change the units to the given format and present your answers in scientific notation.

(a) $127.3\,m =$ ___mm (b) $0.00004578\,cm =$ ___km (c) $920,000,000,000,000\,ks =$ ___s
(d) $0.076\,Mm =$ ___m (e) $4.07\,\mu g =$ ___g (f) $459,000\,mm =$ ___μm
(g) $0.2\,mL =$ ___L (h) $500\,dm =$ ___m

28   Calculate the results. Then, present your answers using scientific notation.

(a) $\frac{12^{-2}}{\sqrt{4}} \cdot 6^2$ (b) $\sqrt[3]{4} \cdot 24^{-1} \cdot \sqrt[3]{54}$ (c) $\left(\frac{\sqrt{24}}{\sqrt{36}}\right)^{-2}$ (d) $\left(\frac{0.0035}{0.007}\right)^{-3}$

(e) $100^{-2} \div \frac{1}{0.01^{-2} \cdot 5^{-2}}$ (f) $\sqrt{\frac{\sqrt[3]{8^2}}{\sqrt[3]{4^3}^{-1}}}$ (g) $\frac{25^{-2} \cdot 45^{-1}}{15^{-4} \cdot \sqrt[2]{25}}$ (h) $(0.008 \cdot 0.0125)^{-5}$

Section 14.8 Introduction to Customary Units

When I introduced international units, Ezra, you mentioned that many people use customary units like inches, feet, and pounds.

The *customary units* are very convenient!

You are correct. Many people use the same units their predecessors used for centuries because these units are easy to estimate.

Are there different customary units in faraway countries?

Of course. Many customary units vary from country to country.

Stella, let's forget about other countries and talk about units in the U.S.

Sure. To become fluent with U.S. customary units, you should confidently:
- A. Estimate the units.
- B. Express units in terms of other units.
- C. Calculate expressions combining different units.
- D. Format answers involving customary units.

I think a *foot* is the best-known customary unit. *One foot* approximately equals the length of an adult's foot. One *inch* is much smaller. An inch has the length of a medial phalange of an adult's index finger.

1 foot

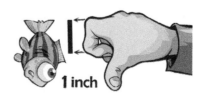

1 inch

There are also *tablespoon* and *cup* units. I will use my spoon and cup for measurements!

A regular spoon or cup would give you only a vague estimation. When baking, you must use a special measuring cup and a measuring tablespoon. Below, I present some popular U.S. customary units. Use them for solving problems.

US Customary Units: Length, Area, and Weight

$Foot = 12\,in$	*ft*	Foot length, 12 in.
$Inch = \frac{1}{12}ft$	*in*	The length of a medial phalange of an index finger, $\frac{1}{12}$ ft.
$Yard = 3\,ft = 36\,in$	*yd*	The distance from the left shoulder to the endpoint of an extended right hand. This is very close to the length of a meter: 1 *yard* $\approx 0.9\,m$.
Miles	*mi*	1760 yards or 5280 feet.
Pound	*lb*	Unit of weight. It is near the weight of a big apple.
Dry Ounce	*oz*	1/16 of pound.
Acre	no standard abbreviation	43,560 square feet or 4,840 square yards.

Ezra, the abbreviations for the units are in the second column and have no period at the end. Until recently, customary units' abbreviations were followed by a period. Now, only inches are sometimes abbreviated with a period at the end.

So, no periods, with one exception: *inches*.

In the American Institute of Standards' publications, a period is absent even after *in*. So, using a period after *in* is your choice. Now, look at units of volume.

US Customary Units: Fluid and Liquid Volume

Fluid ounce	$fl.\,oz$	1/16th of a US liquid pint, about 30 ml.
Gallon or liquid gallon	*gal*	$\frac{1}{7}ft^3$ makes approximately a U.S. gallon or 16 cups.
Quart or liquid quart	*qt*	Quart represents $\frac{1}{4}$ of a liquid gallon or 4 cups.
Pint or liquid pint	*pt*	Pint represents $\frac{1}{8}$ gal of a liquid gallon or 2 cups.
Cup or fluid cup	*cp*	1/16 of a liquid gallon, about 237 ml.
Tablespoon	*Tbsp*	½ of a fluid ounce or 1/16th of a cup.
Teaspoon	*tsp*	1/6 of a fluid ounce or 1/48th of a cup.

Stella, your chart has *gallon or liquid gallon*. But, in a store, Mom buys *dry* plastic gallons...of milk!

In the U.S., we have two types of units: dry units and fluid (or liquid) units. When Mom buys milk, it is in the plastic containers—each contains 1 *liquid gallon* of milk. Liquid gallons and quarts are used to measure the volume of water, milk, and other liquids. We usually skip the word *liquid*.

Also, Stella, what is a *liquid pint*? Today I bought a pint of raspberries. They are juicy, but they are not a liquid.

There are liquid pints and dry pints. There are liquid gallons and dry gallons. A dry gallon has a bit greater volume than the liquid gallon.

Below, I created a chart with customary units used to measure dry volume. You don't have to memorize the units. However, you must use this information when needed. Just remember to add "dry" when using dry gallons, quarts, and pints.

US Customary Units: Dry Volume

Bushel	*bu*	4 pecks or 8 dry gallons.
Peck	*pk*	2 dry gallons or a quarter of a bushel.
Dry gallon	*gal*	Dry gallon is greater than a fluid gallon by about 1/6th of its size.
Dry quart	*qt*	2 pints, 1/4th of dry gallon.
Dry pint	*pt*	½ of dry quart or 1/8th of a dry gallon.

Dry pints and quarts are used to sell small volumes of berries or vegetables. Meanwhile, large quantities are frequently sold in half-bushels and bushels.

I remember we picked a bushel of sour cherries on a farm! Then grandma made blintzes.

Those blintzes with sour cherries were great, but we have a math lesson. So, back to the topic.

Oh, I thought we were done. Wait, Stell, I found a mistake in your first chart. You abbreviated *ounce* as *oz*. However, there is no z in the word *ounce*! The abbreviation must be *oc*!

Ezra, there is no mistake. The abbreviation *oz* comes from Medieval Italian, *onza*.

On-za! Sounds fascinating.

One last remark. When using fluid U.S. customary volume units, I will skip the word *fluid* (or *liquid*). When problems involve volume of a liquid, always use fluid and liquid units.

Sure. It is impossible to pour a liquid in the plastic containers for raspberries or wooden containers for apples.
The liquid will flow away.

Hehe...Ezra, that is quite a joke. Hope you understand the material.

Summary

Use customary units for estimations and abbreviate them according to conventions.

(1) Why is pound abbreviated as lb? (You might need to go online to answer this question.)
(2) Why do you think other units lost their period after their abbreviated version, but inch sometimes keeps its period?
(3) Which customary units have you used already?
(4) Which customary units have you never seen before?
(5) Can you place the units in ascending order? (a) 1ft, 1 mi, 1 yd; (b) 1 in, 1 lb, and 1 hr.

29   Complete these sentences. As units, use one of the following: *in, ft, yd, mi.*

      (a)   Her finger was 2 ____ long.

      (b)   This two-story building is 9 ____ tall.

      (c)   The table was 40 ____ wide.

      (d)   Leah mom's height was 6 ____ and 2 ____ .

      (e)   The baby's feet were 3 ____ long.

      (f)   Caleb was a good runner. He ran 100 ____ in 10 seconds.

      (g)   Her notebook had a thickness of ½ ____ .

      (h)   The distance between two cities was about 150 ____ .

30 *Complete the sentences. Use customary system of units:*

      (a)   Leona usually uses her bike when she goes to the library. It takes her 10 minutes to ride from home to the library that is 5 ____ away from home.

      (b)   Daniela was 12 ____ old when she started walking.

      (c)   Liam caught a fish, which weighed 3 ____ .

      (d)   The length of child's foot was ½ ____ .

      (e)   The school was 40 ____ away from Milena's house, so she walked alone.

      (f)   Paulina's shoe is 7 ____ long.

31 *Fill in the blanks.* Use the words from the list: *dry, liquid, half, giant tomatoes, farm, foot, blackberries, pair, table, bushel, pecks, more.*

      (a)   Ashley bought 1 pint of __ and ½ bushel of __ .

      (b)   Thirty-two __ spoons of milk made __ of cups.

      (c)   Under the table, there was a __ of tomatoes that Lenny picked on a __ .

      (d)   Two __ of pears is the same as a __ .

      (e)   __ quart is greater than __ quart by 1/6th of its volume.

      (f)   In 1 cubic __ , there are 7 __ gallons.

      (g)   Two miles is __ than 5,280 feet.

      (h)   A __ pint is less than __ pint.

32 *Answer the questions:*

      (a) In a store, Luke bought a pint of fresh tomatoes and a pint of dried tomatoes, and the former weighed more. At a farmers' market, Lina bought a pint of dried tomatoes, which weighed more than the fresh tomatoes Luke bought.
How can this happen? Explain your point.

      (b) How many tablespoons would make a pint?

      (c) In the list of U.S. customary units of dry volume, some units are written with the word *dry* and some without. Why?
The list: *bushel, peck, dry gallon, dry quart, and dry pint.*

33 Fill in the blanks. Show your calculations.

      (1) $2\ mi = $ ____ *yards*

      (2) $40\ gal = $ ____ft^3

      (3) $4\ oz = $ ____*lb*

      (4) $8\ dr\ gal = $ ____*pk*

      (5) $3\ tsp = $ ____*Tbsp.*

      (6) $2\ pt = $ ____*qt*

      (7) $8\ cp = $ ____*gal*

      (8) $3\ bu = $ ____*peck*

      (9) $6\ pt = $ ____*qt*

      (10) $7\ in = $ ____*ft*

      (11) $2\ cp = $ ____*Tbp.*

      (12) $2\ cp = $ ____*qt*

      (13) $1\ pk = $ ____*dr qt*

      (14) $0.5\ bu = $ ____*qt*

      In question 14, was it a dry or liquid quart?

Section 14.9 Calculations Using Customary Units

When dealing with international units, we convert all units into a similar format. However, in the case of customary units, it is different. Almost always, it is better to calculate without converting units:

Customer Units Calculations: No Conversion

$2yd\ 2ft\ 8in + 4yd\ 1ft\ 6in = (2+4)yd + (2+1)ft + (8+6)in = 6yd\ 3ft\ 14in = 7yd\ 14in =$
$= 7yd\ 1ft\ 2in$

Looks simple. But maybe the conversion would be even better.

As an exercise, you may try to convert the values into one type of units—inches, feet, or yards—and then add the values. But this would result in complex calculations.

Must I do this? I believe you, Stella. It's better without conversion.

Laziness must never interfere with your point of view. In any case, you will compare different methods of calculations as part of your practice later.
Now, I will teach you how to present your answer in a reader-convenient form.

You already mentioned this in Section 14.6. Any reader must easily understand my answer with the first look!

So, Ezra, you understood why I converted $6yd\ 3ft\ 14in$ into $7yd\ 1ft\ 2\ in$ in the example above, didn't you?

You performed this conversion to present each value in the lowest terms.

Correct. In the example above, $7yd\ 1ft\ 2in$ is a standard presentation for customary units.

A *standard presentation for customary units* means presenting the units in the lowest terms. The standard presentation permits a quality estimation of the value for each measurable attribute. The example below will demonstrate the two-step procedure for converting 372 *inches* into a standard form:

Conversion into Standard Units

Step 1   Convert 372 inches into feet and inches. $373\ in = \frac{372}{12} ft + 1 in = 31\ ft\ 1\ in$

Step 2   Convert 31 ft and 1 inch into yards, feet, and inches. $31 ft\ 1 in = 10 yd\ 1 ft\ 1 in$

It is easier to understand how long $31\ feet$ are than $373\ inches$. However, even this presentation is insufficient because $31 ft$ is a part of a larger unit, yard.

Sure, $10\ yards$ is easier to estimate than $31\ feet$! One yard is like my *big-big* step. Now I understand why we use the *standard presentation for customary units* and how to create it. OK, Stella, I will start practicing.

Summary

Do not convert customary units before calculations. In answers, present customary units in the lowest terms.

(1)   Calculate: 7 Lb 5 oz + 6 Lb 8 oz. (2) Why are lb, oz, and miles called customary units? Are they used in customs control when people enter the U.S.? (3) How many in are in a yard?
(4)   Why was it difficult to read the previous sentence? How can the sentence be written to make it more understandable?

34   Convert feet, yards, and miles to inches: *(a)* 3yd 2ft; *(b)* 45yd 5ft; *(c)* 10miles.

35   Find the answer using three different approaches. For the first approach *(a)*, add yards with yards, feet with feet, and inches with inches. For the second approach *(b)*, convert all units to yards, add the values, and then present the answer in a standard format. For the third approach *(c)*, start with converting to inches. Which approach is better?

$$3yd\ 2ft\ 7in + 6yd\ 1ft\ 5in$$

36   Find the answers, using the best approach. Present your answers the lowest terms.
(a) 6bu 2gal 3qt + 5bu 7gal 2qt; *(b)* 3pt 3cp 9Tbsp + 3qt 2cp 7Tbsp; *(c)* 7Lb 13oz + 4Lb 15oz;
(d) 3gal 5cups– 1gal 7 ups; *(e)* 6gal– 2qt 4pt + 7cp; *(f)* 34bu– 23gal 7pt; *(g)* 2,770yd – 2,345ft.

37   Ron was as tall as Tyler, who was 1 m and 94 centimeters high. Monica and Siri have a 10-gram difference in their weight and some difference in their height. If Monica stands on Siri's head, she would be exactly as tall as Tyler. If 388 divides the total height for all four children, measured in millimeters, the resulting number shows the weight for Siri in kilograms.
   (a) What is the weight of Monica in grams?
   (b) Use the Internet to obtain the answers for these questions: What can you say about the children? Are they short? Tall? What might be their ages?

Chapter 15
Units and Unit Blocks in Word Problems

 Chapter 15 will analyze customary and international units of measure in depth. Some units will combine several other units.

Liters of meters? Pounds of hours? It makes no sense at all.

 Derived units are the units that comprise of several basic units. For example, a speed limit is expressed in miles per hour:
$$v = 55\, mph = 55\, \frac{miles}{hour}.$$

I see. The speed limit on our street is $25\, mph$ which means $25\, miles\ per\ hour$.

 Area of a room is also measured in derived units, square feet:
$$400\, sq.ft = 400\, ft^2.$$
In this chapter, you will use derived units to solve problems involving ratio and proportion. In addition, as part of your practice, you will convert units from the international system to the customary system and *vice versa*.

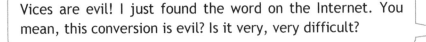

Vices are evil! I just found the word on the Internet. You mean, this conversion is evil? Is it very, very difficult?

 Ezra, there is nothing evil with the conversion. "And *vice versa*" means *and other way around, too.*
You will convert units from the international system to the customary system. Similarly, you will convert units from the customary system to the units of SI.

OK. I'm ready to start.

Section 15.1 Unit Abbreviations

Stella, I already know how to abbreviate units. I use the charts from the Sections 14.5 and 14.8 to abbreviate inches, miles, pounds, kilograms, and feet. I tried to memorize all the abbreviations, but there were too many.

Ezra, Chapter 14 listed various units to provide a general picture. You must memorize only the abbreviations for the most popular units:

International and Customary Units: Conventional Abbreviations

Weight:	kilogram kg	gram g	pound lb	ounce oz
Length:	millimeter mm	centimeter cm	inch in	foot ft
Length:	yard yd	meter m	kilometer km	mile mi
Volume:	quart qt	pint pt	cup cp	tablespoon Tbsp
Volume:	teaspoon tsp	bushel bu	peck pk	gallon gal
Time:	hour h or hr	minute min	second s	microseconds μs
Area:	acre a or ac			
Angle:	degrees deg or ^{0}			

This chart presents only the major units of measure. I don't think it is too much to memorize. However, besides the units that help us measure, there are units that help us specify what we are counting. If we count people or birds, the units are *people* or *birds*.

Are there standards for abbreviating regular words, too?

Four rules allow us to create *comprehensive abbreviations*. The rules for shortcuts help us easily find a connection between a word and its abbreviation.

Rule One: Abbreviate words that start with consonants to include the first group of consonants before the first vowel.

Starting with a Consonant

cat → c.   *block → bl.*   *street → str.*

This idea makes sense. It would be funny to abbreviate *cat* as *ca*. Also, I would never shorten *block* with just one letter *b*.

Rule Two: Abbreviate words that begin with a vowel to include the first group of letters before the second vowel.

Starting with a Vowel

ambulance → amb.   *elephant → el.*

I think this rule is also based on common sense. But for some words it would not work well. For *apple*, the abbreviation would be *appl*. That's too long!

Then abbreviate *apple* with an *a*. The rules are based on common sense. And, if common sense requires you to bend the rules, then bend the rules!

Rule Three: If the abbreviation for a word is too long, abbreviate the word with one letter only.

Too Long

apple → appl. → a.   *eagle → eagl. → e.*   *egg → e.*   *year. → y.*

When bending the rules, just be ready to explain your choice. Logic should always prevail!

Logic is so important, it has a veil? Is it a bridal veil?

The word prev<u>ai</u>l has an *a* and means overcome, succeed, predominate, or conquer. Stella meant, logic must always win.

But how can logic win if two words have the same abbreviations? If a problem talks about *bulbs* in *boxes*, both words must be abbreviated as *b*. No logic at all!

Rule Four: If there is redundancy (repetition), add an extra letter.

Redundancy

bulbs → *bu.*   *boxes* → *bo.*

OK Stella, I will abbreviate according to the rules. But why? Why abbreviate at all? I can write the whole word at the end of calculations.

Ezra, it is frequently necessary to use units in math calculations, and you do not want to write the whole words again and again.

Also, in a Prep or Algebraic Organizer, the abbreviations reduce extra information that can distract you from finding the correct solution to a problem. So abbreviating measuring units helps us with problem solving.

Summary

Memorize the conventional abbreviations. Comprehensive: *cat* → *c.*; *block* → *bl.*; *ambulance* → *amb.*; *apple* → *a.*

(1) *How can you abbreviate these words: sandwich, introduction, story, and electron?*

(2) *Name two units of measure not listed with the units presented earlier in the section.*

(3) *Abbreviate the following units of measure: pound, gallon, bushel, hour, centimeter, meter, peck, teaspoon, quart, cup, kilogram, ounce, gram, yard, feet, acre, minute, tablespoon, foot, second, microsecond, mile, and millimeter.*

38 Make abbreviations for the units below. Also, write the measurable attribute that can be associated with a given unit. It is simple, but not too simple. In this exercise, you cannot use the same attribute more than once.

The units: *inch, meter, cats, days, seconds, liters, pounds, centimeters, acre, feet, and miles.*

39 Write realistic sentences using the given values. Do not use abbreviations.

The values: *3 in, 5 pk, 12 yds, 100 m, 2 cp, and 0.25 ac.*

Section 15.2 Derived Units: Area and Volume

OK, let's introduce the measuring units for area and volume. Most of these units are units of length to the second power:

$$Unit\ of\ Length\ \times\ Unit\ of\ Length.$$

Since these units are made of several simple units, we call them *derived units*.

Measuring Units: Area

In a rectangle:	$Length \cdot Width$	square	meters	$[m^2]$
		square	centimeters	$[cm^2]$
In a circle:	$\pi \cdot radius^2$	square	kilometers	$[km^2]$
		square	inches	$[in.^2]$
		square feet		$[ft^2]$

A unit of area is equal to a square of a unit of length. When a linear unit is changed with the rate of 100, the area unit changes with the rate of 10,000:

Example 1: $1\ m = 100\ cm$. However, $1\ m^2 = 100\ cm \cdot 100\ cm = 10,000\ cm^2$.

Stella, your calculations show that the magic one is different for the <u>length</u> and <u>area</u>. Correct?

It is different. When I convert *centimeters* into *meters*: $Magic\ One_{length} = \frac{100\ cm}{m}$.

However, when I convert cm^2 to m^2, $Magic\ One_{area} = \frac{10,000\ cm^2}{m^2}$.

It's QUITE different. And what about converting cm^3 into m^3?

Look for yourself: $Magic\ One_{volume} = \frac{1,000,000\ cm^3}{m^3}$.

A unit of volume equals a unit of length cubed. When linear unit size changes with the rate of 100, the volume unit changes with the rate of 1,000,000:

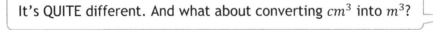

Example 2: $1\ m = 100\ cm$. However, $1m^3 = 100\ cm \cdot 100\ cm \cdot 100\ cm = 1,000,000\ cm^3$.

So, units of volume are made of linear units to the third power:
$Unit\ of\ Length \times Unit\ of\ Length \times Unit\ of\ Length.$

You are correct, Ezra. SI units for measuring volume are units of length to the third power. More examples are presented below.

Measuring Units: Volume

In a rectangular prism: $Length \cdot Width \cdot Height$

In a sphere: $\frac{4}{3} \cdot \pi \cdot radius^3$

cubic	meters	$[m^3]$
cubic	centimeters	$[cm^3]$
cubic	millimeters	$[mm^3]$
cubic	inches	$[in.^3]$
cubic feet		$[ft^3]$

Stella, with SI units it's simple. Can you give me an example of converting customary units?

Unit Conversion for Customary Units

$1ft^2 = 12in \cdot 12in = 144in^2$ $1ft^3 = (12in)^3 = 1,728in^3$

When units of length change, the units of area and volume change much faster than the length.

I see. But it goes against my expectations. I hope, after some practice, my expectations will adjust to reality. Are we done with derived units for area and volume?

Yes. But I would like to review one more topic. As you already know, there are units of area and volume that do not contain the words *square* or *cubic* in their names. You must know how to convert these units, too. So, here are a few more examples of conversion.

Measuring Units: Atypical Area and Volume

Area $1\ hectare = 10,000\ m^2 = 0.01\ km^2$

             $1\ acre = 4,840\ yd^2 = 43,560\ ft^2$

Volume $1\ iter = 1\ dm^3 = 1,000\ cm^3$

             $1\ gal \sim 0.13\ cubic\ feet \sim 231 cubic\ inches$

Ezra, I think it's impossible to memorize how to convert all the units. Rates of conversion are so different. Therefore, use the rates of conversion for simple units to convert derived units.

I'll use the last chart you presented here. Memorizing $1 \, acre = 4,840 \, yd^2$ is too much for me.

Summary

Area → [length unit]². Volume → [length unit]³. To convert derived units, convert each base-unit separately.

Convert and explain the meaning for each conversion.

$300,000 \, cm = \underline{\quad} m$ $300,000 \, cm^2 = \underline{\quad} m^2$ $300,000 \, cm^3 = \underline{\quad} m^3$ $300,000 \, cm^2 = \underline{\quad} m^3$

$1 \, yd = \underline{\quad} in$ $1 \, yd^2 = \underline{\quad} in^2$ $1 \, yd^3 = \underline{\quad} in^3$ $81 \, ft^4 = \underline{\quad} yd^4$

40   *Fill in the blanks. Show your calculations.*

      (a) $54 \, m^2 = \underline{\quad} cm^2$ *(b)* $4,500,000 m^3 = \underline{\quad} km^3$ *(c)* $0.004 \, mm^2 = \underline{\quad} dm^2$

      (d) $254 \, mm = \underline{\quad} m$ *(e)* $1,964 \, g = \underline{\quad} kg$ *(f)* $6,000,000 \, kg = \underline{\quad} Gg$

Solve the following two problems by presenting a solution in the Soft Algebra *format. Show pictures that illustrate your solution.*

41   Lila's property*, like Lola's property, had a rectangular shape and a frontage $72\frac{23}{45}$ yd long. Define the width of the property as the length of the frontage. Lila's property had a length of $150\frac{24}{41}$ *feet*. Lola's property area was twice as big as Lila's. What was the length of Lola's property in yards?

42   The volume of the Cloud Gate (Bean) sculpture in Chicago is about 2,600 cubic meters.
      (a) What is the Bean's volume in cubic centimeters?
      (b) How many such Beans could be contained in 1 cubic kilometer?

---

* In this case, the meaning of the word property is not "a property of matter." It is a property that belongs to a person. It can be a house, parcel, car, and so on.

Section 15.3 Derived Units: Objects in Groups

Below, I will introduce derived units made of two <u>different</u> simple units. These units are used in problems involving groups of objects.

These are *proportion problems* and *ratio problems*. We will discuss the former in the current section.

There are four steps to solving *proportion problems*.
   A. Identify two types of units the problems contain.
   B. Clearly list all given numbers.
   C. Present the problems as a proportion-type chart.
   D. Solve the problems using derived units written in a math format.

I will discuss these four steps using *One Car Proportion* problem as an example.

One Car Proportion Problem

Each car has 4 wheels. How many wheels will 7 cars have?

1 *c.*	4 *wh.*
7 *c.*	? *wh.*

$$4\frac{wh.}{c.} \cdot 7c. = 28 \, wh.$$

Answer: Seven cars will have 28 wheels.

According to <u>Step A</u>, I must identify two types of units—cars and wheels.
Then, following <u>Step B</u>, I must list the numbers: 4 and 7.

Ezra, the problem has three givens: 4, 7, and 1. One is given in the implicit form: *each* here means *one*.
To help you with <u>Step C</u>, I created a Proportion Organizer below.
In a *Proportion Organizer*, each column represents one type of unit. Also, when presenting a problem as a proportion, read the Proportion Organizer to see if your presentation is correct.

One Car Proportion Problem: Proportion Organizer

Cars	Wheels
1 *c.*	4 *wh.*
7 *c.*	? *wh.*

Read? I can read. Cars, wheels, 1 car, 4 wheels, 7 cars, and *question mark* wheels. It doesn't make sense, and it doesn't examine anything!

To read a proportion for this problem means the following:
1 *car has* 4 *wheels, and* 7 *cars have an unknown number of wheels.*

OK, I understand. The presented problem is simple.

Yes, but the units are not. The sentence *Each car has* 4 *wheels* specifies that there are 4 *wheels per car*.
In math format, instead of the word *per*, a *division-line* must be used.
Therefore, the units *wheels per car* appears as $\frac{wheels}{car}$; when abbreviated, $\frac{wh.}{c.}$.
So, instead of writing 4 *wh.*, you must write, $4\frac{wh.}{c.}$. See the summary below.

Derived Units: Everyday vs. Mathematical Formats

English Format	Fraction Format	Abbreviated Form
4 *wheels per car* →	$4\frac{wheels}{car}$ →	$4\frac{wh.}{c.}$

When writing derived units, you may check yourself by reading the units while using the word *per* instead of a fraction line.

You mean, reading $\frac{students}{class}$ as *students per class*?

Yes, Ezra. Just for training, read the numbers with their units in the example below. You will find, in two examples, the units make no sense.

$4\frac{fish}{tank}$	$4\frac{tanks}{fish}$	$4\frac{crs}{wheel}$
4 *fish per tank*	4 *tanks per fish*	4 *cars per wheel*

I see, Stella. I did not think you can make a joke by writing a unit! Sure, we can't put 4 cars on one wheel. And also... 4 tanks for a fish. It's too much.

By following the example presented in this section, you will be able to make Proportion Organizers for quite a few proportion problems.

Proportion problems? Stella, you mean the problems with two types of measuring units?

Oh, sorry Ezra! I was so concerned with explaining derived units, I forgot to define what proportion problems are. Sorry, sorry, and sorry.
Proportion problems are problems that talk about two or more proportional values. *Proportional values* are the values that change in similar ways.

In the *One Car Proportion* problem, when the number of cars increases, the number of wheels increases, too. If the number of cars is tripled, the number of the wheels is tripled. If the number of cars is multiplied by 7, the number of wheels must be multiplied by 7, too.

However, if there are cars with a different number of wheels, then, Ezra, the number of wheels is <u>not proportional</u> to the number of the cars. Therefore, in that case, we could not talk about proportion.

I see. If there are $4\, fish\, per\, tank$, then in ten tanks, we will have $10 \times 4\, fish$. Stella, I think I understand proportion problems and can start my practice.

Summary

Proportion problems: find two types of units, list givens, make a proportion. Use derived units in calculations.

? *Read the units below. What meaning might each of these numbers below have?*

$3\, \frac{glasses}{girl}$ $\quad 4\, \frac{girls}{chair}$ $\quad 5\, \frac{elephants}{forest}$ $\quad 6\, \frac{forests}{elephant}$ $\quad 500\, \frac{km^2}{person}$ $\quad 600\, \frac{persons}{km^2}$

---

43 For the proportions below, perform calculations. Show units of measure for each number.

(a) $\begin{array}{cc} 54\, st. & 3\, cl. \\ ?\, st. & 1\, cl. \end{array}$ (b) $\begin{array}{cc} 1\, pl. & 8\, c. \\ 254\, pl. & ?\, c. \end{array}$ (c) $\begin{array}{cc} 1{,}964\, g & 7\, Ku. \\ 1\, g & ?\, Ku. \end{array}$ (d) $\begin{array}{cc} 45\, h. & 1\, b. \\ 105\, h. & ?\, b. \end{array}$

(e) $\begin{array}{cc} 25\, j. & 1\, m \\ 1\, j. & ?\, m \end{array}$ (f) $\begin{array}{cc} 138\, v. & 18\, k. \\ 1\, v. & ?\, k. \end{array}$ (g) $\begin{array}{cc} 24\, hr & 1\, d. \\ ?\, hr & 20\, d. \end{array}$ (h) $\begin{array}{cc} 450\, m & 36\, d. \\ ?\, m & 1\, d. \end{array}$

44 Jack shared a dozen bananas equally with his oldest sister and youngest brother. How many bananas did everyone receive?

45 Pam's dad said, when Pam contracted a virus, he stayed with her in the emergency room three days and two nights. How many hours did Pam's dad stay with Pam in the emergency room? *Is your answer precise?*

46 Nelly split her 20 candies with her siblings, and each received 4 candies. How many siblings did Nelly have?

47 Glenn walked at a constant speed for 5 hours. He covered 26 km. What was the distance that Glenn covered in one hour? *Use a proportion presentation when solving this problem.*

Section 15.4 Proportion and the Unit-Block Approach

 Ezra, most people calculate answers in proportion problems using formal calculations without giving a second thought.

 I would love to solve problems quickly, too, Stella.

 Sure. But the goal is...a bit more sophisticated. I want you solve complex problems with ease. Not only the simple problems.

 So what is bad about formal calculations?

 Many students and adults do not understand *why* formal calculations work. Therefore, they cannot apply formal calculations for solving challenging problems. I will teach you how to use a *Unit-Block Approach*. In this approach, we break calculations into smaller steps; this helps us understand problems in depth.

 You mean, Stell, using Unit-Block Approach leads to calculation-chunking?

 Yes, Ezra. I will teach you how to apply the Unit-Block Approach using the *Six Cars Proportion* problem as an example.

Six Cars Proportion Problem

Six cars have 30 wheels. How many cars will have 40 wheels?

6 *c.*	30 *wh.*
? *c.*	40 *wh.*

Unit Block

Applying the Unit-Block Approach involves three steps:
1. Identify a unit block.
2. Find the value of the block.
3. Use the value of the unit block to solve the problem.

The *unit block* in the problem above is *the number of the wheels in one car.*

Other examples of unit blocks are number of apples in a box, weight of fish in an individual tank, number of tables in one room, area of each tile, volume of a glass, number of beats per second, and so on.

I see. And how do I find the size of a unit block?

Calculate a unit block using givens from a proportion chart. Then, mark it with lowercase b.

In the *Six Cars Proportion* problem, 6 *cars* have 30 *wheels*. Therefore, one car has 5 wheels. Using b as a label for *the value of a unit block*, I calculated,
$$b = \frac{30\text{wh.}}{6\text{c.}} = 5\frac{\text{wh.}}{\text{c.}}.$$

Since you found that each car has 5 *wheels*, finding the number of cars having 40 *wheels* is straightforward: $40\ wh. \div 5\frac{wh.}{c.} = 8c.$
Now, I will present this problem and its solution.

Six Cars Proportion Problem: Unit-Block Approach

Six cars have 30 wheels. How many cars will have 40 wheels?

6 c.	30 wh.	b is the number of wheels for one car.
? c.	40 wh.	$b = \frac{30wh.}{6c.} = 5\frac{wh.}{c.}, \quad 40\ wh. \div 5\frac{wh.}{c.} = 8c.$

Answer: Eight cars will have 40 wheels.

As you can see, I started the solution by defining a unit block, b. Then, I calculated b and used it to solve the problem.

I think I can solve the next problem myself.

OK. Then solve the *Four Bricks Proportion* problem using Unit-Block Approach.

Four Bricks Proportion Problem

Four bricks have the weight of 11 kg. How much will 7 bricks weigh?

4 br.	11 kg
7 br.	? kg

As you see, Ezra, the problem deals with bricks and their weight.

I see, Stella. In this problem, a unit block, b, is *the weight of one brick* with the unit of measure, $\frac{kg}{brick}$.

As for a unit block...the weight of one brick is $b = \frac{11kg}{4br.} = 2.75\frac{kg}{br.}$. So, one brick weighs $2.75\ kg$. Now, I will use the size of a unit block to solve this problem.

Four Bricks Proportion Problem: Unit-Block Approach

Four bricks have the weight of 11 kg. How much will 7 bricks weigh?

4 *br.*	11 *kg*	$b = \frac{11kg}{4br.} = 2.75\frac{kg}{br.}$, where b is the weight of a brick.
7 *br.*	? *kg*	$2.75\frac{kg}{br.} \cdot 7br. = 19.25kg$

Unit Block

Answer: Seven bricks will weigh 19.25 kg.

Nice work, Ezra.

Don't mention it. I just followed your instructions: find a unit block, calculate it, and use it.

In the end, I want to mention one more point regarding unit blocks. The Unit-Block Approach allows us to perceive the nuances for each problem and understand the meaning for each value.

Perceive the nuances? Can you be more specific? Down to Earth, Stella. Puh-lease.

Finding a unit block allowed you to see that each car has 5 wheels. This infor-mation generates a question: "Why?" Also, you determined the weight of one brick. This makes you think about the size and material of the bricks.

Calculating unit blocks always adds meaning to word problems. You saw it with the problems in this section. You will also see it later, when solving problems involving percentages and parts. And now, it is time to practice!

Summary

Unit-Block Approach: Identify a unit block. Calculate the value of the block. Use the value to solve the problem.

What are the unit blocks in each situation below? Is it always obvious?

    (1) There are 12 fish in 4 tanks. How many fish are in 9 tanks?

    (2) There are 10 dogs in 5 dog houses. How many dogs are in 15 dog houses?

    (3) If 6 similar apples weigh 2 kg, what is the approximate weight of one apple?

48-55 *Solve the problems using Unit-Block Approach. Some problems will require using the Internet.*

48   If 16 identical pencils make a length of 0.5 m, what would be the length of 20 such pencils?

49   *(a)*   The problem above is not a good problem. *Explain why.*

        (b)   The problem can be fixed by changing one word (in all its instances) or number only. *Propose three different ways for changing the problem.*

50   Mr. Connor paid 2,000 dollars per month for a property he was renting. This property had 4 rooms with a total area of 1,250 square feet. When Mr. Connor decided to expand his business, he started looking for a unit with an area of 2,000 square feet and found one. Although he thought the price per square foot would be lower when he rented a larger space, he found in his area, this is not the case for properties below 3,000 square feet. So, for his new 2,000 square foot unit, he will need to pay per square foot the same amount of money he was paying for his old space. What will be Mr. Connor's monthly rent for the new place?

51   A good doctor can touch the hand of a patient and provide a pretty good estimation of the patient's heart rate, i.e., the number of heart beats per minute. Solve the problem below and then explain how doctors can do this.

    How many heartbeats will Leila have in 5 minutes, if in 20 seconds she has 30 heartbeats?

52   Using her car for a business trip, Darya received 172.5 dollars as a reimbursement for using her car. In her company, the reimbursement is calculated on a "per mile" basis. What was the distance covered during the trip, if for her shorter trip, 20 miles, Darya received a reimbursement in the amount of 11 dollars 50 cents? All the trips were made during the same year, so the payment per mile was the same.

53   *Use the Internet if needed.* In the previous problem, Darya received reimbursement for her trip. Basically, Darya used her car to drive from downtown Chicago to a university where she had a meeting with a professor who had a proposal for an interesting type of technology, which involved high tech engineering research in energy exploration. Her company was interested in this technology. What university did she visit? Using the last problem's data, estimate the distance from the university to downtown Chicago. Do you have sufficient data to determine the answer?

54   A solid sphere made from copper weighs 134.4 kg. Estimate its volume in cm³ and liters. *Find the copper's density elsewhere.*

55   Rosemount had not received any snow yet. The first snow came in an intense and frightening way. It felt as if it would never end. The snow was accumulating at a constant rate for one day and one night. After the first 7 hours of snowing, Abigail went outside at 8 a.m. and found 5 inches of snow. At what time will the snow reach 12 inches?

Section 15.5 The Ratio-of-Elements Approach

4 : 5

$\dfrac{4}{5}$

4 to 5

Ezra, we will discuss ratios in the following few sections.
A *ratio of two numbers* is a relationship representing the quotient of the first and second numbers.

So, Stella, the ratio of 4 and 5 is $\dfrac{4}{5}$.

Yes. But, this ratio, in algebraic language, must be written as 4 : 5. You can understand a ratio from the following example.

On a team, a ratio of girls and boys is 2 : 3 (*two to three*).

This means, the quotient of the number of girls and boys is $\dfrac{2}{3}$. In terms of the *Ratio-of-Elements Approach*, for every two girls, there are three boys.

Do you mean, a team can contain 2 girls and 3 boys, 6 girls and 9 boys, or 8 girls and 12 boys?

Yes, Ezra. You got the point.

When solving problems involving the ratio of two numbers, follow these rules:
 1) Reduce ratios when possible. Instead of 8 : 6, use 4 : 3.
 2) Pay close attention to the order of the words describing ratios. The ratio 4 : 3 is not the same as 3 : 4.
 3) When using the Ratio-of-Elements Approach, explain the ratio as a proportion.

Reduce ratios just like fractions: reduce a ratio 10 : 15 to 2 : 3.

Why make a special rule about the order?
Sure, 2 : 3 is not the same as 3 : 2!

The rule is about sentences, Ezra, not formulas. If <u>the ratio of girls and boys is 2 : 3</u>, there are 2 girls for every 3 boys.
When <u>the ratio of boys and girls is 2 : 3</u>, there are 3 girls for every 2 boys. The ratio is reversed.

Stella, I am OK with your second rule. But... how will I explain a ratio as a proportion?

I will clarify the third rule using the *Girls and Boys* problem as an example.

Girls and Boys Problem

There are 42 girls on a team. The ratio of girls and boys on the team is 2 : 3. How many boys are there?

<u>To make a proportion</u>, I will rewrite the problem without changing its meaning using different words.

Girls and Boys Problem: Ratio-of-Elements Approach

Alternative Problem: There are two teams of girls and boys. In each team, the number of girls is proportional to the number of boys. The smallest team has 2 girls and 3 boys. Find the number of boys on a team with 42 girls.

2 *g.*	3 *b.*	*b* is the number of girls per boy.
42 *g.*	? *b.*	$b = 2 \,.\div 3\, b. = \frac{2}{3}\frac{g.}{b.}$ and $42\, g. \cdot \frac{2}{3}\frac{g.}{b.} = 63\, b.$

Answer: There are 63 boys on the team.

The new problem does not have a ratio but has the same answer as the original problem.

Look, Stella. There is a very strange unit block, $\frac{2}{3}$ *of a girl per boy*. Does this mean, one boy has a friend, $\frac{2}{3}$ of a girl? Hee-hee. It is a funny couple: a boy and $\frac{2}{3}$ of a girl.

I agree, Ezra, the meaning of a unit block in this solution is somewhat abstract. However, that strange unit block helps obtain the answer to the problem. Below, I will show you even a better couple. Look at the solution I placed below.

Girls and Boys Problem: *Boys per Girl*

Alternative Problem. There are two teams of girls and boys. In each team, the number of girls is proportional to the number of boys. The smallest team has 2 girls and 3 boys. Find the number of boys on a team with 42 girls.

2 g.	3 b.	b is the number of boys per girl.
42 g.	? b.	$b = 3\,b. \div 2\,g. = \frac{3}{2}\frac{b.}{g.}$
		$42\,g. \div \frac{3}{2}\frac{b.}{g.} = 63\,b.$

Answer: There are 63 boys on the team.

Stella, in this solution, there is 1.5 of a boy for each girl. It's so weird!
Here, Stella, the meaning of a unit block is as abstract as in the first case. So, it does not make any difference what ratio I will choose as a unit block for this problem.

By the way, Ezra, the unit blocks in the Ratio-of-Elements Approach are not always meaningless. Below, I present the *Water and Sugar* problem. The problem has a *meaningful* unit block. Way too meaningful.

Water and Sugar Problem

The ratio of the volume of Coca-Cola in liters to the weight of sugar in *grams* is 3 : 320. How much sugar does the 0.222-liter can of *Coca-Cola* contain?

320 g	3 l	b is the weight of sugar (in *grams*) in a liter of *Coca-Cola*.
? g	0.222 l	$b = 320\,g \div 3\,l = \frac{320\,g}{3\,l} = 106\frac{2}{3}\frac{g}{l} \approx 107\frac{g}{l}$
		$0.222\,l \cdot \frac{320\,g}{3\,l} = 1.11 \cdot 32\,g = 23.68\,g \approx 24\,g$

Answer: A mini can of *Coca-Cola* contains 24 grams of sugar.

I agree, Stella, a unit block, 107 grams of sugar in a liter of Coca-Cola, does have meaning. It is about a half cup of sugar!

You see, Ezra, the unit block helped you more deeply understand the problem.

Sure, Stella. Too much sugar is not good for your health.

Definitely. Now, I will summarize. The introduced approach considers ratios of numbers. Each number represents the quantities of objects (elements). Therefore, I called this the *Ratio-of-Elements Approach*.
In the next section, we will discuss one more method for solving the problems with a ratio: we will use the Ratio-of-Groups Approach.

Summary

Ratio problem → Ratio-of-Elements Approach → Proportion. The order of the words in a ratio is important.

Create a simple word problem that involves a ratio and then solve the problem.

56-58 *Solve the problems using the Ratio-of-Elements Approach.*

56   *Use two alternative unit blocks.*
The ratio of dogs and cats in house number 463 on 128th Street is 6 : 8. How many dogs are there if there are 28 cats in the house? *Which solution was easiest? Why?*

57   *Use two alternative unit blocks.*
The ratio of white and red roses in each vase is 5 : 10. How many white roses are in a vase with 36 red roses?

58   The ratio of the salt (in grams) to the volume of Black Sea deep waters in milliliters is 7:200. How much salt is in an 80-liter bathtub with Black Sea deep water?

Section 15.6 The Ratio-of-Groups Approach

In the previous section, a ratio was interpreted as a quotient between the numbers of elements. However, many ratio-problems would benefit from an alternative, the **Ratio-of-Groups Approach**.
I will use the *Girls and Boys* problem to compare the Ratio-of-Elements and Ratio-of-Groups Approaches.

You mean, Stella, you presented the picture on the left-hand side below just to show the comparison?

I did. On the right-hand side, five rectangles represent 2 groups of girls and 3 groups of boys. It illustrates how the *Ratio-of-Groups Approach* presents the *Girls and Boys* problem.

Girls and Boys **Problem:** Girls ∶ Boys = 2 ∶ 3

Ratio-of-Elements Approach

Ratio-of-Groups Approach

b is a unit block

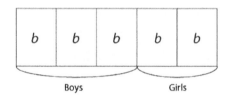

Numbers of girls and boys on a team are proportional to the numbers of girls and boys on a smallest team with 2 girls and 3 boys.

On a team, there are 3 groups of boys and 2 groups of girls.
Each unit group has b children.

In the *Girls and Boys* problem, according to the Ratio-of-Groups Approach, a unit block b represents the number of children in one group.

You mean, there are three b-children groups of boys and two b-children groups of girls?

Something like that. Also, it is known, two b-children groups of girls have 42 children.

Cool. Then, each *b*-children group has 21 children. It's easy.

Girls and Boys Problem: Ratio-of-Groups Approach

There are 42 girls on a team. The ratio of girls and boys on the team is 2:3. How many boys are on the team?

$G : B = 2 : 3$	G – the number of girls.	**Alternative Problem**
$G = 42 \, ch. = 2 \cdot b$	B – the number of boys.	A unit block, b, represents the number of children
$b = G \div 2$		in a *unit*-group. There are two b-children groups
$B = 3 \cdot b$	$b = 42 \, ch. \div 2 = 21 \, ch.$	of girls and three b-children groups of boys. There
	$B = 3 \cdot 21 \, ch. = 63 \, ch.$	are 42 girls in the two b-groups. How many boys
$B = ? \, ch.$		are in the three b-groups?

Answer: There are 63 boys on the team.

For this solution, first, I used the Ratio-of-Groups Approach to create an alternative problem. Then, I found the size of a b-children group (unit block). Finally, I calculated the number of boys in 3 groups.

Stella, I think for the *Girls and Boys* problem, the Ratio-of-Groups Approach makes more sense than the Ratio-of-Elements Approach.

Ezra, the Ratio-of-Groups Approach will help you solve quite challenging problems. However, for some problems, the Ratio-of-Elements Approach will work better.

Summary

Ratio-of-Groups Approach helps solve problems with ratios. Create an alternative problem and find a unit block.

Create a word problem involving a ratio. For solving the problem, apply Ratio-of-Groups Approach: present the problem as an alternative problem with a ratio between the groups' numbers. Make an illustration and solve the problem.

59-60 *Use the Ratio-of-Groups Approach. Present the ratio in the lowest terms. Then, present an alternative problem, which approaches a ratio using the ratio of groups. Illustrate the problem and create an Algebraic Organizer. Solve the problem using a Unit-Block Approach.*

59 The ratio of dogs and cats in house number 132 on 19th Street is 12 : 10. How many cats are there if there are 90 dogs in the house?

60 The ratio of red and white roses in each vase is 18 : 20. How many white roses are in a vase with 36 red roses?

Section 15.7 Challenging Proportions and Ratios

In this section, we will discuss two more examples involving ratios. It will prepare you for solving slightly more challenging word problems.

The first example will present a ratio with three numbers.

Long Proportion Problem

The ratio of pears, apples, and strawberries on a table is 10:3:15, and there are 84 fruits altogether. How many pears, apples, and strawberries are on the table?

Parameters A – the number of apples
P – the number of pears
S – the number of strawberries
N – the total number of groups

$P : A : S = 10 : 3 : 15$
$P + A + S = 84\ fr.$
$N = (10 + 3 + 15)gr.$
$b = (P + A + S) \div N$
$P = 10 \cdot b$
$A = 3 \cdot b$
$S = 15 \cdot b$

$P =?\ fr.\ \ A =?\ fr.\ \ S =?\ fr.$

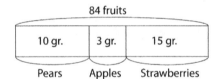

84 fruits

| 10 gr. | 3 gr. | 15 gr. |
| Pears | Apples | Strawberries |

$N = (10 + 3 + 15)gr. = 28\ gr.$
$b = 84\ fr. \div 28\ gr. = 3\ \frac{fr.}{gr.}$
$P = 3\ \frac{fr.}{gr.} \cdot 10\ gr. = 30\ fr.$
$A = 3\ \frac{fr.}{gr.} \cdot 3\ gr. = 9\ fr.$
$S = 3\ \frac{fr.}{gr.} \cdot 15\ gr. = 45\ fr.$

Answer: There are 30 pears, 9 apples, and 45 strawberries on the table.

Stella, to find the unit block in this problem, you divided the total number of fruits by the number of groups (blocks). However, in the visual model, you failed to put three question marks: for Pears, Apples, and Strawberries.

My fault, Ezra. When you make visual models, do not miss anything.

The second example will present proportion with a *unit adjustment*. The units in the problem below are kilograms. However, to emphasize the difference in units, I will write *kg of apples* and *kg of pears*.

Ratio of Weights Problem

The ratio between the weights of fruits in each box is the same. Small boxes have 78.3 kg of apples and 45 kg of pears. Big boxes have 135 kg of pears. What is the weight of apples in the big boxes?

kg of apples → a.	**kg of pears → p.**
78.3 a.	45 p.
? a.	135 p.

$b = 78.3\,a. \div 45\,p. = 1\frac{33.3}{45}\frac{a.}{p.} = 1\frac{3.7}{5}\frac{a.}{p.} = 1\frac{7.4}{10}\frac{a.}{p.} = 1.74\frac{a.}{p.}$

$1.74\frac{a.}{p.} \cdot 135\,p. = 8.7 \cdot 27\,a. = 234.9\,a.$

Answer: The weight of the apples in the big boxes is 234.9 kg.

I see the adjustments! Instead of *kg of a.* and *kg of p.*, you used *a.* and *p.* So, this section has two topics: three-number ratios and unit shortening.

Ezra, you missed the point. The topic for this section is the following—use logic to adjust your approach when a problem requires it.

Summary

Adjust your approach when a problem requires it.

Create a word problem where the sum of two values is known as well as the ratio between the values. Make an illustration and solve the problem.

61-62 *Define parameters, present the ratio in the lowest terms, finally, illustrate and solve the problem using the Ratio-of-Groups Approach. Then, present an alternative solution to the problem.*

61 The ratio of students and teachers in all schools of Geoppolis is the same. In the first school, there are 700 students and 22 teachers. In the second school, there are 350 students. How many teachers are in the second school?

62 The ratio of students with freckles to students without freckles in a school is 1 to 75. If the school has 2 girls and 3 boys with freckles, how many students attend this school in all?

63-67 *Solve the problems using the Unit-Block Approach. Illustrate the problems where the Ratio-of-Groups Approach is applied.*

63 A recipe for yellow cake requires 8 eggs, one cup of sugar, and one cup of flour. In case you have a dish with a capacity for 1.5 cakes, how many eggs do you need?

64 At 60 mi per hour a car is traveling 88 ft/s. How many feet per second does a car travel at $75\frac{mi}{hr}$?

65 The ratio of guitar players, piano players, and clarinet players in Lintoppo's schools of music is 37 : 26 : 15. Lintoppo's largest school has 1,560 students. How many students play a clarinet?

66 The ratio of pears and apples on each table is 36 to 24. There are 40 fruits on an oval table. How many of them are apples?

67 The ratio of decorative grass, roses, and edible plant areas in a botanical garden is 18 : 27 : 65. The grass and roses combined cover 9 acres. What is the area used for edible plants?

Section 15.8 Unit Conversion

When students need to convert measuring units from the customary system to international or *vice versa*, they can use *step-by-step substitution*.

Ezra, for the system-to-system conversion, it will be convenient to use the unit equivalents from the list below. I rounded them unremorsefully.

Unit Conversion: Approximated Equivalents

Customary	International	International	Customary
1 mi	1.6 km or 1,600 m	1 km	0.6 mi
1 yd	0.9 m	1 m	1.1 yd or 3.3 ft
1 in	2.5 cm	1 cm	0.4 in
1 ft	0.3 m or 30 cm	1 mm	0.04 in
1 gal	3.8 l	1 l	0.26 gal
1 lb	0.45 kg or 450 g	1 kg	2.2 lb
1 oz	28 g	1 g	0.035 oz
1 fluid oz	29.6 mL	1 mL	0.034 fl. oz
1 ac	4,050 m^2	1 km^2	250 acre
1 tbl sp	15 cm^3	1 cm^3	0.07 Tbl sp

Un-re-mor-se-fully. From your word, I only understand the last part. Fully. Or rather, folly.

Ezra, unremorsefully means without any remorse (regret, sorrow). I <u>signifi-cantly</u> rounded these numbers. They are very easy to work with. These equivalents will help you develop your intuition regarding the units of measure. Also, in *Soft Algebra* problems, many calculations will become easier when you use the approximated values from this list.

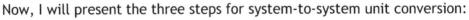

Now, I will present the three steps for system-to-system unit conversion:
  A. Choose an equivalent (a *magic one*) using the values presented above.
  B. Substitute units by their equivalents after separating units from a number.
  C. Complete calculations.
Two examples below will demonstrate how the *step-by-step substitution* works.

Miles-to-Meters Problem

| $D = 10\ mi = ?\ \text{m}$ | $1\ mi\ =\ 1,600\ m$ | A |
| | $D = 10\ mi = 10 \cdot 1\ mi = 10 \cdot 1,600\ m = 16,000\ m$ | B-C |

Answer: $D = 16,000\ m.$

I see, Stella. At first, you presented the substitution equivalent, $1\ mi = 1,600\ m$. Then, you separated a unit, $1\ mile$, from a number: $10\ mi = 10 \cdot 1\ mi$. Next, you substituted $1\ mile$ by its equivalent and completed the calculations. I think I got it and am ready to see your second example.

Mph-to-SI Problem

$v = 4.5\ mph\ = ?\ \text{m/s}$	$1\ mi\ =\ 1,600\ m$ $1\ hr\ =\ 60 \cdot 60\ s = 3,600\ s$	A
	$v = 4.5\ mph = 4.5\ \frac{mi}{hr} = 4.5 \cdot 1\ mi \div 1\ hr = 4.5 \cdot 1,600\ m \div 3,600\ s$	B
	$v = 4.5 \cdot 1,600\ m \div 3,600\ s = \frac{4.5 \cdot 1,600\ m}{3,600\ s} = 2\frac{m}{s}$	C

Answer: $v = 2\frac{m}{s}.$

Since $1\ mph = \frac{mi}{hr}$, I converted $\frac{mi}{hr}$ into $\frac{m}{s}$: I converted miles into meters and hours into seconds. Also, I presented steps A, B, and C on separate rows. With practice, you will be able to reduce the number of steps.

I'm sure, after minor practice, I will perform system-to-system conversion with ease.

Summary

For conversion, substitute units with their equivalents. In this book, use rounded numbers for the equivalents.

(1) *Why do you need unit conversion?* (2) *Present 3,274 seconds in its lowest terms.*
(3) *Present 4 miles per hour in meters per second.*
(4) *Which material has a greater density if material A has the density of 4 g per cubic centimeter, and material B has the density of 400 lb per cubic foot.*

68 *Convert units from one system of measure to another. When presenting your answer, use scientific notation. (a)* $15L = \_\_Gal$; *(b)* $22\ yd = \_\_cm$; *(c)* $50mph = \_\_\frac{km}{hr}$; *(d)* $25\ oz = \_\_kg$;
    (e) $44\ km^2 = \_\_acre$; *(f)* $50\ sec^{-1} = \_\_hr^{-1}$; *(g)* $50\ km = \_\_ft\ per\ s$; *(h)* $17\ m^3 = \_\_tbs.$

69 The first hour, a car was moving 60 miles per hour. During the second hour, the car was moving with a speed of 60 km per hour, and the final hour the car was moving with a speed of 50 meters per second. *(a) Find the highest and lowest speeds of this car. (b) Find the average speed by adding the speed of the car at each hour and dividing it by the number of hours. Express your answer in System International rounded to the nearest integers. (c) Are all the speeds given realistic? If not, why?*

Chapter 16
Elements of Kinematics

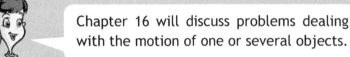
Chapter 16 will discuss problems dealing with the motion of one or several objects.

Several?! You mean, there will be more than one puma? I think one running predator is more than enough!

Ezra, concentrate.
The branch of science that deals with moving objects is called K-I-N-E-M-A-T-I-C-S. Consequently, the problems dealing with motion are called *kinematic problems*.

The word *kinematics* reminds me of cinema.

The words do have a common root...Ezra, return to the topic. To solve simple kinematic problems, you can use proportions. However, this would not work with complex kinematic problems. Therefore, you will learn a new method, which I call the d-t-v approach.

I knew it was something about TV, Stella!

Ezra, the name has nothing to do with TV. The approach involves specific parameters, Freestyle Models, and graphs.
The kinematic approach is a technique, which can be applied to a wide range of problems—some are not kinematic. Later, you will utilize this approach in your physics class.

(1) What is kinematics?

(2) List the methods used for solving kinematic problems.

(3) When "movie theater" is translated into Russian, the word sounds like a combination of two words, kino and theater. Do you have any idea why?

Section 16.1 Constant Velocity

 In general, kinematic problems talk about objects that move: trains, animals, people, airplanes, or bicycles.

 The parameters for these problems are distance, time, and velocity (speed).

 Kinematic problems can also involve acceleration. However, we will discuss only problems, where acceleration equals zero. I will refer to these problems as *distance-time-velocity* problems with velocity as the unit block.

Kinematic Parameters

Distance	Time	Speed or Velocity
d	t	v

Velocity? What is it?

 I use the word *velocity* instead of the word *speed* for two reasons. First, velocity involves direction. Second, velocity can be negative. You will see why these features are important for problem solving later. For now, just get used to the word. In this section, velocity has the same meaning as speed. To find average velocity, divide distance by time: $v = d/t$.

Finding Velocity

Distance covered in a unit of time	$\dfrac{Distance}{Time}$	$[\frac{m}{s}]$

To find the distance covered by a moving object, multiply the average velocity by time: $d = vt$. To calculate time of a trip, divide distance by the average velocity, $t = d/v$.

 Mr. Refiner, I found two interesting examples of velocity:
- ✓ an ant crawls 8 cm/sec, and
- ✓ a rocket needs a velocity of 11,200 m/s to leave the Earth.

Nice examples, Ezra. When solving problems involving constant speed, follow the rules for the d-t-v method:
- A. Rewrite the problem as a chart specifying speed, time, and distance.
- B. Convert all units of measure to the same type.
- C. Use visual models for challenging problems. See next sections for details.

The *Peter's Car* problem will illustrate what a d-t-v format is.

Peter's Car Problem: d-t-v Approach

Peter drives a car at a constant speed along a straight road for 175 miles in 2.5 hours. How much time will it take him to drive 260 miles?

$d_1 = 175\ mi$
$d_2 = 260\ mi$
$t_1 = 2.5\ hr$

$v = 175\ mi \div 2.5\ hr = \frac{1750}{25}\frac{mi}{hr} = 70\ \frac{mi}{hr}$

$t_2 = 260\ mi \div 70\ \frac{mi}{hr} = 3\frac{5}{7}\ hr = 3hr\ \frac{300}{7}min = 3hr\ 42min\ 51\frac{3}{7}s$

$t_2 = ?\ hr$

Answer: It will take Peter $3\ hr\ 42\ min\ 51\frac{3}{7}s$ to drive 260 miles.

The problem has two instances of motion with the same velocity, v. The first time, the car drives $175\ miles$. Then the car drives $260\ miles$.
Index 1 denotes the first instance: d_1-t_1-v.
Index 2 denotes the second instance: d_2-t_2-v.

There can be a lot of subscripts in these problems! If a car moves from a library to a bank and then from the bank to school, I can use parameters d_{LB}, t_{LB}, v_{LB}, d_{BS}, t_{BS}, and v_{BS}. Or, I can use d_1, t_1, v_1, d_2, t_2, and v_2, instead. Can't I?

It is your choice. Also, it is appropriate to use u and v for the velocities of two different objects. For example, if a freerunner runs with velocity v atop a train, it is convenient to use u for the velocity of the train.

OK, rule A is clear. Rule B is also simple, I think. Don't worry, Stella, I will remember to convert units and will use the rounded equvalents from the list in Section 14.7.

From the list in Section 14.8, Ezra. Be precise when you talk to people. As for rule C, wait for the next section.

Summary

In *distance-ime-velocity* problems, use d, t, and v as parameters. Convert units. Use visual presentations.

(1) Why do we need to use velocity if we can use the word speed?

(2) What four parameters are used in kinematic problems?

(3) What do the parameters d, t, and v represent in d-t-v problems?

(4) Can all kinematic problems be referred to as d-t-v problems?

(5) List the formulas that can be used to find d, t, and v.

(6) When solving kinematic problems, what are the three steps to follow?

70-72 *Solve the problems. Present your solution in the d-t-v format.*

70   Cleo looked at her phone at 12:15 p.m. and found she had some extra time before she needed to be elsewhere. So, she sat on a bench for 10 minutes and then started walking toward the library with a constant speed of $4\frac{km}{hr}$. In a quarter hour, she arrived at the library. How far is the library from the bench where Cleo was sitting?

71   Two drivers were going from their homes to Lake on the Moon, a city. The first driver drove 3 hours and 40 minutes with a speed of 60 miles per hour. The second driver drove 2 hours and 8 minutes with a speed of 120 km per hour. Which driver lives closer to Lake on the Moon? How much closer?

72   Cindy walked with a speed of $5\frac{km}{hr}$ the first 5 miles. Then, she jogged a mile with a speed of $3.5\frac{mi}{hr}$. How much time did she spend on her trip in total? Using *1.6 km in a mile* as a coefficient, calculate time to the nearest minutes.

Section 16.2 Freestyle Model

When solving challenging kinematic problems, use a *Freestyle Model* to portray problems in a simplified manner.

Does freestyle mean "do what I want"? No rules?

Mm...There are three rules about "no rules" presentation in a Freestyle Model.
- ✓ Values do not necessarily have units.
- ✓ Values can be described using English or parameters.
- ✓ Information might be presented as pictures, sentences, lines, or other.

The *Bike and Car* problem will help you understand what a Freestyle Model is.

Bike and Car Problem

At 6:00 a.m., a bicyclist started biking from village A to village B at the same speed for 2.5 hours. During this time, he covered 32 kilometers. After stopping for 30 minutes, he continued biking. At this time, he increased his speed by 3 kilometers per hour to compensate for the 30-minute break he took. At 7:30 a.m. on the same day, a car driver started driving from village B to village A on the same road. The car continued at the same speed, 50 kilometers per hour, for the entire trip. Villages A and B are 120 kilometers apart.

(a) At what time will the bicyclist arrive at village B?

(b) At what time will the car driver reach village A?

(c) At what time will the driver and the bicyclist pass one another?

The answers should not deviate from the exact solution by more than 5 minutes.

Bike and Car Problem: Freestyle Model

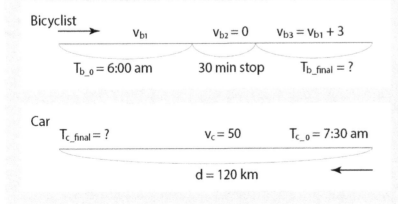

The bicyclist and the driver move in opposite directions.

When do they meet?

Stella, your Freestyle Model has two maps. Also, you added a block with text. Why?

The block with the sentences is also part of the model. The text helps me understand the meaning of the problem. As always, the main goal of a model is to help us understand the problem.

Your model did help me understand what's going on. However, I would mark villages A and B. Also, for the car, I would change the order...

Your Freestyle Model should not be like mine. However, the goal must stay the same—your model should help you better understand the problem.

Now we have completed discussing Freestyle Models. So, it is time to describe all unclear parameters and create an Algebraic Organizer.

Bike and Car Problem: Parameters

T_{bc} is the time when the bicyclist and the driver pass one another.
t_{bc} is the time-period from 6:00 a. m. until the moment they pass one another.

Mr. Refiner, there are many parameters in the problem. Why did you define only two of them?

All other parameters are self-explanatory.

Bike and Car Problem: Algebraic Organizer

Before the Stop	30 min Stop	After the Stop	Opposite Direction
$T_{b\_0} = 6:00\,a.m.$	$v_{b2} = 0$	$v_{b3} = v_{b1} + 3\frac{km}{hr}$	$T_{c\_0} = 7:30\,a.m.$
$d_{b1} = 32\,km$	$t_{b2} = 30\,min = .5\,hr$	$d_{b3} = d - d_{b2}$	$d_c = 120\,km$
$t_{b1} = 2.5\,hr$	$d_{b2} = 0$	$t_{b3} = \frac{d_{b3}}{v_{b3}}$	$v_{c1} = 50\frac{km}{hr}$
$v_{b1} = \frac{d_{b1}}{t_{b1}}$			$t_{c_1} = \frac{d}{v_{c1}}$
$T_{b\_final} = ?$	$T_{bc} = ?$		$T_{c\_final} = ?$

I see now, Mr. Refiner. You organized data in four blocks; the names of the blocks tell us the meaning of the parameters. Also, you defined d_c and v_{c1} as negative to emphasize that the bike and the car move in opposite direction.

The calculations below will help find the distance the bicyclist covered after the stop and determine the unknown velocities.

$$d_{b3} = d - d_{b2} = 120\,km - 32\,km = 88\,km,$$

$$v_{b1} = \frac{d_{b1}}{t_{b1}} = \frac{32\,km}{2.5\,hr} = 12.8\,\frac{km}{hr},$$

and $v_{b3} = v_{b1} + 3\,\frac{km}{hr} = 12.8\,\frac{km}{hr} + 3\,\frac{km}{hr} = 15.8\,\frac{km}{hr}.$

A lot of calculations. But now that we found the distance and velocities, it is easy to calculate the unknown times, t_{b3} and t_{c1}:

$$t_{b3} = \frac{d_{b3}}{v_{b3}} = \frac{88\,km}{15.8\,\frac{km}{hr}} = \frac{440}{79}\,hr = 5\,hr + \frac{45}{79} \cdot 60\,min \approx 5\,hr\ 34\,min,\ \text{and}$$

$$t_{c1} = \frac{d}{v_{c1}} = \frac{-120\,km}{-50\,\frac{km}{hr}} = 2.40\,hr = 2\,hr + 60 \cdot 0.4\,min = 2\,hr\ 24\,min.$$

But, Mr. Refiner and Stella! We still don't know when the bicyclist and driver pass one another!

Since we know the times and velocities, we can draw graphs. The graphs will show how the velocities of the bicyclist and driver depend on time. It will provide further insight. The graphs will be presented in the next section.

Summary

When you cannot comprehend kinematic problems, create a Freestyle Model.

(1) Why do we need a Freestyle Model?
(2) What does the name "Freestyle Model" tell us?
(3) What are the main features of a Freestyle Model?

73   At 6 a.m. two fishermen came to a river. The first fisherman fished from a bridge and stayed there the entire time. The second fisherman took a boat that had been tied to the bridge and rowed with the river's flow. The boat moved with a speed of *4 miles per hour* <u>relative to the water</u>. The speed of the current is *2 miles per hour*. After two hours, the second fisherman made a U-turn, which took *4 minutes*, and began rowing back to the bridge at the same speed relative to the water. He rowed until he met the first fisherman, who was still fishing from the bridge. At what time did the two fishermen meet?

Draw a Freestyle Model before solving the problem.

Section 16.3 Constructing *v(t)* Graphs

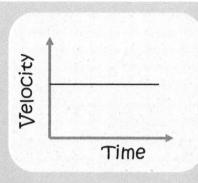

 Until now, Ezra, you used x-y graphs only for training. Now, you will utilize the graphs for solving problems, starting with the *Bike and Car* problem.

But Stella, the problem has no x and y!

 In $v(t)$ graphs, *time* is utilized instead of x, and *velocity* instead of y. Here the graphs will show how the velocity of the bike and car depends upon time.

Instead of x-y charts, we will create *time-velocity* charts?

 Correct. Below is a presentation of the velocity of the bike at different times.

Bike and Car Problem: Bicyclist's $v_b(t)$ Chart

Δt, period of time	$t_{b1} = 2\ hr\ 30\ min$	$t_{b2} = 30\ min$	$t_{b3} = 5\ hr\ 34\ min$
t	$0\ hr - 2\ hr\ 30\ min$ $6\ a.m. - 8:30\ a.m.$	$2\ hr\ 30min - 3\ hr$ $8:30\ a.m. - 9\ a.m.$	$3\ hr - 8\ hr\ 34\ min$ $9\ a.m. - 2:34\ p.m.$
v_b	$v_{b1} = 12.8\ \frac{km}{hr}$	$v_{b2} = 0$	$v_{b3} = 15.8\ \frac{km}{hr}$

 In addition to the periods of time t_{b1}, t_{b2}, and t_{b3}, I inserted the time elapsed from the beginning of the trip, t:
$$t_{b1} + t_{b2} + t_{b3} = 2.5\ hr + 30\ min + 5\ hr\ 34\ min = 8\ hr\ 34\ min.$$
Also, I calculated the time of the day:
$$T_{b\_final} = 6:00\ a.m. + 8\ hr\ 34\ min = 2:34\ p.m.$$

The $v_b(t)$ graph below visualizes the data from the chart. Besides the lines, the graph presents units of measure (hr and $\frac{km}{hr}$) and measurable attributes, *time* and v_b. For convenience, the time of the day is presented, too.

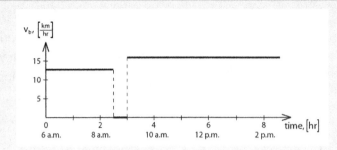

Bike and Car Problem: Bicyclist's $v_b(t)$ Graph

Making a $v_b(t)$ graph involves three steps.
1. Identify the analogues of x and y.
2. Create an x-y chart.
3. Draw a graph that presents
   - Points and lines that reflect information in the chart.
   - Axes, grids, units of measure, and the names of measurable attributes.

 Mr. Refiner, I will analyze these steps to make the second graph, $v_c(t)$. In the case of the car, the analogues of x and y are time and v_c:

A.   *Bike and Car* Problem: Car's *x* and *y* Analogues

x Time, t, measured in *hours* and *minutes*. Time starts at 6 *a.m.*

y The velocity of the car, v_c, is measured in *kilometers per hour*.

Using the car's velocity, v_c as y and t as x, we can create the $v_c(t)$ chart.

B.   *Bike and Car* Problem: Car's $v_c(t)$ Chart

Δt, period of time	$t_{c0} = 1\ hr\ 30\ min$	$t_{c1} = 2\ hr\ 24\ min$
t	$0\ hr - 1\ hr\ 30\ min$ $6\ a.m. - 7:30\ a.m.$	$1\ hr\ 30\ min - 3\ hr\ 54\ min$ $7:30\ a.m. - 9:54\ a.m.$
v_c	$v_{c0} = 0\ \frac{km}{hr}$	$v_{c1} = -50\ \frac{km}{hr}$

 And where did you find $T_{c\_final} = 9:54\ a.m.$?

I calculated: $T_{c\_final} = 7:30\ a.m. + 2\ hr\ 24\ min = 9:54\ a.m.$
And now, Ezra, draw graph $v_c(t)$.

C.   *Bike and Car* Problem: Car's $v_c(t)$ Graph

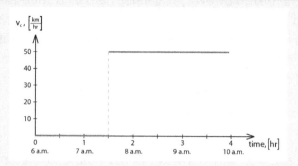

 Besides the axes and lines, my graph has the names of the measurable attributes, $v_c(t)$ and $time$, and the units of measure, hr and $\frac{km}{hr}$.

I see, Ezra. You also marked the time of day, 6 a.m. to 10 a.m. Showing two types of time is not necessary but, in some problems, is beneficial.

 In some. Let me summarize. We still did not complete the original problem but obtained the answers to the first two questions of the problem. See below.

Bike and Car Problem: Solution to (a) and (b)

The bicyclist will reach village B at 2:34 p.m. The car will reach village A at 9:54 a.m.

Mr. Refiner, how can I find when the car and bicyclist pass one another? Maybe if I combine the $v_b(t)$ and $v_c(t)$ graphs, it will help me to find the answer!

Bike and Car Problem: Combined $v_b(t)$ and $v_c(t)$ Graphs

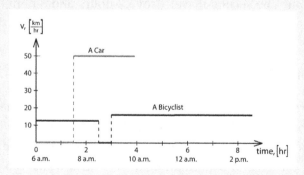 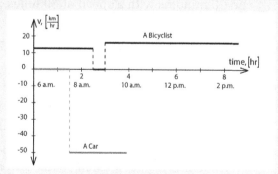

Stella, I made two graphs. In the left-hand side graph, the car and the bike have positive velocity. In the right-hand side graph, the car's velocity is negative. However, none of the graphs tells us when the driver will pass the bicyclist.

You are correct. The right-hand side graph demonstrates how the $v(t)$ behave for the car and the bike; however, it cannot help us to find the time of the meeting. We will need to draw the graphs that show how the distance depends on time. These graphs will tell us when the driver passes the bicyclist!

So, in the next section, we will draw $d(t)$ graphs for the *Bike and Car* problem. Right?

Not yet, Ezra. Section 16.4 will discuss simple $d(t)$ graphs and prepare you for drawing $d(t)$ graphs for the *Bike and Car* problem in Section 16.5.

Summary

From x-y charts and graphs to $v(t)$ charts and graphs. To combine graphs, use common axes and grids.

(1) In $v(t)$ graphs, what is used instead of y?
(2) In $v(t)$ graphs, what is used instead of x?
(3) What type of chart must be made before drawing a graph?
(4) What are the three steps that allow creating $v(t)$ graphs?
(5) What is the difference between graphs like $y = 2x$ or $y = 3$ and the graph for $v(t)$?
(6) What can you see from a combination of two $v(t)$ graphs?

74-77 *Draw v(t) graphs, for each object mentioned in the problems below. On each Cartesian plane, use a different color for different objects. The situations below are from the problems you already solved. Therefore, you may use your solutions to make the graphs.*

74 Cleo looked at her phone at 12:15 p.m. and found she had some extra time. So, she sat on a bench for 10 minutes and then began walking towards the library with a constant speed of $4\frac{km}{hr}$. In a quarter hour, she arrived at the library. *Start your graph at 12:15 p.m.*

75 Two drivers were going from their homes to Lake on the Moon, a city. The first driver drove 3 hours and 40 minutes with a speed of 60 miles per hour. The second driver drove 2 hours and 8 minutes with a speed of 120 km per hour. Both drivers started driving towards Lake on the Moon at the same time and drove in the same direction.

76 Cindy walked with a speed of $5\frac{km}{hr}$ the first 5 miles. Then, she jogged a mile with a speed of $3.5\frac{mi}{hr}$.

77 At 6 a.m. two fishermen came to a river. The first fisherman fished from a bridge and stayed there the entire time. The second fisherman took a boat that had been tied to the bridge and rowed with the river's flow. The boat moved with a speed of *4 miles per hour* <u>relative to the water</u>. The speed of the current is *2 miles per hour*. After two hours, the second fisherman made a U-turn, which took *4 minutes*, and began rowing back to the bridge at the same speed relative to the water. He rowed until he met the first fisherman, who was still fishing from the bridge. *Since the second fisherman, after the U-turn, was going in a direction opposite his initial velocity, use a negative velocity when graphing the second part of the trip. Mark the fisherman on the bridge with red.*

Section 16.4 Discussing *d(t)* Graphs

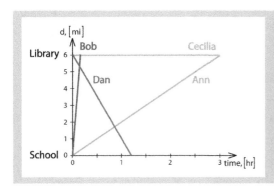

The graph on the left tells what is happening with Ann, Bob, Cecilia, and Dan.

Stella, the graph has no mouth. It can't talk.

Ha, ha. The graph shows which student goes to or from the library, who walks and who—possibly —rides a bike, and who does not move at all. Ezra, we will start by discussing Ann's motion.

Ann's graph shows that at time $t = 0$, Ann was at school ($d = 0$).

And, at time $t = 1$ hour, Ann moved 2 *miles* closer to the library.

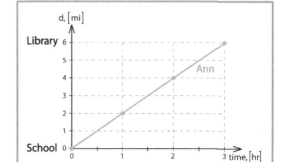

For three hours, Ann was moving 2 *miles per hour* toward the library. In other words, $v_{Ann} = 2 \frac{mi}{hr}$. The straight line shows Ann was moving with a constant speed. The chart below summarizes the findings.

Graph $d_{Ann}(t)$: Description

Motion: Ann was moving from the school to the library with a constant velocity.

Total time: $t_{Ann} = 3 \, hr$

Total Distance: $d_{Ann} = 6 \, mi$

Velocity: $v_{Ann} = 2 \, \frac{mi}{hr}$

Conclusion: Ann probably walked. Riding a bicycle or running would result in a higher speed.

I understand all the numbers. But how did you know Ann did not ride a bicycle?

I found the typical velocities for walking, running, and riding a bike on the Internet. Now, look at Bob's line on the graph. The graph of Bob's motion reveals Bob was also moving from the school to the library with a constant velocity.

However, Bob's speed was much higher than Ann's. In ten minutes, Bob reached the library, which was $6\ mi$ from the school!
So, Bob's speed was...
$$v_{Bob} = \frac{6\ mi}{\frac{1}{6}\ hr} = 36\ \frac{mi}{hr}.$$

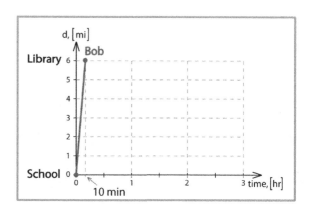

You are correct, Ezra. Bob moved fast. Do you have any idea how he did it?

Bob is a good runner, Stella. He runs very, very fast!

The best runner in the world, Usain Bolt, runs the $100\text{-}meter$ sprint with a speed close to $28\ mph$. Since your idea is not realistic, I stated my opinion below.

Graph $d_{Bob}(t)$: Description

Motion: From the school to the library with a constant velocity.

Total time: $t_{Bob} = 10\ min = \frac{1}{6}\ hr$

Total Distance: $d_{Bob} = 6\ mi$

Velocity: $v_{Bob} = 36\ \frac{mi}{hr}$

Conclusion: Bob took a bus, or someone gave him a ride. This velocity is typical for cars.

You think someone gave Bob a ride? Maybe....
Now, I'll analyze the graphs myself!

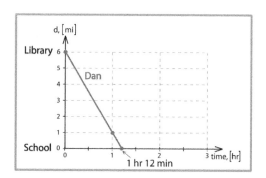

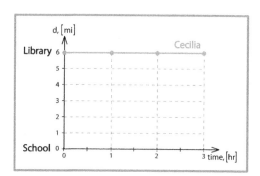

Cecilia and Dan were in the library at time $t = 0$. Cecilia remained in the library. So, her velocity was zero, $v_{Cecilia} = 0 \frac{mi}{hr}$.

Dan was moving toward the school. The trip took him $1\ hour\ 12\ minutes$. He was moving with a constant speed (*straight line*) covering $5\ miles\ per\ hour$. So, $v_{Dan} = 5 \frac{mi}{hr}$.

Graph $d_{Dan}(t)$: Description

Motion: From the library to the school with a constant velocity.

Total time: $t_{Dan} = 1\ hr\ 12\ min$

Total Distance: $d_{Dan} = 6\ mi$

Velocity: $v_{Dan} = 5 \frac{mi}{hr}$

Conclusion: Dan probably was riding a bike. This time is realistic for a good runner as well.

Nice touch, Ezra. As each graph is analyzed, we can discuss their combination. To the combined $d(t)$ graph, for clarity, I added grids and dashed lines.

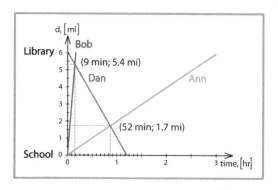

Why did you add the lines?

The dashed lines show, at $t = 9\ min$, Bob and Dan were at the same distance from the school, $d = 5.4\ miles$.

Ezra, since the two students were on the same road at the same time and the same distance from the school, we can conclude they met or passed one another.

I see now. The graphs really talk! And I will use a $d(t)$ graph to solve the *Bike and Car* problem.

So, at $t = 9\ min$, Dan met or passed Bob. It happened 5.4 *miles* from the school.

Similarly, Ann and Dan met or passed one another at time $t = 52\ min$, 1.7 *miles* from the school.

The time and place of the meetings are not exact, but for many applications, proximity is sufficient.

I hope we will discuss how to draw $d(t)$ graphs for the *Bike and Car* problem in the next section.

Summary

$d(t)$ graphs → speed, direction of motion, distance, time, and meeting place. Straight lines → constant speed.

The graph on the right provides information about red and brown ants. (1) Describe the ants' motion.
(2) What do the straight lines on the $d(t)$ graph mean?
(3) What can you say from a comparison of the red and brown ants' motions? Explain.

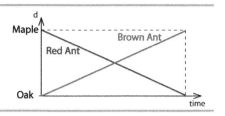

78 Landon travelled to school and made graphs to represent his whereabouts from 8:00 to 8:30 a.m. *Find Landon's speed, direction of motion, and distance to home and/or school. Find the incorrect graph. Explain why it is incorrect.*

Monday

Tuesday

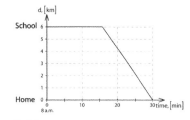

Wednesday

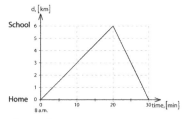

Thursday

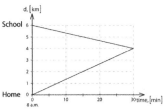

Friday

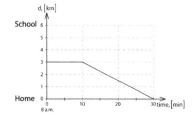

Saturday

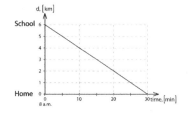

Section 16.5 Constructing *d(t)* Graphs

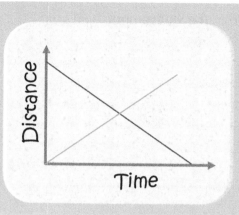

This section will return to the *Bike and Car* problem introduced in Section 16.2.

First, we will construct graphs that show how the distance depends on time for the bike and car.
Then, we will combine the $d_c(t)$ and $d_v(t)$ graphs to solve the problem.

When creating $d(t)$ graphs, we will follow the rules defined in Section 16.3. When creating a graph:
    A. Identify the analogues for x and y. In $d(t)$ graphs, t works as x, and d—as y.
    B. Create an x-y chart. In our case, we should make t-d_c and d_b-t charts.
    C. Draw a graph and show all necessary labels.

Oh, I remember these rules. I will begin with defining x and y for the car's motion.

A. *Bike and Car* Problem: The x and y Analogies for Car's Motion

x Time elapsed, t, measured in *hours* and *minutes*. Time starts at 6 *a.m.*

y The displacement of the car from B is measured in *kilometers*.

At time $t = 0$, the car was at village B. It remained there for 1.5 hours. So, at $1hr\,30\,min$, the distance to village A was still $120\,km$.

The third point on the chart can be placed at $t = (1.5 + 1)\,hr$, i.e., after the driver drove for 1 hour with a constant speed of $50\,\frac{km}{hr}$ toward village A.

Then the car covered $50\,km$ in an hour again. And again. The fifth point has time coordinate $t = 3hr\,54\,min$. At this time the car driver reached village A.

B. *Bike and Car* Problem: $d(t)$ Chart for Car's Motion

t elapsed	0 hr	1.5 hr	2.5 hr	3.5 hr	3.9 hr
d_c	0 km	0 km	−50 km	−100 km	−120 km

Since the car was moving with a constant speed, we can use the chart's data and construct $d_c(t)$ graph, point-by-point.
The graphs below show the driver was $120\ km$ from the village until $7:30\ a.m.$

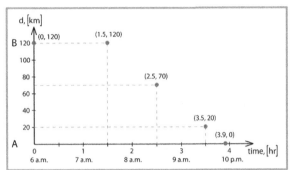

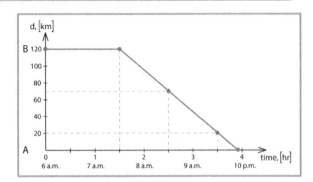

Then the driver gradually reduced the distance to zero.
Stella, on the graph $d_c(t)$, I marked the variables, d and t, and their units. Now, I will construct the graph for the bike.

A. *Bike and Car* Problem: The *x* and *y* Analogies for Bicyclist's Motion

x   Time elapsed, *t*, measured in *hours* and *minutes*. Time starts at 6 *a.m.*

y   The displacement of the bike from village *B* is measured in *kilometers*.

At time $t = 0$, the bicyclist started moving from village *A* toward village *B* with a constant velocity, $v_{b1} = 12.8\frac{km}{hr}$. Later, after $2.5\ hours$ (marked t_{b1}), the bike stopped for $30\ min$ (t_{b2}) and then started moving with a faster speed, $v_{b3} = 15\frac{km}{hr}$.

B. *Bike and Car* Problem: $d(t)$ Chart for Bicyclist's Motion

t elapsed	0 *hr*	1 *hr*	2 *hr*	2.5 *hr*	3 *hr*	4 *hr*	5 *hr*	8 *hr* 34 *min*
d_b	0 *km*	12.8 *km*	25.6 *km*	32 *km*	32 *km*	47.8 *km*	63.6 *km*	120 *km*

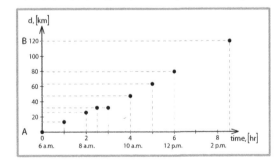

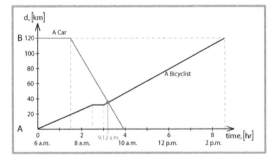

A combined graph on the right will help us answer the last question of the problem—*when do the bicycle and the car pass one another?*

Stella, the intersection of the purple and brown lines shows the bike and the car met at $9\colon 12\ a.m.$ So, we can complete the *Bike and Car* problem.

Bike and Car Problem: Answer for the Third Question

The bicyclist and the car will pass one another at 9:12 a.m.

You can see how Freestyle Models, d-t-v parameters, and graphs help us with solving kinematic problems. What is most exciting is that we can apply the very same methods for solving many non-kinematic problems, too. Section 16.6 will illustrate it using two examples.

Summary

$d(t)$ graphs provide information about the time and place where the objects met or passed one another.

An average speed for an ant was mentioned in Section 16.1. Using this speed as a guide, add units and grids to the graph on the right. These units on the graph must make sense.

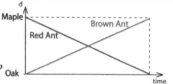

(1) Based on your units, what is the distance between the maple and oak trees?
(2) What is the speed of the brown ant? (3) At what distance from the maple tree and when did the ants meet? (4) What information can be obtained from a combination of two or more $d(t)$ graphs?

79-82 *Draw d(t) graphs for each object mentioned in the problems. Use different colors for different objects. The situations below are from the problems you already solved. Therefore, you may use your solutions when constructing the graphs.*

79   Cleo looked at her phone at 12:15 p.m. and determined she had some extra time. So, she sat on a bench for 10 minutes and then started walking towards the library with a constant speed of $4\frac{km}{hr}$. In a quarter hour, she arrived at the library. *Start your graph at 12:15 p.m.*

80   Two drivers were going from their homes to Lake on the Moon, a city. The first driver drove 3 hours and 40 minutes with a speed of 60 miles per hour. The second driver drove 2 hours and 8 minutes with a speed of 120 km per hour. The drivers began driving toward Lake on the Moon at the same time and drove in the same direction.

81   Cindy walked with a speed of $5\frac{km}{hr}$ the first 5 miles. Then, she jogged a mile with a speed of $3.5\frac{mi}{hr}$.

82   At 6 a.m. two fishermen came to a river. The first fisherman fished from a bridge and stayed there the entire time. The second fisherman took a boat that had been tied to the bridge and rowed with the river's flow. The boat moved with a speed of *4 miles per hour* <u>relative to the water</u>. The speed of the current is *2 miles per hour*. After two hours, the second fisherman made a U-turn, which took 4 *minutes*, and began rowing back to the bridge at the same speed relative to the water. He rowed until he met the first fisherman, who was still fishing from the bridge. At what time will the two fishermen meet? *Since the second fisherman, after the U-turn, was rowing in a direction opposite his initial velocity, use a negative velocity when graphing the second part of the trip.*

Section 16.6 The *d-t-v* Approach

Section 16.6 will demonstrate how the *d-t-v* method can be applied for solving the *Cell Phone Payment* and *Filling a Pool* problems.

Why these problems, Stell? Not because my cell phone fell into a pool last summer?

Cell phones have neither legs nor wings. Ezra, you dropped it in the pool. But *Cell Phone Payment* and *Filling a Pool* problems are very popular in math textbooks and on standardized tests.

Cell Phone Payment Problem

Two cell phone companies propose the following payment plans. Company *A* charges a monthly $5 fee and an additional 4 cents per minute for the time used by customers. Company *B* does not charge a basic monthly fee but collects 10 cents per minute for the first 40 minutes, then 6 cents per minute thereafter. Which company is better for a customer who uses the phone one hour per month? Two hours per month? Three hours per month? Four hours per month?

Start by identifying the values that correspond with a distance and velocity. Such connections for the *Cell Phone Payment* problem are presented below.

Can I use the *d-t-v* method for any problem?

If a problem does not involve a constant rate, we cannot apply the *d-t-v* technique. In the *Cell Phone Payment* problem, rate of payment works as velocity.

Cell Phone Payment Problem: *d-t-v* Approach

$distance_A$ and $distance_B$ – payments for companies *A* and *B*
$velocity_A$ and $velocity_B$ – rates of payment for companies *A* and *B*

Understanding the problems in terms of *d-t-v* results in creating a *Total Price*(*time*) graph, an analogue to the *d*(*t*) graph.

Cell Phone Payment Problem: Incorrect Graph, *Total Price(time)*

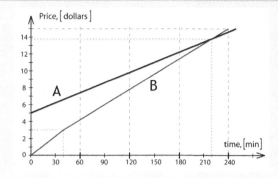

Thick – Company *A*

Thin – Company *B*

Stella, the title of the graph makes no sense. You wrote "Incorrect Graph."

This graph has a mistake. The correct graph is similar but not the same.

What? Why did you present an incorrect graph?

I made this mistake and spent 20 minutes trying to find it. Ezra, can you find the mistake faster than me? Please, find this mistake before turning the page.

OK, I'll try. I'll work on the graph while you define parameters.

Cell Phone Payment Problem: Parameters

d_{A0} is the initial payment for Company *A*

v_A is the rate of payment (dollar per min) for Company *A*

v_{B1} is the initial rate of payment for Company *B*

v_{B2} is the rate of payment for Company *B* after the time $t_{B1} = 40\ min$

$t_1, t_2, t_3,$ and t_4 are the times at which we need to compare plans *A* and *B*

Your parameters, Stella, are self-explanatory. The subscripts point to a company and the number of hours. Good job!

Did you find a mistake in my graph?

Not yet. I'll keep working while you make an Algebraic Organizer.

You are mischievous!

Cell Phone Payment Problem: *d-t-v* Algebraic Organizer and Solution

$d_{A0} = 5\ d.$

$v_A = 0.04\ \frac{d.}{min}$

$v_{B1} = 0.1\ \frac{d.}{min}$

$t_{B1} = 40\ min$

$v_{B2} = 0.06\ \frac{d.}{min}$

$t_1 = 60\ min$

$t_2 = 120\ min$

$t_3 = 180\ min$

$t_4 = 240\ min$

$d_{A1} = ?\ d.$ $d_{A2} = ?\ d.$ $d_{A3} = ?\ d.$ $d_{A4} = ?\ d.$
$d_{B1} = ?\ d.$ $d_{B2} = ?\ d.$ $d_{B3} = ?\ d.$ $d_{B4} = ?\ d.$
Which *d* is lower at 1, 2, 3, and 4 hours?

$d_{A1} = 5\ d. + 0.04\ \frac{d.}{min} \cdot 60\ min = (5 + 2.4)d. = 7.4\ d.$

$d_{A2} = (7.4 + 2.4)d. = 9.8\ d.$
$d_{A3} = (9.8 + 2.4)d. = 12.2\ d.$
$d_{A3} = (12.2 + 2.4)d. = 14.6\ d.$

$d_{B1} = 0.1\ \frac{d.}{min} \cdot 40\ min + 0.06\ \frac{d.}{min} \cdot 20\ min =$
$\qquad = (4 + 1.2)d. = 5.2\ d.$

$d_{B2} = 5.2\ d. + 0.06\ \frac{d.}{min} \cdot 60\ min =$
$\qquad = (5.2 + 3.6)d. = 8.8\ d.$

$d_{B3} = (8.8 + 3.6)d. = 12.4\ d.$
$d_{B4} = (12.4 + 3.6)d. = 16\ d.$

Answer: If a user talks 1 or 2 hours per month, the pricing for Company *B* ($5.20 or $8.80) is better than the pricing for Company *A* ($7.40 or $9.80). For a user who talks 3 or 4 hours per month, the pricing for Company *A* ($12.20 or $15.60) is better than that of Company *B* ($12.40 or $16).

Ezra, I am done with the problem's presentation. What about the graph?

I tried hard. Really. I couldn't find what is wrong.

It is a pity. You probably need more practice with graphs.
OK, I will show you the mistake. But first I will present a $v(t)$ graph for the *Cell Phone Payment* problem. Oh, $v(t)$ means the *price per minute* as a function of time.

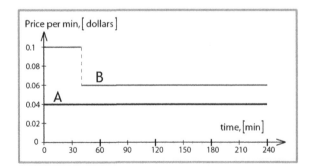

I understand the graph. The blue line shows the *price per minute* for Company *A*. And the red line shows the price per minute for Company *B*. Correct?

Sure. The blue line shows Company A charges 4 cents per minute. The initial payment of $5 is not presented on the graph.

For Company B, Ezra, the red graph shows two prices: 10 cents and 6 cents per minute.

To better understand the pricing, you, Ezra, must examine how the total price depends on time. The graph $Total\ Price(time)$ will help you with this.

Stella, in terms of the d-t-v approach, the graph $Total\ Price(time)$ will be the same as a $d(t)$ function. Correct?

Yes, Ezra. $Total\ Price(time)$ is an analogue to $d(t)$.

The thick $Total\ Price(time)$ line on the right starts at $(0, 5)$. Its first point shows, at the initial time, $t = 0$, customers of Company A must pay $5.

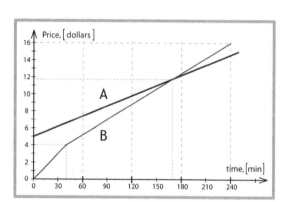

And then the thick line goes straight.

The straight line demonstrates the price increases with a constant rate.

Stella, in the graph you made earlier, did you have a mistake with the blue or red line?

In the <u>incorrect graph</u>, the first part of the red line had a lower rate than needed. *At* 40 *minutes, the incorrect red line marked the price as* $3 *instead of* $4.

Now I see the mistake. I had to find it myself!

Sure, you had to... Now, let me analyze the $Total\ Price(time)$ graph. The graph shows us which price is higher at each time.

The red line is below the blue line for the first two hours. So, if someone talks from one to two-and-a-half hours during a month, it is better to use Company B.

OK. But at about 2 hours and 50 minutes, the price for calls becomes equal for both companies.

You are correct, Ezra. The graph demonstrates that if you talk 3 hours or more, it is much better to use Company A than Company B. Calculations and graphing resulted in the same answer. However, graphs carry more information about the relative pricing of the two companies and allow prediction of what will happen at various times.

Sure, graphs show a lot of things, but you solved the problem before drawing the graphs!

A combination of calculations and visual representations allows a deeper understanding of problems and helps prevent mistakes. Besides, you will need graphs for some challenging problems...and really, Ezra, you are not exactly drowning in extra practice.

Peace, guys! Now we are done with cell phones, and I am ready to present the solution to the *Filling a Pool* problem. I will use the *d-t-v* approach.

Filling a Pool Problem

Two pumps are connected to a pool. The first pump can fill the pool in 5 hours. The second pump can fill the pool in 8 hours. How fast will the pumps fill the pool when working together if the volume of the pool is 400 cubic meters? *The answer must be correct to the nearest minute.*

Parameters

v_1 is the rate of filling the pool by the first pump
v_2 is the rate of filling the pool by the second pump
d is the volume of the pool

d-t-v Algebraic Organizer

$$d = 400 \, m^3$$
$$t_1 = 5 \, hr$$
$$t_2 = 8 \, hr$$
$$v_1 = \frac{d}{t_1} \frac{m^3}{hr}$$
$$v_2 = \frac{d}{t_2} \frac{m^3}{hr}$$

$$t = ? \, hr$$

$$v_1 = \frac{d}{t_1} \frac{m^3}{hr} = (400 \div 5)\frac{m^3}{hr} = 80 \frac{m^3}{hr}$$
$$v_2 = \frac{d}{t_2} \frac{m^3}{hr} = (400 \div 8)\frac{m^3}{hr} = 50 \frac{m^3}{hr}$$
$$v = v_1 + v_2 = 80\frac{m^3}{hr} + 50\frac{m^3}{hr} = 130\frac{m^3}{hr}$$
$$t = \frac{400 \, m^3}{130\frac{m^3}{hr}} = 3\frac{1}{13}\,hr = 3hr + \frac{60 \, min}{13} = 3hr + 3\frac{4}{13}\,min \approx 3hr \, 3in$$

Answer: The two pumps will fill the pool in 3 hours and 3 minutes when working together.

In the *Filling a Pool* problem, using the *d-t-v* approach was helpful. But why, Stella, didn't we draw graphs?

The problem did not involve comparison; therefore, graphs were not needed. In various problems which describe values changing with time, some or all aspects of the *d-t-v* method can be applied.

Summary

Use the *d-t-v* approach to create a *d-t-v* Algebraic Organizer in word problems that involve values changing with a constant rate.

(1) What type of problems can be solved using the d-t-v approach? (2) What is the difference between the v-d-t and d-t-v approaches? (3) What do the parameters d, t, and v represent for the cell phone problem presented in this section?

There are two graphs presented in this section to illustrate the cell phone problem. (4) Which of the graphs can help you find the best company for you if you talk 5 hours per month? (5) Which company is better for you if you talk 5 hours per month, A or B? How can you be sure if the graph does not go that far?

83   Three telephone companies proposed the following payment plans:

Flying Cats asks for a $9 payment per month and 3 cents per minute. Power Cats collects $3 in advance and then 6 cents per minute. Fighting Cats collects 20 cents per minute for the first 30 minutes and then 5 cents per minute thereafter.

Which company is better for a customer who uses the phone 1 hour per month? Two hours per month? Three hours per month? Four hours per month? Ten hours per month?

Make graphs that show rate changes over time for each company. Then, on the next page, draw graphs that show how the total cost for each plan changes. Finally, solve the problem.

84   *Make graphs that help you understand the problem. Then, solve the problem.*

You need to fill a pool with a volume of 12,000 m³. The pump can work on three different settings: economy, regular, and forced. On the economy setting, the pump can fill the pool in 20 hours. On the regular setting, the pump can fill the pool in 15 hours, and on the forced setting, it can fill the pool in 13 hours and 20 minutes. However, due to a drought, the pump only works on one of the following three 12-hour programs. The pump turns off automatically when the pool is filled or when 12 hours have passed.

         Program 1: 12 hours of economy regime.

         Program 2: 6 hours of regular setting and then 6 hours of economy setting.

         Program 3: 3 hours and 15 minutes of forced setting and then 8 hours and 45 minutes of
                     economy setting.

The pump can be programmed to work according to any one of the three programs during each 12-hour period or until the pump stops by itself once the pool is filled. If desired, the programs can be switched from one to another every 12 hours. How fast can you fill the pool by using the available programs?

Chapter 17
Basic Geometry and Problem Solving

In Chapter 17, Ezra, you will learn how to chunk and organize data presented in a geometric form. Later, you will use the very same methods to solve problems in mathematics and physics classes.

How will I chunk a geometric data?

You will draw additional lines, add color, and move figure parts by crossing out old lines and drawing new lines. But first, since you will use measurements, let's recall what a measurement *is*. A *measurement* is the act of comparing two values, where one value is defined as a unit.

I remember. And length is the number of units of length that fit into a given line segment.

1 unit of length

Length is 5 units

Perfecto! And relatedly, **area** is the number of unit squares that fit inside a "flat" figure or 3-dimensional surface. Mostly, you will work with flat figures. However, you will define volume of some 3D shapes, too.

1 unit of area

Area equals 6 square units

Volume is the number of unit cubes that fit inside a three-dimensional figure.

1 unit of volume

Volume is 8 cubic units

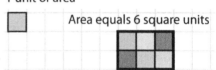

In the example, you can see and count unit cubes within a 3-dimensional shape. In this chapter, you will work on finding perimeters, areas and volumes of various geometric figures.

Will I use formulas?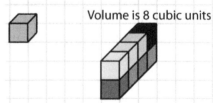

Yes, Ezra. You will use formulas, but not too many.

Section 17.1 Perimeter

The castle, Ezra, has a strong perimeter. It includes a double battlement and a moat between the walls. To calculate the number of guardians needed to protect the castle, you must know the length of the perimeter.

You mean the length of the wall around the castle?

Yes. In geometry, the word perimeter carries a similar meaning. The *perimeter of a figure* is defined as the length of its borderline.

So, how can I find the length of the perimeter for the castle?

You can find the castle's perimeter the same way as the perimeter of any geometric shape—use measuring devices and mathematical calculations.
  A. Find the perimeter by applying measuring devices:
      ✓ measure the length of each side and then add the lengths,
      ✓ measure the approximate length of curved lines' pieces, or
      ✓ measure the length of a curve that represents the perimeter of a figure using a *curvimeter*.
  B. Calculate the perimeter by using a given formula.

Stella, what is a curv-i-meter?

A mechanical device, Ezra. It has another name too: *o-pi-so-meter*. See the picture on the left-hand side.

I never heard the words *curvimeter* and *opisometer* in my life!

Now you have. A *curvimeter* can help you find the perimeter of a figure by measuring the length of each curved boundary line.

91

If a figure is comprised of straight lines, a ruler is sufficient. Stella, I can calculate the perimeter of a polygon as the sum of the lengths of its sides.

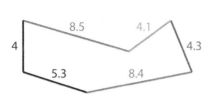

Sure, you can. The perimeter of the *six-sided* polygon on the left is found using *line-segment addition*.

$P = 4 + 8.5 + 4.1 + 4.3 + 8.4 + 5.3 = 34.6$

But what if the boundary line is curved and I don't have a curvimeter?

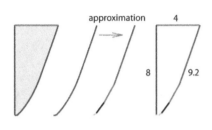

You still may use the line-segment addition by substituting the curves with short line segments and then adding their lengths. In the *Curved Triangle* on the left, I substituted the curved line on its right with four straight lines of different length.

However, for curved boundaries, line-segment addition provides only an approximate value for the perimeter! So, the most precise method is to use a curvimeter?

Not really, Ezra. The most precise method for finding the perimeter of a figure with curved boundaries is using formulas and substitution.

The *Curved Triangle* has the boundaries $x = 0$, $y = a$, and $y = \sqrt{x^3}$. Therefore, the perimeter can be calculated using the formula,

$$P = a + \sqrt{a^3} + \frac{8}{27}\sqrt{(\frac{9a}{4} + 1)^3} - \frac{8}{27}, \text{ where } a = 4.$$

The resulting perimeter is: $P = 21.073415289\ldots$

How did you find the formula?

I used integration, a topic of mathematics you will learn in a few years. Do not forget, Ezra, we live in the era of computers. Formula and parameters were fed to a computer...and *voila*! The precise result was ready.

Stella, will we discuss circles, too?

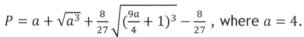

For curved figures, the perimeter is frequently called *circumference*. You can calculate the circumference of a circle with radius r using the formula $P = 2\pi r$, where $\pi = 3.14159265359...$

To calculate a trajectory of a satellite, you will need 40 digits of π^*.

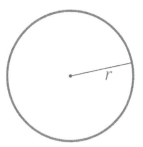

And for *Soft Algebra* problems?

It is usually sufficient to use $\pi \approx 3.14$. Moreover, for some problems, an estimation $\pi \approx 3$ will be satisfactory, too.

Summary

There are two ways to find a perimeter—use measuring devices or calculate mathematically.

What method or methods can you use to find the perimeter of a figure that represents a half-circle if no measurements are provided?

85   *Find the perimeters of the figures below using the best approach. The total of all the answers is 190.*

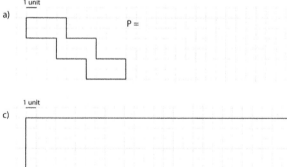

a)   1 unit   P =

b)   1 unit   P =

c)   1 unit   P =

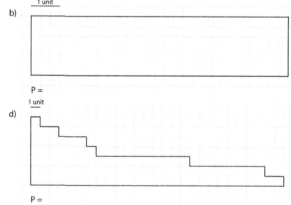

d)   1 unit   P =

86   *Find the perimeter of a figure if the formula for the perimeter is given:*

$$P = a + \sqrt{a^3} + \frac{8}{27}\sqrt{\left(\frac{9a}{4} + 1\right)^3} - \frac{8}{27},$$ *where $a = 9$. Not using a calculator, estimate the square root to the nearest tenth. When you found the answer to the problem, round it to the nearest integer.*

---

*Cosmologists say 40 digits will suffice to compute the volume of the observable universe with a precision of one atom (*Unknown source*).

87   *Find the perimeter of the figure on the right using the*
        given measurements. Do not use approximations.

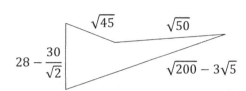

88   *Find the perimeter of the figures below using the given measurements. Although the figures are not*
        drawn to scale, all angles are right angles.

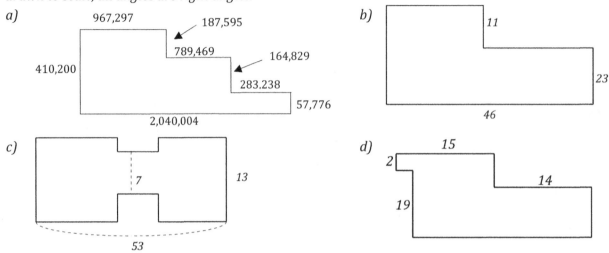

89   There are two numbers. The second number is $\sqrt[2]{8}$ more than the first number. The first number is
        eight less than the square root of ninety-eight. What is the sum of these numbers? Provide an exact
        answer.

90   There are four numbers. The first number is three less than the square root of seven. The second
        number is as large as the product of negative one and the square root of 28. The third number is the
        sum of the first two numbers and the fourth number. What is the sum of all these numbers if the
        fourth number cubed equals the square root of seven taken seven times?

91   There are two numbers. Their GCF is 6 and their LCM is 30. What are these numbers?

92   In a rectangle, the length to width ratio is 4:7. The perimeter is 154 in. By how much is the width
        longer than the length?

93   Lanita and Shanita came to Matamata Forest Preserve together. The Preserve has two trails. The
        Paramita trail loops around Paramita Lake while the Maricossa trail loops around the wetlands. The
        Paramita trail has a circular shape with a one-kilometer radius. The Maricossa trail has six sharp
        turns and amazingly straight roads in between the turns. The trail starts by going 750 meters north
        and then turns right abruptly. After the turn, the trail stays eastbound for a while and then turns
        south. After reaching a huge red oak, the Maricossa trail becomes eastbound again. Right after a
        miniature bridge, the trail has its second southbound piece. The road goes south for almost a kilo-
        meter when it reaches an alcove. Right after the alcove, the trail turns right and continues west-
        bound for 1.6 km. Finally, the trail turns north and after one kilometer reaches the parking lot.
        Lanita and Shanita frequently run together. They always run at the very same speed and never
        change their pace on their way. This time, Lanita took the Paramita trail, and Shanita took the Mari-
        cossa trail. When Lanita completed her trail, she looked at her watch—it was 3:00 p.m. When the
        girls started jogging, it was 1:00 p.m. or 2:00 p.m. Lanita did not remember for sure. Therefore,
        Lanita did not know whether she jogged for 1 or 2 hours. How long will she wait for Shanita?
        For this problem, use π = 3.14 and use the Internet. Round your answer to the nearest minute.

Section 17.2 Area

 Ezra, do you know about the Chicago area marathon for non-professional athletes?

 Sure. People come together and run. It's fun.

 The word *area* in this context means a part of a city.

 In geometry, it's different. In geometry, area is *the amount of space the surface of a place covers.*

 It sounds a bit...unnatural. I like Stella's definition better: <u>the number of unit squares</u> that fit inside a "flat" figure or a 3-dimensional surface.

Use whatever definition suits you. Measure an area using square units like $km^2, mi^2, inches^2, feet^2, cm^2, mm^2$....
To find area, we almost always combine measurements and calculations.
   A. Count square units covered by a given figure using graph paper.
   B. Subdivide the figure into rectangles and right triangles, then calculate the area for each part.
   C. Use formulas to calculate the exact areas of complex figures.

 If there is a rectangle that holds an integer number of squares, you can calculate area by counting the squares. You can count or multiply the length of a rectangle by its width, $A = ab$.

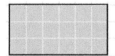   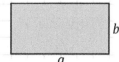

b

a

$A = a \cdot b$

 However, Mr. Organizer, counting units will not help for a triangle.

Ezra, for a right triangle, you can find the lengths of the legs, a and b. Their product equals the area of a rectangle made of a double triangle.

In the picture below, can you see how the black and white triangles make up the rectangle? The rectangle is made of two identical triangles. Therefore, the formula for the area of each right triangle is $A = \frac{ab}{2}$.

$$A = \frac{a \cdot b}{2}$$

This formula works for any right triangle! Moreover, you can use this formula for complex figures, too. When finding the area of a complex figure, you can present the figure as a sum of several rectangles and right triangles. I call it the *right-block* method.

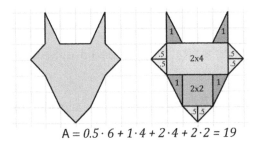

$$A = 0.5 \cdot 6 + 1 \cdot 4 + 2 \cdot 4 + 2 \cdot 2 = 19$$

I see. But, what if a borderline of the figure is curved?

Then, you can use the right-block method for a rough approximation. Precise calculation is only possible when you know the formula for finding a complex area.

approximation

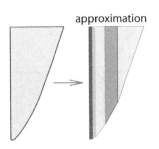

It is like with perimeters, using a formula is best. So, Stella, to find the area of a circle, I will need to use a formula. Correct?

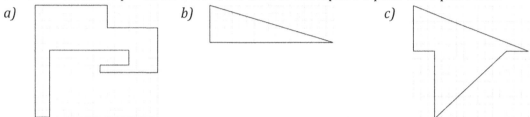

Sure. The formula for finding the area of a circle with a radius r is the following: $A_{Circle} = \pi r^2$.
Use this formula for solving some of your practice problems.

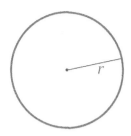

Summary

To find area, count squares using graph paper or use the right-block method. Use formulas if available.

 What method or methods can you use to find the area of a rectangular piece of paper with a round hole in the middle?

94   *Find the area.* In the problems below, the area of one square equals one square unit.

a)   b)   c)

95   *Find the area of the figures using chunking. Mark all dimensions you use in calculations. In all figures, 1 square = 1 unit².*

a)   b)   c)

96   *Find the area and the perimeter of a quarter of the circle and the figure with half-circles removed. 1 square = 1 unit². For calculations, use $\pi = 3.14$.*   a)   b)

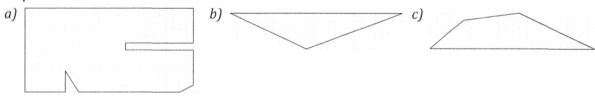

97   *Find the area of the figure on the right without using chunking. Explain your solution.*

1 square = 1 unit².

98   There are four numbers. The second number is twenty-four and a multiple of all the other numbers. The third number is eight times the first number. The fourth number is not a multiple of 3 and is not the square root of sixteen. All four numbers are different and positive. What is the sum of all four numbers?

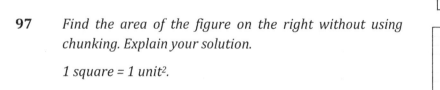

99   There are two numbers. The first number is six more than the second number and is the LCM of 14 and 49. What is the second number?

100   The second number is the product of the cubic root of negative one hundred twenty-five and the first number. The second number is –30. What is the sum of these numbers?

Section 17.3 Volume

 Stella, will you discuss speakers or measuring cups?

Volume is indeed the word that unites sound and measuring cups, Ezra.

 Yeah. Sound and measuring cups can both have different volumes. When a sound has a low volume, we say the sound is quiet.

When a measuring cup has low volume, we say the cup is small. Volume can be measured using several different methods.
- A. Employ measuring vessels to measure volume:
  Use a <u>direct measurement</u> of volume for liquid or granular materials and the <u>displacement method</u> when dealing with solid objects.
- B. For a rectangular block, use the formula: $V = abc$, where a, b, and c are the sides.
- C. For complicated figures, use complex algebraic formulas if available.

 Stella, you go too fast. I have several questions. First, what are granular materials?

You can *directly measure the volume* of liquid as well as the volume of sugar, salt, or sand using a measuring cup, measuring spoon, measuring cylinder, or any other vessel with marked volume.

 I see. I can measure the volume for gran-u-lar sugar the same way as I measure the volume of water.

Sure. Besides, when you use a measuring vessel, you can find a volume of a solid objects by placing an object into a liquid and measuring the volume of the displaced liquid.

 Stella, from now on, slower please.

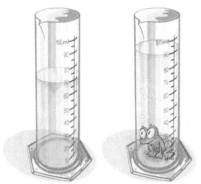

Here is a description of the *displacement method*. When a measuring cylinder has no toy inside, the volume of water is $70\,ml$. When I placed a toy frog inside the cylinder, the level of water increased to $90\,ml$. So, the displacement method demonstrated the volume of the toy is $20\,ml$.

Stella, I think you just love those frogs...

Below, I will discuss strategies for measuring volume without using measuring vessels.

I can find the volume of a rectangular prism or a block using the formula $V = abc$, where a, b, and c are the sides of the block. The sides, usually, are given.

Ezra, but what if you have a real block and must find the volume?

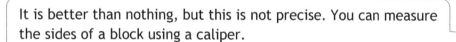

Mm...I will use a ruler.

It is better than nothing, but this is not precise. You can measure the sides of a block using a caliper.

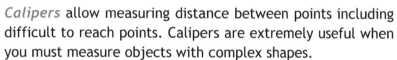

Ca-li-per?

Calipers allow measuring distance between points including difficult to reach points. Calipers are extremely useful when you must measure objects with complex shapes.

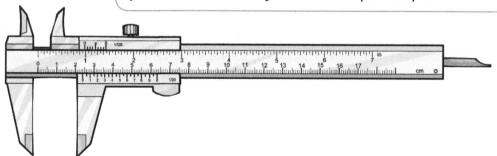

I see. Calipers will help me to measure the sides of rectangular blocks. Can I then present any 3-dimensional figure as a combination of rectangular blocks?

Volume is 16 un.³

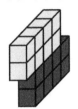

1 un.³

You can. You can use that method for block-made figures like the one on the left. But I do not think you will ever apply it in real life for anything besides *very, very* rough estimations...

Then, how will I calculate the volumes of complex shapes?

Using formulas, Ezra. Below, I wrote the complex *volume formulas* to help you find the volumes of the following solids: a sphere, a cylinder, and a cone. *Solids* is the name for three-dimensional solid (filled inside) figures. Also, I presented the formula for the *surface of a sphere* and the *lateral* (side) *surface* of a cone and a cylinder.

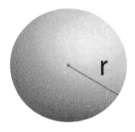

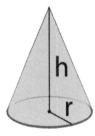

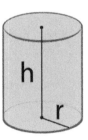

$$V_{sphere} = \frac{4}{3} \cdot \pi \cdot r^3$$

$$A_{sphere} = 4 \cdot \pi \cdot r^2$$

$$V_{cone} = \frac{1}{3} \cdot \pi \cdot r^2 \cdot h$$

$$A_{cone.side} = \pi \cdot r \cdot \sqrt{r^2 + h^2}$$

$$V_{cylinder} = \pi \cdot r^2 \cdot h$$

$$A_{cylinder\_side} = 2 \cdot \pi \cdot r \cdot h$$

Why do you call these formulas complex? Formulas like any other...

Because you do not have a sufficient level of mathematics knowledge to understand any of these formulas. Therefore, for now, you must believe me the formulas are correct. Believing is...not mathematical.

So, Stella, maybe it's better to calculate an approximate volume using the *vol-block* method?

Maybe...but the approximate measurements for volume are not as precise as those for perimeter and area.

Summary

Use direct measurement, the displacement method, or formulas to measure volume. $V_{block} = abc$.

 What method or methods can you use to find the volume of a phone? A pencil? An eraser? A glass?

101-109 *In this section, use π = 3.14.*

101   Find the volume of a sphere with a radius equal to the cubic root of three halves.

102   Find the volume of the oval object inside the measuring cylinder on the right-hand side. The first cylinder is the same cylinder before the object was placed inside.

103   In a rectangle, the width to length ratio is 8:15. The perimeter is 138 in. What is the area of the rectangle? *Express your answer in square feet.*

104   Find the volume of the object inside the measuring cylinder on the right-hand side. The first cylinder is the same cylinder before the object was placed inside.

105   What are these four numbers? *(a)* All numbers are different positive factors of 42 in descending order. The first number multiplied by itself results in 49. *(b)* How many solutions exist?

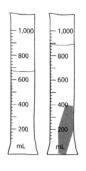

106   To make a cylinder with the diameter of 6 *cm*, two circles with the diameters of 6 cm and an 8 cm long rectangle were cut off from an aluminum sheet with the thickness of 0.4 mm and the density of $2.7 \frac{g}{cm^3}$. In addition to the aluminum, 7 grams of a duct tape were utilized in the construction. To make the cylinder, a tube with a joint was made from the rectangle and then the joint was fastened with a duct tape. The joint had neither gaps nor overlaps. Finally, the two circles were connected to the tube with a duct tape.
(a) Use a construction paper to create a paper model for the cylinder. *(b)* Find the total weight of the aluminum cylinder and round your answer to the nearest tenth of a gram. *(c)* Estimate the volume of air inside the cylinder in cubic centimeters and round to the nearest integer.

107   Find the volume of the three-dimensional figure on the right. The figure is symmetrical and looks the same from both sides. *Explain your solution.*

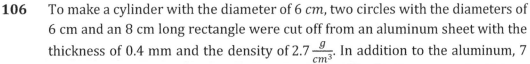
1 cubic unit

108   A sphere, a cone, and a cylinder have the same radius, $r = 12$ *inches*. In addition, there is a block with two 12-*inch* sides and one side with the length of 40 *inches*. The height, h_{cone}, of the cone is 36 *inches* while the height, h_{cyl}, of the cylinder is 16 *inches*. List the shapes according to their volume. Begin with the greatest-volume shape. List equal-volume shapes alphabetically.

109   A cone with a radius of 2 cm has a height of 3 cm. If the cone were made of actinium, the material with the density of $10 \frac{g}{cm^3}$, what would be the weight of the cone? *Estimate your answer to the nearest gram.*

Section 17.4 Auxiliary Elements in Geometry

Ezra, many important problem-solving methods use *auxiliary (helping) elements.*

Au-xi-li-a-ry!? Why do you need to use such bizarre words, Stell? The word "helping" would suffice!

Auxiliary elements is the term used in problem solving all over the world.

If you want to communicate with other problem-solvers, you must use terminology they comprehend, Ezra.

OK, OK. I will communicate the nice way. Now I remember, Mr. Chunker already used this word two books ago when talking about parameter-difference.

We call artificially introduced elements that help solve problems *auxiliary elements.* For example, artificially introduced symbols (parameters, for example) or geometric constructions. Although there are several kinds of auxiliary elements, here we will only discuss the elements used in geometry.

To solve geometric problems, additional lines are used to

   A. Emphasize symmetry of the system.
   B. Subdivide the figure into simpler parts.
   C. Add figures to increase symmetry and make a drawing more complete.
   D. Move parts of a picture from place to place.

Stella, why do I need to emphasize symmetry?

If you color a high symmetry pattern, *drawing symmetry axes* helps to see what parts must be colored the same way.

The habits of drawing symmetry lines and/or outlining repeating patterns will help you develop skills needed for future geometry classes.

I see. And the other three applications?

The three examples below will demonstrate how auxiliary elements can be used to find the area of the figure below.
The first example is *chunking*. With additional lines, we subdivide the figure into smaller parts and color the parts to better illustrate the solution.

Chunking $A = 1 + 1 + 1 + 1 + 4 = 8$

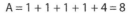
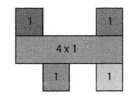

I see, Stella. You used the *right-block* approach. And the lines helped you to artificially create the blocks. And what is the *adding parts* method?

The second example shows how to find the area of the figure by *adding parts* that increase symmetry of the figure.

Adding Parts $A = 3 \times 4 - (1 + 1 + 2) = 8$

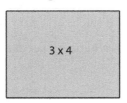
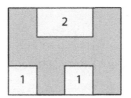

You made the figure fatter. Will you make it leaner at the end?

Yes, Ezra, at the end, we subtract the added parts. The last example shows how area can be determined when you use shuffling.

Shuffling...? I know Great-Grandpa shuffles when walking. Great-Grandpa can also shuffle a deck of cards.

I mean *shuffling* in the sense of moving pieces from one place to another. In the figure below, I cut the lower two pieces and added them on the top. Thus, I obtained a highly symmetric figure, a 4 by 2 rectangle.

Shuffling

A = 4 x 2 = 8

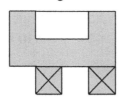

4 x 2

I think shuffling is the coolest approach.

Chunking, adding parts, and shuffling can be used independently or in combination. Your goal is always to find the best approach for a problem, draw auxiliary lines, and color the parts to clearly present your solution. You will solve quite a few area problems for practice.
Using auxiliary elements in geometry will help you develop the idea of auxiliary elements and use them later in various problems.

Hmm... Now I finally understood why you put <u>making a parameter-difference</u> on the list of problem-solving techniques. It was just a mini example of creating auxiliary elements. Now I see auxiliary elements can be used everywhere.

Summary

Additional lines (auxiliary elements) are used to emphasize symmetry, subdivide figures into simpler parts, add figures, and move the parts of a picture from place to place.

What method or methods can you use to find the perimeter of a figure that has a string taped along its strangely shaped borders?

110-115   *For these problems,*
- *Unless another unit is given, use the length of a square as a unit of length, use the area of a square as the unit of area, and the smallest cube shown as a unit of volume.*
- *Mark all dimensions used for calculations.*
- *Mark auxiliary elements with a red pencil.*
- *Shade each chunk you make with colored pencils.*
- *Each vertex is set on a node, i.e. where lines cross on the graph paper.*
- *If a line "appears" to go through a node, you cannot use it to solve the problem; you may use only node-centered vertices.*

110 Copy the given figures. *Mark all axes of symmetry in each figure below with red.*
If you find a line where you can attach a mirror and the picture in the mirror will be the same as what you see on the other side of the figure, this is the line of symmetry. There are 10 axes of symmetry in these figures. Draw all of them. *How many symmetric figures did you find?*

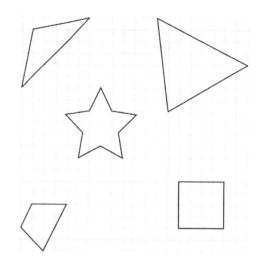

111 Find the perimeter by using shuffling. *Draw the figure the way it looks after shuffling.*

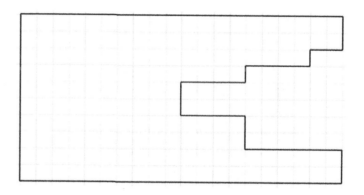

112 Copy the figure. Find the area by adding and then subtracting parts. What is the name of a problem-solving technique used?

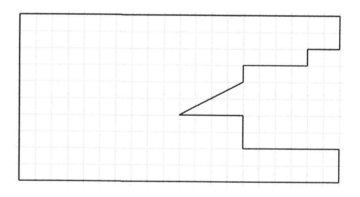

113 Copy the figure. Find the area using two methods. First use chunking, then use adding and subtracting parts. Which method is better? Can you think of a better way of solving the problem?

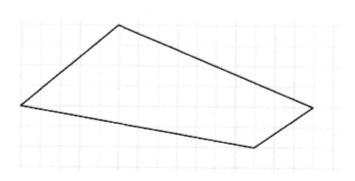

114 Copy the figures and find their areas. Explain your solutions visually.

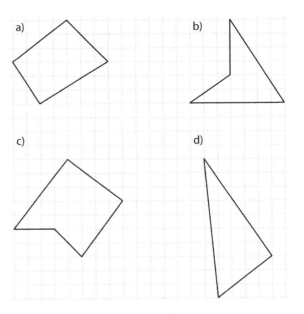

115 Find the areas for the figures, Happy Fish and Angry Fish, to the nearest one-hundredth.
Pay attention. Do not forget to subtract the areas for the holes: the "eyes."
Explain your solutions.

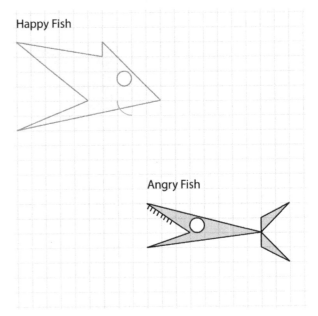

116^{Prep} The second number is less than the first number by as much as the fourth number is less than the third number and as much as the fifth number is less than the fourth number. What is the difference between the second and fourth numbers if the difference between the first number and the fifth number is 11, and the second and third numbers are equal?
To solve, begin by making an outline. Use an auxiliary element to solve the problem. Identify the auxiliary element you used.

117 There are three numbers. What is their product if the second number is 5 less than the first number, and the third number is 3 more than the second number and is the GCF of 12 and 20?

118 A machine was digging a 2-foot-deep rectangular (4 by 6 feet) trench for a pond, moving on average 1 cubic foot of dirt in 5 minutes. If the machine works at the same speed, how much time it will take the machine to dig the trench for a second pond with dimensions of 8 by 6 feet and a depth of 2.5 feet?

Part C Exploration

Stella, Part C taught me how to perform unit conversion, solve simple geometric problems, and present problems as proportions. Also, I know how to draw $v(t)$ and $d(t)$ graphs, and much more.

The problems below will help you examine whether you know Part C material superficially or can apply your knowledge for exploring the world around you. Besides exploration, you will solve some recreational problems here too.

C1-4 **Exploring Shapes:** *You have probably seen colorful metal wind sculptures in gardens and backyards. With a slight wind, the metallic characters start moving; they seem alive. There is a secret behind the liveliness: the horizontal upper part of the construction can swing freely while the left and right sides of the construction are well balanced.*

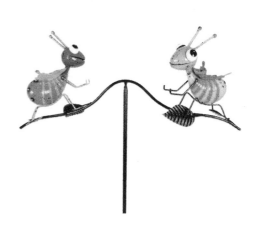

*Zeva has several wind sculptures with red-headed ants on one side and blue-headed ants on another. To make the ants funnier, Zeva attached a 10 cm metal stick to each of them. So, now her ants hold the sticks. Now, Zeva plans to do more. She wants to attach extra decorations to the sticks. Zeva has a big box with geometric shapes. Some shapes are made of solid metal. Other shapes are made of metallic sheets. The shapes had various dimensions, however all the lengths of the sides in rectangular blocks have integer numbers of centimeters. In cylinders, spheres, discs and cones, the radii, and heights (if there are heights) have integer numbers of centimeters as well. From her huge stock of shapes, Zeva wants to choose the shapes that will provide the best balance and then adjust the weights by inserting small weights inside the ants. So, when solving the problems **C1-4**, you can use only integer numbers for heights, radii, and sides.*

C1 For the first wind sculpture, Zeva found a nice 2-mm-thick cone, which she decided to paint as a butterfly net. She planned to find a disc to make an umbrella for the second ant on the swing. The "net" cone had a height of 8 cm and a base with the radius of 6 cm. Zeva attached the "net" to the stick of the red-headed ant. The cone did not have a metallic base. For the blue-headed ant, Zeva had to choose one of her 2-mm-thick discs. *(a)* Find the disc to balance the butterfly net. *(b)* During the final weight adjustment, which ant will need an extra weight?

C2 To decorate the second wind sculpture, Zeva will use a solid cylinder with a diameter of 10 cm and height of 12 cm to decorate the red-headed ant. For the blue-headed ant, she will use two or three solid cubes, choosing them from her stock of cubes, though she found the 1 cm and 2 cm side cubes were missing. *(a)* What set of 2 or 3 cubes will provide the best balancing option? *(b)* Which ant will need an extra weight?

C3   For the third wind sculpture, Zeva has chosen a disc with radius of 12 cm and thickness of 2 mm to attach to the red-headed ant. The disc has a circular hole in the middle with a radius of 10 cm. For the blue-headed ant, Zeva wants to attach a disc the same size that would have two circular holes. Zeva has tools to make the holes with radii that have integer numbers of centimeters. However, her 2 mm thick metal can bend if some parts of the disk are narrower than 1 cm. What must the radii of the holes be to provide the best possible balance while not diminishing the quality of the blue-headed ant's disc?

C4   For the fourth wind sculpture Zeva has chosen a hollow sphere with radius of 9 cm and thickness of 1 cm to attach to the red-headed ant. For the blue-headed ant, Zeva wants to choose a fitting solid sphere. *(a)* What must be the solid sphere's radius? *(b)* Which ant will need an extra weight?

C5-10 Exploring Piecewise Functions. *Sometimes, to present your graph in a mathematical form, you must subdivide the graph into several pieces. Each piece must be presented by a separate formula. The following problems will help you understand the idea of piecewise functions, which you will apply to solve the kinematics problems later in this section.*

C5   The graph on the right represents a piecewise function. Find the missing formulas.

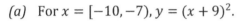

    (a) For $x = [-10, -7)$, $y = (x + 9)^2$.

    (b) _____

    (c) For $x = [-3, 1)$, $y = (x + 1)^2$.

    (d) _____

    (e) For $x = [5, 9)$, $y = (x - 7)^2$.

    (f) _____

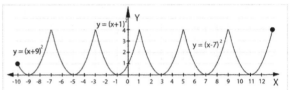

C6   The graph on the right represents a piecewise function. Find the missing formulas.

    (a) For $x = [-6, 0)$, $y = 1.5x + 6$.

    (b) _____

    (c) _____

    (d) For $x = [9, 13]$, $y = 1.5x - 13.5$.

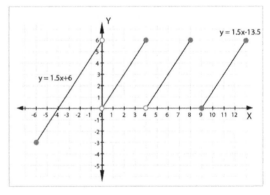

C7   Draw the following piecewise function:

    (a) For $x = [-8, 0]$, $y = 0.5x + 4$.
    (b) For $x = (0, 3)$, $y = (x - 2)^2$.
    (c) For $x = [3, 10)$, $y = -x + 4$.
    (d) For $x = (10, 17]$, $y = 2x - 26$.

C8   The graph on the right represents a piecewise function. Find the missing formulas.

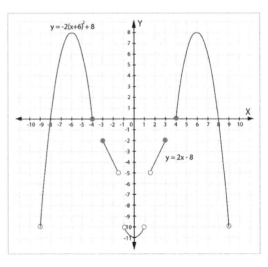

    (a) For $x = (-9, -4]$, $y = -2(x + 6)^2 + 8$.

    (b) _____

    (c) _____

    (d) For $x = (1.5, 3]$, $y = 2x - 8$.

    (e) _____

C9   Draw the following piecewise graph:

(a)   For $y = [1, 7]$, $x = -10$, $x = -8$, $x = -5$, $x = -2$, $x = 1$, $x = 4$, $x = 6$, and $x = 9$.
(b)   For $x = [-4, 0]$, $y = 7$.
(c)   For $x = [7, 11]$, $y = 7$.
(d)   For $x = [-8, -5]$, $y = -2x - 9$.
(e)   For $x = [1, 4]$, $y = 2x - 1$.

C10   The graph on the right represents a piecewise function. Find the missing formulas.

(a)   For $x = (-13, -9]$, $y = (x + 11)^2 - 2$.
(b)   _____
(c)   _____
(d)   For $x = (-1, 3]$, $y = (x + 1)^2 + 4$.
(e)   For $x = (3, 7]$, $y = -(x - 5)^2 + 4$.
(f)   _____
(g)   For $x = (11, 14]$, $y = -(x - 13)^2$.

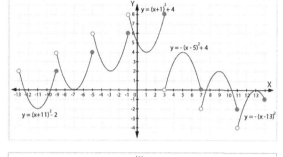

C11   The graph on the right represents a piecewise function. Find the missing formulas.

(a)   _____
(b)   For $x = (-6, 6)$, $y = 0.5x^2 +$ ____.
(c)   For $x =$ _____, $y = -2(x - 9)^2 + 5$.

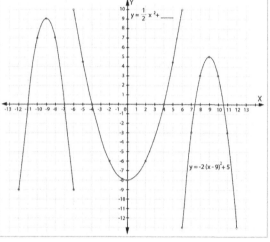

C12-14   Recreational Math

C12   I have three three-digit numbers in my mind. For each number, the square root of the sum of the digits is an integer number, which is greater than the unit digit. Also, in each number, the tens' place digit is an average of the other two digits. I added my three numbers and wrote the result on a card. What number did I write?

C13   **No-Nine Problem**. Decode the multiplication problem below. Here, different letters mean different numbers. Also, the code does not have the digit 9.

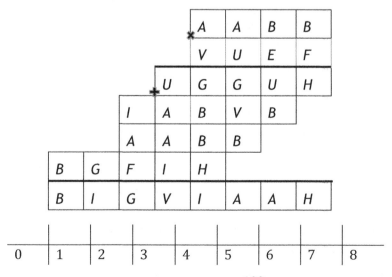

C14   In the problems below, the Roman numerals and mathematical operations are made of toothpicks. Make a single change to create a correct equality: change position of one of the sticks in the equation. *Hint: Problem (a) has four answers. Problems (b) and (c) have two answers.*

Roman Numerals from one to ten: I, II, III, IV, V, VI, VII, VIII, IX, X.

Here are a few more examples: $XI = 11, XII = 12, XIII = 13, XIV = 14, XIX = 19, XX = 20$, $XX1 = 21, XXII = 22, XXX = 30, XL = 40, XLII = 42, L = 50, LI = 51, LIX = 59$, and $LX = 60$.

a)   VIII – II = IV   b)   IV – III = VIII   c) $\frac{LX}{XI} = V$ d)   X = V – V   e)   LX = L

f)   X / VI = I   g) V^I = XXVI   h)   LI – XVII = III   i)   VII = I

C15-20   **Exploring Kinematics.** *These problems will help you explore the distance(time), displacement(time), and velocity(time) functions in depth. First, the difference between the words distance and displacement must be elucidated.*

If a body moved from A to B, the distance covered by the body equals the length of the body's trajectory. In its turn, the displacement of the body is the distance between A and B. The example on the right shows that displacement and distance can be quite different.

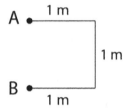

Displacement = 1 m

Distance Covered = 3 m

To solve the problems below, you must know that the area under v(t) graphs gives you a valid information about d(t) functions.

First, we consider the case when <u>an object is moving in the same direction all the time</u>.
1)   *In this case, the total area under the v(t) graph equals the distance (and displacement as well) covered by the object.*
2)   *The area under each piece of v(t) graph is equal to the increase of the d(t) function. Therefore, to construct a d(t) graph, subdivide the v(t) graph into small parts. Finding the area under the v(t) for each unit of time will allow you to draw d(t) graph point by point.*

The situation is a bit different when a body moves sometimes forward and sometimes backwards. In this case, adding the areas under the positive v(t) parts will tell us what the displacement was in the positive direction. Adding the areas under the negative v(t) parts will tell us what the displacement was in negative direction: the <u>displacement</u> and <u>distance covered</u> is different when an object moves back and forth.

C15   A material body was moving in northeast direction for 40 minutes until it suddenly stopped. For the first 10 minutes, it was moving at a speed of 50 meters per minute. During the second 10-minute period, the speed was $25\frac{m}{min}$. Then, for 10 minutes, the speed was reducing gradually until it reached $5\frac{m}{min}$. In the third 10-minute period, each minute, the speed was steadily reducing by $2\ m/min$. After the speed of $5\frac{m}{min}$ was reached, the body continued moving without changing the speed until it suddenly stopped.
(a)   Draw a *v(t)* graph for the material body movement described above.
(b)   Find the distance covered by the body during each 10 minutes of the movement.
(c)   What is the total displacement and the distance covered by the body?

C16 Create a piecewise function for the problem **C15**. Fill in the blanks.

(a) For $t = [0, 10min)$, $v =$ _____ $\frac{m}{min}$.   (c) For $t = [20min, 30min)$, $v = -2\frac{m}{min^2} \times t +$ _____ $\frac{m}{min}$.

(b) _____.   (d) _____.

C17 A car started at 8:00 am and after accelerating (gradually increasing velocity) for 5 seconds, it reached the speed of 108 km per hour and continued driving at the same speed in a south-southeast direction till 10 am.

(a) For the first 7 seconds of movement, build $v(t)$.

(b) Supplement the graph with the related piecewise function.

(c) For the first 7 seconds of movement, build $d(t)$ using your $v(t)$ graph.

(d) Supplement the graph with the related piecewise function.

C18 An object started moving north with the speed of 8 meters per second and never changed its speed. After covering 76 meters, it turned 45 degrees left and continued its movement for 2 seconds. Then the object turned 90 degrees left. After staying for 5.5 seconds on the path, the object turned 45 degrees left and continued its movement for 32 meters when it abruptly turned 90 degrees left. After 24 meters going forward, the object turned somewhat right and, after going just for 4 seconds, stopped. To return on its initial point, it would take the body only 750 milliseconds. *(a)* Present a free style presentation for the movement of the object. *(b)* What is the distance covered by the object? *(c)* What is the displacement of the object? *(d)* What is the measure of the last turn?

C19 The graph on the right-had side describes the movement of the body in a long straight tube with east-west orientation.

(a) Create a piecewise function that describes the velocity of the body.

(b) Find the total distance covered by the body.

(c) Find the displacement of the body.

(d) What is the minimal length of the tube, which can accommodate the described motion?

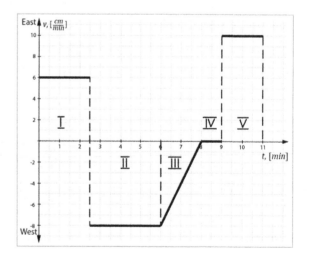

C20 Pytyepa ran south on a trail with a speed of 8 km per hour. Putyopa ran on the same trail with the speed of 12 km per hour in the north direction. The girls started running at the same time from opposite sides of the trail. The length of the trail was 2 km. As Pytyepa started to run, a fly from her hat flew straight toward Putyopa. The fly just touched Putyopa's nose and flew back toward Pytyepa, touched her nose, and flew back... The fly was flying from one girl's nose to the other girl's nose again and again until the girls met. What was the distance covered by the fly if its speed stayed the same, $10\frac{m}{s}$? *Ignore the time when the fly was changing the direction of its flight.*

Approximate your answer to the nearest hundreds of meters.

Part D

fractions, percentages, comparison, and change

PARTS & WHOLES

Stella, in my experience, learning fractions means eating pizza....

Oh, Ezra, there is a deeper meaning in what you say! Knowing fractions and percents will help you to find a good job and earn your own pizza and do anything else you want.

Ezra, Part D will discuss several models and approaches. You will practice using the Unit-Block and Formal-Calculation Approaches. Also, you will create many Area-Box and Length-Box Models. All of these are necessary for developing deep understanding and solving problems involving fractional parts and percents.

Mm...I understand why I need to know how to visualize problems. However, why do I need two approaches for these problems?

The Formal-Calculation Approach works much faster than the Unit-Block Approach. However, unit blocks lead to deeper understanding. So, you will need to develop fluency with both methods. In the end, you will solve change-problems involving parts and percents and learn the specifics of logical conversion for these problems.

Here are the prerequisites: you must know the problem-solving techniques from Parts A and B as well as the Unit-Block Approach from Part C.

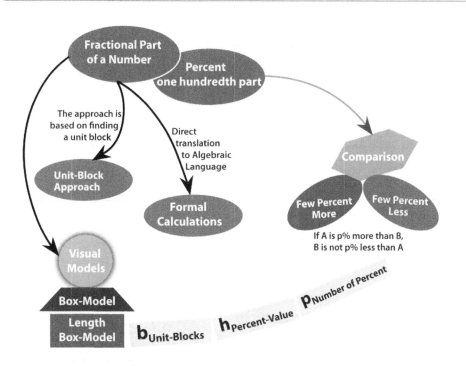

Prerequisites

Algebraic Models and Organizers	**Visual Models**	**Prep**	**Formatting Problems**
Logical Conversion	**Mapping**	**Subscript**	**Alien Eye**
Time & Change Organizers	**Time Lines**	**Time Planes**	**Time Coordinates**

Unit-Block Approach Think of each value as comprised of uniform small parts (unit blocks). Calculate the size of the unit blocks and use this information to find all unknowns.

Chapter 18
Fractions

 Ezra, Chapter 18 will discuss problems dealing with fractional relationships between numbers using the Unit-Block Approach.
Do you remember this approach, Ezra?

Sure, Stella. I applied the Unit-Block Approach when solving proportion problems.

 Unit blocks are everywhere. Think of unit blocks like bricks, specially cut stones, or cement formations: people create blocks to use them for constructing walls, buildings, roads, bridges, etc.

In this chapter, unit blocks represent the greatest common part for two or more values. To illustrate the idea, look at how we use the Unit-Block Approach to add two fractions, $\frac{1}{14}$ and $\frac{3}{4}$.

 The unit block in this problem is $\frac{1}{28}$. The first fraction, $\frac{1}{14}$, is made of two blocks: $\frac{1}{14} = \frac{1}{28} \cdot 2$. The second fraction contains twenty-one blocks: $\frac{3}{4} = \frac{1}{28} \cdot 21$.

Using the unit block, we add the fractions: $\frac{1}{14} + \frac{3}{4} = \frac{1}{28} \cdot 2 + \frac{1}{28} \cdot 21 = \frac{2}{28} + \frac{21}{28} = \frac{23}{28}$.

 Stella, it is a normal addition of two fractions! Your example shows me I have been using the Unit-Block Approach all my life!

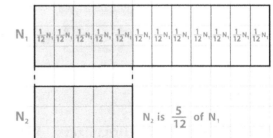

N_2 is $\frac{5}{12}$ of N_1

Yes, Ezra. You did. Every time you found a common denominator.

 In this chapter, you will solve problems and visualize relations between values using unit blocks. In addition, you will use formal calculations and logical conversion in problems with parts.

Section 18.1 Unit-Block Approach

Unit Block

Let's visualize a problem involving parts of a number.

Using the Unit-Block Approach?

 Yes, Ezra. With the *Unit-Block Approach*, we start solving problems by finding the value of the smallest part—a unit block.

Three-Fifths Problem: Digital Model[*]

The first number is 30. What is the second number if it makes $\frac{3}{5}$ of the first number?

N_1 [blocks] 30

N_2 [blocks] 3 unit blocks

b_5 [block] Unit block

 Stella, in the *Three-Fifths* problem, the unit block is 6. It makes $\frac{1}{5}$ of N_1.

 Yes, Ezra. Also, as the picture shows, three blocks make up the second number, and five blocks make up the first number—a whole. A unit block is marked as b_5 because five b_5 blocks make a whole.

Three-Fifths Problem: Unit-Block Approach

$N_1 = 30$	$b_5 = 30 \div 5 = 6$
$b_5 = N_1 \div 5$	$N_2 = 3 \cdot 6 = 18$
$N_2 = 3 \cdot b_5$	
$N_2 = ?$	

Answer: $N_2 = 18$.

---

[*] Digital Models were introduced in Chapter 11.

Stella, you taught me to always define parameters. Why didn't you define b_5?

Look, a lowercase b says it is a unit block. The subscript 5 says *five such blocks make a whole*.
Since the definition of the block is in its name, no explanation is needed.

The Unit-Block Approach is very convenient and especially powerful when we have several numbers made from the same blocks.

Summary

For $\frac{k}{m}$ of N, $b_m = \frac{N}{m}$. In this equation, b_m means, there are m unit blocks in a whole.

 Use the Unit-Block Approach to answer the following questions: (1) What is 2/13 of 130?
(2) What is 13/10 of 130?   (3) What is 4/5 of 20? Illustrate this example.

1   *Find N_2 using the Unit-Block Approach:*
   (a) $N_1 = 17$, N_2 makes 5/3 of N_1.   *(b) $N_1 = 144$, N_2 makes 17/24 of N_1.*
   (c) $N_1 = 144$, N_2 makes 5/9 of N_1.   *(d) $N_1 = 50$, N_2 makes 7/100 of N_1.*
   (e) $N_1 = 256$, N_2 makes 13/64 of N_1.   *(f) $N_1 = 1690$, N_2 makes 11/26 of N_1.*

2   *M is 18 and makes $\frac{9}{10}$ of K. What is the value of K?*
   Finish the discrete visual model and find K using the
   Unit-Block Approach.

3   *Find N_2 using the Unit-Block Approach:*
   (a) $N_1 = 30$, N_1 makes 5/3 of N_2.   *(b) $N_1 = 204$, N_1 makes 17/24 of N_2.*
   (c) $N_1 = 450$, N_1 makes 5/9 of N_2.   *(d) $N_1 = 700$, N_1 makes 7/100 of N_2.*
   (e) $N_1 = 48$, N_1 makes 12/65 of N_2.   *(f) $N_1 = 121$, N_1 makes 11/26 of N_2.*

4   The first number is 20. The second
   number makes $\frac{5}{4}$ of the first. What
   is the second number?

   Finish the model. Apply the Unit-
   Block Approach.

Section 18.2 Visualizing: Area-Box Model

Ezra, this section utilizes an Area-Box Model.

But Stell, the example below is impossible. I cannot subdivide 7 dots into 12 groups!

Agreed. Therefore, instead of dots, I use rectangles. I call them *boxes*. In *Area-Box Models*, the numbers are represented by rectangles. The rectangles are subdivided into unit blocks.

Five-Twelfths Problem: Area-Box Model

The first number is 7. What is the second number if it makes $\frac{5}{12}$ of the first number?

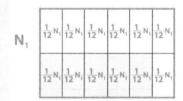

N_2 is $\frac{5}{12}$ of N_1

Unit block: b_{12}

The upper rectangle represents the first number, N_1. I subdivided this rectangle into 12 unit-blocks. For convenience, I chose the area to be divisible by 12.

Five-Twelfths Problem: Unit-Block Approach

$N_1 = 7$	$b_{12} = 7 \div 12 = \frac{7}{12}$
$b_{12} = N_1 \div 12$	
$N_2 = 5 \cdot b_{12}$	$N_2 = 5 \cdot \frac{7}{12} = \frac{35}{12} = 2\frac{11}{12}$
$N_2 =?$	

Answer: $N_2 = 2\frac{11}{12}$.

> That was simple, Stell. I'm ready to practice.

Summary

When making an Area-Box Model for "$\frac{k}{m}$ of N," draw rectangles with the area divisible by m.

(1) What is 2/13 of 5? Visualize the problem and solve using the Unit-Block Approach.

(2) Imagine visualizing the relationship 5/6 of N. What are the best dimensions for the box that represents N? (a) 6 by 64 (b) 6 by 8 (c) 3 by 13 (d) 4 by 5.
Explain why. Illustrate your answer.

5   The rectangles below have the following areas: *(a)* 24; *(b)* 480; *(c)* 36; *(d)* 11; *(e)* 90; *(f)* 7; *(g)* 5.
Find the sizes of the unit blocks and determine the value of the shaded area, A.

(a)

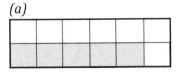

(c)

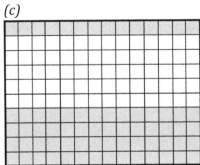

(e)

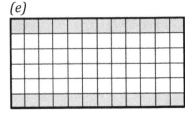

(b)

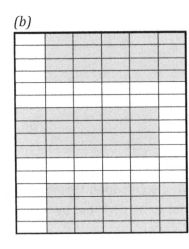

(d)

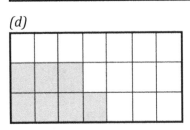

(f)

(g)

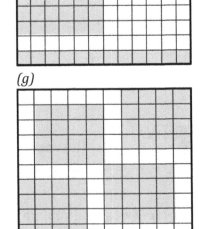

6   *Solve the problems graphically using Area-Box Models. Shade the fractional part and specify its value.*

     (a) Find $\frac{1}{55}$ of M *(b)* Find $\frac{7}{48}$ of P *(c)* Find $\frac{11}{12}$ of N

7-8   *Solve the problems using an Area-Box Model and the Unit-Block Approach.*

7   The first number is 11. The second number makes $\frac{5}{2}$ of the first. What is the second number?

8   The first number is 20 and makes two-thirds of the second number. What is the second number?

Section 18.3 Visualizing: Length-Box Model

 I call it a *Length-Box* Model if the length of each box is proportional to its size.

Stella, why do we need one more model?

 The Length-Box Model can be used in *scaled* and *unscaled* fashions.

I like scaled fashion, but only if it is real body armor! But what do scale armor and visualizing fractions have in common?

 Nothing, really. I used the word *fashion* with the meaning "type or kind." And the word *scaled*...you know, Ezra, you will understand it from the next example.

Five-Twelfths Problem: Scaled Length-Box Model

The first number is 7. What is the second number if it makes $\frac{5}{12}$ of the first number?

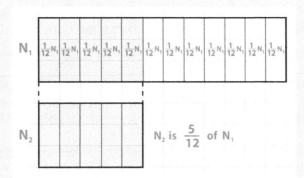

 The picture demonstrates that the <u>length</u> of the rectangle in the scaled version is divisible by a denominator of the fraction. In a scaled Length-Box Model, all unit boxes lay in one line, block by block.

But what if the denominator is large? How can you place, let's say, 121 unit-boxes in one line?

 In that case, you would use an *unscaled* model. Look at this.

One-Twenty-One Problem: Unscaled Length-Box Model

The first number is 7. What is the second number if it makes $\frac{5}{121}$ of the first number?

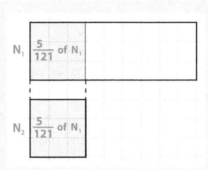

Hmm, the shaded part, $\frac{5}{121}N$, should be much smaller.

In an unscaled model, size is not shown precisely. In the non-scaled picture, we *pretend* the section marked as $\frac{5}{121}N$ has the area of $\frac{5}{121}N$. I oversized the shaded part to fit the label. If I made the part as small as it would be in a scaled version, the label would not fit.

So, the part stays small, but it becomes big enough to fit the label. I see. In an unscaled model, we combine good approximation with clear labeling.

Summary

For $\frac{k}{m}$ of N, use a scaled Length-Box Model with the rectangle length divisible by m. For an unscaled Length-Box Model, combine approximation with clear labels.

For each relationship, choose the best model. Then, explain your choice.
(1) 5/73 of 100: (a) non-scaled model; (b) box 6×63; (c) box 6×14; (d) box 7×73; (e) box 4×7.
(2) 4/7 of P: (a) non-scaled model; (b) box 6×63; (c) box 6×14; (d) box 7×73; (e) box 4×7.
(3) 6/133 of 5: (a) non-scaled model; (b) box 6×63; (c) box 6×14; (d) box 7×73; (e) box 4×7.

9   Each Length-Box Model below has one mistake. Match each model with the description of the mistake.

(1)   Find $\frac{2}{3}$ of T.

T

| $\frac{1}{3}$T | $\frac{1}{3}$T | |

$\frac{2}{3}$T

(2)   Find $\frac{4}{7}$ of D.

D

| $\frac{1}{7}$D | $\frac{1}{7}$D | $\frac{1}{7}$D | $\frac{1}{7}$D | | | |

(3)   Find $\frac{2}{6}$ of N.

N

| $\frac{1}{6}$N | $\frac{1}{6}$N | | | | |

$\frac{2}{6}$N

(4) Find $\frac{1}{2}$ of Q.      (5) Find $\frac{1}{8}$ of M.

(A) The size of the fractional part we must find is not specified.

(B) Not all parts are shown.

(C) The length of the rectangle is not optimal. The rectangle does not fit into the space provided.

(D) Incorrect shading.

(E) The size of the rectangle is not optimal. The length of the rectangle is not divisible by a denominator, although the space allows us to make it divisible.

Pictures (1), (2), (3), (4), and (5) match with: _____ _____ _____ _____ _____

10 Present the problems graphically using a scaled Length-Box Model. Shade the fractional parts and specify their values. *(a)* Find $\frac{1}{8}$ of N. *(b)* Find $\frac{4}{5}$ of P. *(c)* Find $\frac{3}{6}$ of N. *(d)* Find $\frac{1}{30}$ of R.

11 Each unscaled model below has exactly 1 mistake. Match each model with the description of the mistake.

(1) Find $\frac{3}{77}$ of N.   (2) Find $\frac{107}{110}$ of N.   (3) Find $\frac{13}{65}$ of N.

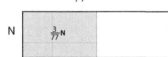   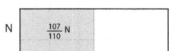

(4)   Find $\frac{2}{3}$ of N.   (5)   Find $\frac{11}{201}$ of N.

(A) The height of the rectangle is not optimal. The rectangle takes too much space.

(B) The shaded part is too small. Label does not fit well.

(C) The size of the fractional part that must be found is not specified.

(D) The shaded part is much larger than it should be.

(E) The shaded part is much smaller than it should be.

Pictures (1), (2), (3), (4), and (5) match with: _____ _____ _____ _____ _____

12 Represent the problems graphically using an <u>unscaled</u> Length-Box Model. Shade the fractional parts and specify their values. *(a)* $\frac{19}{800}$ of N; *(b)* $\frac{417}{419}$ of P; *(c)* $\frac{3}{601}$ of M; *(d)* $\frac{151}{300}$ of R.

13-16 *Solve the problems using a Length-Box Model and the Unit-Block Approach.*

13 The first number is 33. The second number makes $\frac{9}{10}$ of the first number. What is the second number?

14 The first number is 20 and it is $\frac{13}{18}$ of the second number. What is the second number?

15 The first number is 11. The second number makes 0.63 of the first number. What is the second number?

16 The first number is 2. The second number makes $\frac{13}{50}$ of the first number. What is the second number?

Section 18.4 Formal-Calculation Approach

 Ezra, this section introduces formal calculations—calculations done without thinking. Just following the rules.
Some students forfeit their problem-solving abilities by only using formal approaches.

Stella, do I need to wear formal dress to perform formal calculations?

 Don't be silly, Ezra. You will see an example of formal calculations in a minute. For comparison, take another look at the Unit-Block Approach we used to solve the *Five-Twelfths* problem.

Five-Twelfths Problem: Unit-Block Approach

The first number is 7. What is the second number if it makes $\frac{5}{12}$ of the first number?

$$N_1 = 7 \qquad\qquad b_{12} = 7 \div 12 = \frac{7}{12}$$
$$b_{12} = N_1 \div 12$$
$$N_2 = 5 \cdot b_{12} \qquad N_2 = 5 \cdot \frac{7}{12} = \frac{35}{12} = 2\frac{11}{12}$$
$$N_2 = ?$$

Answer: $N_2 = 2\frac{11}{12}$.

 In the <u>Unit-Block Approach</u>, we start by finding the unit block, b_{12}. This approach provides superior understanding but slows us down.
In the Formal-Calculation Approach, in an Algebraic Organizer, we translate *fraction of a number* into algebraic language using a *multiplication sign* instead of the preposition "*of*":

Five-Twelfths Problem: Formal-Calculation Approach

The first number is 7. What is the second number if it makes $\frac{5}{12}$ of the first number?

$$N_1 = 7 \qquad\qquad N_2 = \frac{5}{12} \cdot 7 = \frac{35}{12} = 2\frac{11}{12}$$
$$N_2 = \frac{5}{12} N_1$$
$$N_2 = ?$$

Answer: $N_2 = 2\frac{11}{12}$.

Stella, you translated $\frac{5}{12}$ of N_1 as $\frac{5}{12}N_1$. Where is the multiplication sign you mentioned?

Ezra, when multiplying a fraction or integer times a parameter, the multiplication sign in the expression is frequently omitted. So, the expression $\frac{5}{12}N_1$ is the same as $\frac{5}{12} \cdot N_1$.

Thanks, Stella, now I remember. I have already done multiplication without writing a multiplication sign.

Summary

$\frac{2}{3}$ of N → $\frac{2}{3} \cdot N = \frac{2}{3}N$. Fraction of a number means fraction times a number, *Fraction* × *N*.

(1) *How would you algebraically represent $\frac{5}{7}$ of P?*

(2) *How would you write $\frac{t}{w}$ of 20, where t and w are some number?*

(3) *Draw a sketch showing that the number M makes three-hundredths of 678.*

17   Write each expression in a mathematical form using the Formal-Calculation Approach. When possible, find the answer in numeric form:

(a) $\frac{1}{24}$ of N (d) $\frac{17}{18}$ of 36   (g) $\frac{2}{3}$ of 300   (j) $\frac{3}{26}$ of P

(b) $\frac{11}{25}$ of K (e) $\frac{3}{20}$ of 40   (h) $\frac{1}{10}$ of 30   (k) $\frac{2}{35}$ of M

(c) $\frac{4}{15}$ of 30   (f) $\frac{15}{22}$ of 44   (i) ½ of 24   (l) $\frac{3}{28}$ of D

Convert mixed numbers into improper fractions and reduce if possible.

18   Take the fractions of the given numbers. Show your calculations and express your results in the form of integers or decimal fractions:

(a) $3\frac{5}{4}$ of 6;   (b) 0.03 of 2/3;   (c) ½ of $25\frac{1}{2}$;   (d) $11\frac{7}{13}$ of 26;   (e) $1\frac{7}{8}$ of 1.2;   (f) $\frac{6}{3}$ of 7.

19   The first number is 31. The second number makes 0.7 of the first number. What is the second number?

20   It is known that K is 252 and M makes $\frac{5}{9}$ of K. What is the value of M?

Section 18.5 Logical Conversion and Fractions

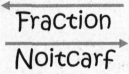

When using formal calculations, Ezra, we can easily apply logical conversion. I will illustrate this using the *Five and a Third* problem.

Five and a Third Problem

The second number is $5\frac{1}{3}$ times the first number. If the second number is 7, what is the first number?

This problem provides plenty of information about N_2. It says, $N_2 = 7$ and $N_2 = 5\frac{1}{3} \cdot N_1$. However, we must find another number, N_1.

To find N_1, convert the formula $N_2 = 5\frac{1}{3} \cdot N_1$ into an expression that helps find the first number: $N_1 = N_2 \div 5\frac{1}{3}$.

But Stell! It is better to convert $5\frac{1}{3}$ into an improper fraction, $\frac{16}{3}$.

You are correct. Look, I created an improper fraction, $5\frac{1}{3} = \frac{16}{3}$, performed logical conversion, $N_1 = N_2 \div \frac{16}{3}$, and then simplified N_1 in my Algebraic Organizer.

Five and a Third Problem: Logical Conversion and Formal Calculations

$N_1 = N_2 \div \frac{16}{3} = \frac{3}{16} \cdot N_2$

$N_2 = 7 = 5\frac{1}{3} \cdot N_1 = \frac{16}{3} \cdot N_1$

$N_1 = ?$

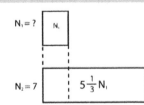

$N_1 = \frac{3}{16} \cdot 7 = \frac{21}{16} = 1\frac{5}{16} = 1.3125.$

Answer: $N_1 = 1.3125.$

Stella, I think the main idea is to simplify everything before applying logical conversion. I will always convert mixed numbers and decimals into fractions before applying logical conversion and simplify "division by a fraction" when needed.

Summary

Before logical conversion, change mixed numbers or decimals into $\frac{P}{Q}$. Simplify: use multiplication by a fraction.

(1) Which number format is the best for solving a word problem involving logical conversion: $\frac{7}{3}$, $2\frac{1}{3}$, or 0.7? Why? (2) You have $2\frac{1}{3}$ times the amount of money I have. What fraction of your money do I have? Solve and illustrate your solution.

21   Transform each decimal and mixed number to an integer or a fraction, proper or improper.

(a) 0.05   (b) 0.7   (c) $25\frac{5}{7}$ (d) $11\frac{4}{9}$ (e) $33\frac{6}{3}$ (f) 35.45   (g) $1\frac{3}{7}$

(h) $11\frac{7}{133}$ (i) $23\frac{15}{45}$ (j) $K\frac{16}{8}$ [read *K and sixteen-eights*]

22   Translate each sentence into algebraic language, converting mixed numbers and decimals into fractions. Express N in terms of P and calculate it.

(a) P makes $1\frac{1}{24}$ of N, P = 125.   (b) P makes $\frac{11}{25}$ of N, P = 44.   (c) P makes $20\frac{4}{15}$ of N, P = 10.

(d) P makes *0.07* of N, P = 2.8.   (e) P makes $24\frac{3}{20}$ of N, P = 1.5.   (f) P makes 1.5 of N, P = 0.45.

(g) P makes $\frac{2}{3}$ of N, P = 200.

23   The first number is 3,000. It makes $\frac{2}{3}$ of the second number. What is the second number? *Apply the Formal-Calculation Approach.*

24   The first number is 30. It makes three-fifths of the second number. What is the second number? *Apply the Unit-Block Approach.*

25   The first number is 2. It makes $\frac{7}{15}$ of the second number. What is the second number? *Apply the Formal-Calculation Approach.*

26   The first number is 26. It makes 0.13 of the second number. What is the second number? *Apply the Unit-Block Approach.*

27^P   There are four numbers. The second number makes seven-tenths of the third number, which makes one and one-ninth of the first number. The first number, in turn, is $\frac{6}{7}$ less than the fourth number, which is equal to the quantity of all the different factors of eighteen. What is the second number?

28^P   There are three numbers. Each is 7/11 greater than the previous number. What is the quotient of the first and third numbers if the greatest number is as big as $\frac{7}{9}$ of one?

29   Find the sum of the first two numbers if the first number makes a quarter of the third number, and the second number makes three-quarters of the third number. The third number is $6,785\frac{398}{399}$.

30   The first number makes $\frac{3}{5}$ of the second number. The second number makes $\frac{3}{5}$ of the third number, and the third number makes $\frac{3}{5}$ of the fourth number, which is as big as $\frac{3}{5}$ of one-sixteenth. What is the square root of the first of these four numbers?

31   There are three numbers. The first number makes $\frac{91}{110}$ of the second, which is 187. The third number makes $\frac{182}{220}$ of the second number. What is the difference between the first number and the sum of the other two numbers?

32   There are two numbers. The second number makes two-thirds of the first. What is the first number if we know the second number is 7? *Make a visual model and solve the problem using the Unit-Block Approach.*

Chapter 19
Percents

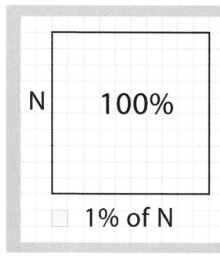

N   100%

1% of N

Chapter 19 introduces percents, Ezra. To take *1 percent of a value*, take a one-hundredth part of this value.

Write one percent as 1%. One percent of N means $\frac{1}{100}N$.

Then, taking *3 percent* of a number means taking $\frac{3}{100}$ of the number. Three percent must be written as 3%.

Above, Ezra, you can see an Area-Box Model. The model helps you visualize 1% of N. In the model, N is represented as a 10×10 box.

And the area for each small square is 1% of N. Right, Stell?

Sure. The box represents a whole and has 100 unit-blocks; each unit block equals $\frac{N}{100}$. We can label each block b_{100}, but it would be too long. Since we use percent a lot, I propose using the letter h. This letter emphasizes that a unit block makes one <u>h</u>undredth part of a whole, $h = \frac{N}{100}$.

Great, I will use h. It is faster than writing b_{100}.

Chapter 19 will introduce the algebraic language needed for solving problems involving percentages and several visual models. You will predominantly draw Length-Box Models.

I MAKE 1% OF YOUR BODY.

Sure. Drawing boxes should be easier than drawing elephants and worms.

Section 19.1 Unit-Block Approach to Percents

 In *percent* problems, *Soft Algebra* proposes the following notation...

 Stella, it was in the introduction. For a unit block, use h instead of b_{100}. The meaning of h is 1% or a hundredth part of a number.

 Of what number, Ezra?

 Hmm...aah...some number. Stella, we can use $h(N)$ to mark the percent of N. I mean, we can write, $h(200) = 1$. This will mean, one percent of 200 is 1.

 Yes, Ezra, except one percent of 200 is 2. We can write $h(N) = \frac{N}{100}$. It works for any number. Below, I will apply it to present the *Eighty-Eight Percent* problem.

Eighty-Eight Percent Problem: Unit-Block Approach and Length-Box Model

The second number makes 88% of the first number, which is 150, and the third number makes 75% of the second number. What is the third number?

$N_1 = 150$
$h(N_1) = N_1 \div 100$
$N_2 = 88 \cdot h(N_1)$
$h(N_2) = N_2 \div 100$
$N_3 = 75 \cdot h(N_2)$

$N_3 = ?$

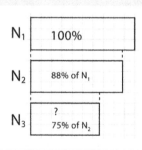

$h(N_1) = 150 \div 100 = 1.5$
$N_2 = 88 \cdot 1.5 = 132$
$h(N_2) = 132 \div 100 = 1.32$
$N_3 = 75 \cdot 1.32 = 99$

Answer: $N_3 = 99$.

 Ezra, in this problem, $h(N_1)$ means 1% of N_1, and $h(N_2)$ means 1% of N_2. Also, in this example, $h(150) = 1.5$ and $h(132) = 1.32$. Since N_2 is less than N_1, 1% percent of N_2 is less than 1% of N_1 as well:
If $N_2 < N_1$, then $h(N_2) < h(N_1)$.

 I see, the size of a percent changes if the number representing 100% changes. OK, Stella, I will remember that the size of a percent can change.

Summary

$h(N)$ is the value of 1% of N. When a problem talks about the percent value of a single number, use h.

(1) In the Eighty-Eight Percent *problem, what is the value for $h(N_3)$?*

(2) If K makes 4% of M and 7% of G, and it is known G is 200 greater than K, which is greater, $h(M)$ or $h(G)$? Illustrate your solution.

33-43 *This section requires use of the Unit-Block Approach.*

33   Make Area-Box Models for the relationships below. Draw 10×10 squares and shade the area of interest. *(a) K makes 26% of N. (b) K is $\frac{13}{50}$ of N.*

34   Make Area-Box Models for the relationships below. Find Q. Start by drawing 10 by 10 squares.

        (a) Q is 200% of 2. (b) Q is 75% of 46.

35   Find N_2.

      (a) $N_1 = 17$; N_2 makes 50% of N_1.   *(b) $N_1 = 144$; N_2 makes 5% of N_1.*
      (c) $N_1 = 144$; N_2 makes 25% of N_1.   *(d) $N_1 = 50$; N_2 makes 240% of N_1.*
      (e) $N_1 = 0.25$; N_2 makes 12% of N_1.   *(f) $N_1 = 400$; N_2 makes 2.7% of N_1.*

36   *M is 18. K makes 9% of M. What is the value of K? Illustrate the problem using an Area-Box Model. Solve the problem.*

37   Find N_2. Pay attention: in these problems N_2 makes *100%*, not N_1.

      (a) $N_1 = 30$; N_1 makes $\frac{5}{3}$% of N_2.   *(b) $N_1 = 204$; N_1 makes 200% of N_2.*

      (c) $N_1 = 30$; N_1 makes $17\frac{1}{7}$% of N_2.   *(d) $N_1 = 7$; N_1 makes 0.7% of N_2.*

      (e) $N_1 = 48$; N_1 makes 10% of N_2.   *(f) $N_1 = 12$; N_1 makes 50% of N_2.*

38   *Solve the problems described by Length-Box Models.*

      (a) 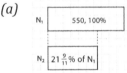   *(b)*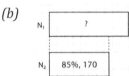

39   *M is 18 and makes 9% of K. What is the value of K? Illustrate the problem using a Length-Box Model.*

40   The first number is 200. The second number makes $\frac{5}{4}$% of the first number. What is the second number? *Present a Length-Box Model and solve the problem.*

41   The first number makes 20% of the second number, which, in turn, makes 30% of the third number. What is the first number if the third number is 500? *Illustrate your solution.*

42   The first number makes 50% of the second number. The second number makes 40% of the third number. What is the first number if the third number is 100? *Illustrate your solution.*

43   *M makes 21% of six million and two-hundred fifty thousand, K makes 25% of T, and T, in turn, makes 84% of the number that is as big as 50 to the fourth power. What is the quotient of M and T? Illustrate your solution.*

Section 19.2 Formal-Calculation Approach to Percents

 Calculations frequently become easier after we convert percentages into numeric form. Below, I will perform a conversion using the $\frac{1}{100}$ part of the number instead of 1%.

So, instead of 1% *of a number*, you will write $\frac{\text{Whole Number}}{100}$. Correct?

Correct. Look at the four examples below.

Presenting Percentages in Numeric Form

1) $\quad 7\% = 7 \cdot 1\% = 7 \cdot \frac{1}{100} = 0.07$

2) $\quad \frac{8}{9}\% = \frac{8}{9} \cdot \frac{1}{100} = \frac{2}{225}$

3) $\quad 200\% = \frac{200}{100} = 2$

4) $\quad 64\frac{1}{3}\% = 64\frac{1}{3} \div 100 = \frac{192+1}{300} = \frac{193}{300}$

 The *First-Sixty* problem will demonstrate how this conversion is applied.

First-Sixty Problem: Formal-Calculation Approach

The first number is 60. What is the second number if it makes $64\frac{1}{3}\%$ of the first number?

$N_1 = 60$

$N_2 = 64\frac{1}{3}\% \cdot N_1 = 64\frac{1}{3} \cdot \frac{1}{100} \cdot N_1 = \frac{193}{300} \cdot N_1$

$N_2 = ?$

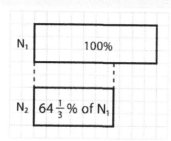

$N_2 = \frac{193}{300} \cdot 60 = 38.6$

Answer: $N_2 = 38.6$.

Stella, the conversion $64\frac{1}{3}\% = \frac{193}{300}$ really simplified calculations.

For formal calculations, always start with converting percents into proper or improper fractions. The %-to-fraction conversion and simplification must be part of an Algebraic Organizer. After the percentage is presented in a form of a proper or improper fraction, you can use logical conversion.

Summary

When using formal calculations, convert %-values into regular numbers. $\frac{Percent\ Value\%}{100\%} = Normal\ Fraction.$

(1) Convert into fractions or integers: (a) 7%; (b) 300%; (c) 0.2%; (d) $2\frac{1}{3}$%.

(2) What is ½% of 1,000?

---

44 Represent each percentage below as a regular number in the form of a fraction or an integer (if possible). Show your calculations.

(a) 5%   (b) 7%   (c) 125%   (d) $11\frac{4}{7}$%   (e) $37\frac{2}{3}$%

(f) 200%   (g) $137\frac{3}{11}$%   (h) $\frac{7}{13}$%   (i) $35\frac{1}{2}$%   (j) K%

45 Take the given percentage of the numbers below. *Show your calculations and express your results in the form of integers or decimal fractions.*

(a) $2\frac{5}{4}$% of 6   (b) 0.9% of 2/3   (c) $\frac{1}{2}$% of $5\frac{1}{2}$ (d) $5\frac{2}{3}$% of 600   (e) $\frac{3}{4}$ % of 104

(f) 2.8% of 70   (g) $1\frac{3}{7}$% of 154   (h) 10% of M   (i) Find p% of 40   (j) $\frac{5}{13}$% of 169

46 Solve the problems described by the visual models below. *Use formal calculations and data conversion when needed.*

(a) 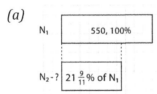   (b)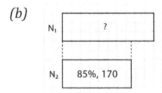

47 Half of these statements are incorrect. Mark them with the letter F. *Present your calculations.*

(a) 3% · 40 = 12   (b) (1/3 of 69) = (30% of 69)   (c) (¾ of G) = (75% of G)

(d) (93% of 77) = (77% of 93)   (e) (½ of 50) = (25% of 100)   (f) (3/7% of 70) = 30

48 The first number is 200. The second number makes $\frac{1}{3}$% of the first number. What is the second number? *Present a Length-Box Model and solve the problem using the Formal Calculation Approach.*

49 Match each problem with the correct letter. *(1) 2% of 310   (2) 960% of 2/3   (3) $\frac{1}{2}$ of $12\frac{2}{3}$*

(4) $\frac{3}{4}$% of 880   (5) 2.8% of 220   (6) 9% of 70

Letters: *(C) 6.4, (S) 6.3, (O) 6.2, (P) 6.6, (U) 6.16, (T) $6\frac{1}{3}$.*

1	2	3	1	4	5	6

50   The first number makes 50% of the second number. The second number makes 40% of the third number. What is the first number if the third number is 100?
Solve the problem using the Formal-Calculation Approach. Illustrate your solution.

51   Find the additive and multiplicative inverses to the numbers below. Express your answer as an integer or decimal fraction when possible. In other cases, express the answer in a form of a proper fraction or mixed number. *(a)* $-33\frac{6}{3}$ *(b)* 30 *(c)* $-1\frac{56}{7}$ *(d)* $\frac{1}{11}$ *(e)* $23\frac{45}{15}$ *(f)* $-\frac{1}{K}$

52   Find *M* using formal calculations. Start by converting percentages to proper or improper fractions.
   (a) *K* makes 10% of *M*. *K* = 26.   *(b)* *P* makes 0.9% of *M*. *P* is 9/10.
   (c) *T* makes $\frac{1}{2}$% of *M*. *T* is $5\frac{1}{2}$.   *(d)* *R* makes $5\frac{2}{3}$% of *M*. *R* is 3.4.
   (e) *L* makes *p*% of *M*. *L* = 20.   *(f)* *Q* makes 20% of *M*. *Q* = 20.

53   The first number makes 20% of the second number and 30% of the third number. What is the difference between the second and the third numbers if the first number is 60?
Solve the problem using the Formal-Calculation Approach. Illustrate your solution.

54   *M* is 27 and makes 9% of *K*. What is the value of *K*?
Solve using formal calculations. Illustrate the problem using a Length-Box Model.

55   There are three numbers. The first number makes $42\frac{2}{7}$% of 35 and is 37 times the second number. The third number is the greatest two-digit prime. What is the second number?

56   *Represent each percentage below as a regular number in fraction or (if possible) integer form. Show your calculations.*
   (a) .025%   *(b)* 17%   *(c)* $12\frac{19}{20}$%   *(d)* $\frac{4}{7}$%   *(e)* $717\frac{300}{3}$%
   (f) 2,007%   *(g)* $17\frac{8}{11}$%   *(h)* $1\frac{7}{613}$%   *(i)* $\frac{1}{2}$%   *(j)* $\frac{K}{M}$%

57   The second number makes 0.28% of the first number, which is as large as $\frac{3}{7}$ of $\frac{5}{6}$. What is the second number?

58   There are four numbers. The second number makes five-thirds of the third number, which makes five-ninths of the first number as well as three-fifths of the second number. The first number makes 27% of the fourth number, which is as big as one percent of the cube of twenty. Find the <u>mean</u> of all the numbers.

59   There are four numbers. The first number is the reciprocal of the second number and is the additive inverse of the third number. If the fourth number is the additive inverse of the second number and is equal to $-57\frac{3}{7}$, what is the sum of all four numbers?

60   There are four numbers. The second number makes 41 and 3/7 percent of the fourth number, which makes 7 and 7/29 percent of the first number, which is as big as 100 1/3. If the third number makes 11/1450 of the first number, what is the 37th part of the sum of all four numbers?

Section 19.3 Find the Percentage

In this section, you will identify percentages using the Unit-Block and Formal-Calculation Approaches: you will find $p_{part}(Whole)$.

Stella, what does $p_{part}(Whole)$ mean?

I will show you, Ezra: $p_{24}(200) = 12\%$ means 24 makes 12% of 200. Here, 200 is the whole, which makes 100%.

And 24?

Twenty-four is a part of 200, which makes 100%. So, $p_{24}(200) = 12\%$.

Cool. And what about the two methods for finding the percentage?

In the Unit-Block Approach, we first calculate $h(Whole)$ and then the percent. In the Formal-Calculation Approach, we convert percentages into regular numbers and then find the percent.
Below, look at the examples with 200 and 24 in a form of a problem.

Percent-24 Problem

What percent does 24 make if the number that makes a whole is 200? If a whole is 20?

First, I will use the Unit-Block Approach. As you can see, the first step is finding the value of 1%, $h(Whole)$:

Percent-24 Problem: Unit-Block Approach

(a)   Whole = 200 $h(200) = \frac{200}{100} = 2$ $p_{24}(200) = \frac{24}{h(200)}\% = \frac{24}{2}\% = 12\%$

(b)   Whole = 20 $h(20) = \frac{20}{100} = 0.2$ $p_{24}(20) = \frac{24}{h(20)}\% = \frac{24}{0.2}\% = 120\%$

I see. Knowing the value of one percent, Stella, you found what percent 24 makes. The division was not difficult.

Now, Ezra, let us turn to the Formal-Calculation Approach. First, I will calculate what part of a whole 24 makes. You must read $Part(200)$ as *part of* 200.

Percent-24 Problem: Formal-Calculation Approach

(a)   Whole = 200 $Part(200) = \frac{Part}{Whole} = \frac{24}{200} = 0.12$ $p_{24}(200) = 0.12 \cdot 100\% = 12\%$

(b)   Whole = 20 $Part(20) = \frac{Part}{Whole} = \frac{24}{20} = 1.2$ $p_{24}(20) = 1.2 \cdot 100\% = 120\%$

In the second step, I made a translation from a fraction to a percent using the formula, $p_{part}(Whole) = Fractional\ part \cdot 100\%$.

Now, Ezra, you know how to translate percent problems into algebraic language and can apply both the Unit-Block and Formal-Calculation Approaches.

Yes, Stella, I can use any of these models but...just one more example of translation, please. How should I translate *K makes 7% of M?*

K makes 7% of M is translated as $p_k(M) = 7\%$, and N_1 *makes 5% of* N_2 is translated as $p_{N_1}(N_2) = 5\%$. I think you have it now! Let's move on.

Summary

If $p_{N_3}(N_2) = 4\%$, we can say N_3 makes 4% of N_2. Unit-Block Approach: $p_{Part}(Whole) = \frac{Part}{h(whole)}\%$. Formal-Calculation Approach: $p_{Part}(Whole) = \frac{Part}{Whole} \cdot 100\%$.

    Explain your steps using the Unit-Block and Formal-Calculation Approaches:

(1)   *Five percent of a number is 20. What percent of the number does 28 make?*

(2)   *What does this mean:* $p_{N_2}(N_4) = 88\%$?   (3) *What does this mean:* $p_G(L_1) = 8\%$?

61   In each problem $N_1 = 400$, $N_2 = 500$, and $p = 20\%$. Find N_3. *Illustrate each solution.*
(a) If $p_{N_3}(N_1) = 20\%$, $N_3 = ?$ (b) If $p_{N_3}(N_2) = 20\%$, $N_3 = ?$
(c) If $p_{N_2}(N_3) = 20\%$, $N_3 = ?$ (d) If $p_{N_1}(N_3) = 20\%$, $N_3 = ?$

62   Use percent notation to label the following percent-values:

(a) 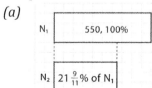 $p\_(\_\_) = 21\frac{9}{11}\%$ (b) 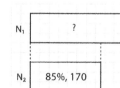 $p\_(\_\_) = 85\%$

Review the section material if needed.

63   What percentage of each rectangle is shaded? Show your calculations.

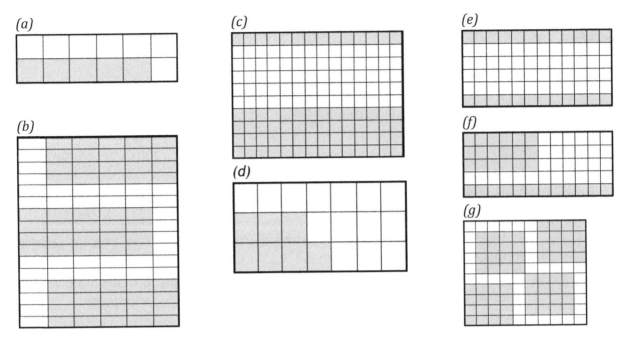

64   Convert the numbers to percentages. Show your calculations.

(a) 2.5   (b) 0.7   (c) $\frac{19}{20}$ (d) $\frac{40}{7}$ (e) $\frac{3}{30}$ (f) 2   (g) $\frac{0.7}{10}$ (h) $\frac{7}{600}$ (i) $\frac{1}{2}$ (j) $\frac{K}{M}$

65   There are five numbers. The first number is the additive inverse of the second number, which is $\frac{3}{7}$ less than -119. The third number is the multiplicative inverse of the first number, and the fourth number is the reciprocal of the fifth number, which equals $7\frac{34}{51}$. What is the product of the numbers?

66   There are three numbers. The second number is as big as 3% of the first number. The third number makes 34% of the first number and is as big as 17. What is the second number? *Solve the problem using both the Formal-Calculation and Unit-Block Approaches. Which works better?*

67   There are four numbers. The first number tells us what percentage of the second number the third number makes. The fourth number equals the number of digits in the first number. It is known the second number is 20 times the third number and equals 2 to the 10th power. Find the fourth number.

68   If we take 37 and three-sevenths percent of the first number, we will calculate the second number and it equals 26. What is the quotient of the first and second numbers?

69   The second number makes 37/50 of the first number and makes 27% of the third number. If the difference between the first and third numbers is 212, what percentage of the first number does the second number make?

70   There are five numbers. The third number is as large as one and one-half of the fifth number. In addition, the third number has the value of three-sevenths and is $\frac{1}{7}$ of the first number. The second number is 7/12 and makes a quarter of the fourth number. Find the product of all the numbers.

71   There are six numbers. The third number is as large as a fifth of the fifth number. It is also as big as one-sixth of the sixth number. The fourth number makes one-fourth of the third number and is as big as the first number. The second number is $\frac{1}{30}$ of the third number and is the quotient of eight hundred and eighty tens. Find all the numbers.

Chapter 20
Comparison

Ezra, you already know how to translate sentences with comparison into algebraic language.

Sure. Here are a few examples.

Previous Examples of Comparison

A is $\frac{4}{5}$ greater than B.	$A = B + \frac{4}{5}$
A is $\frac{4}{5}$ less than B.	$A = B - \frac{4}{5}$
A is 4 times B.	$A = B \cdot 4$
A is one-fourth of B.	$A = B \div 4$

As you can see, I know how to compare numbers, Stella.

In Chapter 20, we will examine novel ways of comparing values. Ezra, you will learn how to translate into algebraic language the comparison relations shown below.

Novel Types of Comparison

A is greater than B by $\frac{4}{5}$ of its value.	$A = B + \frac{4}{5} \cdot B$
A is less than B by $\frac{4}{5}$ of its value.	$A = B - \frac{4}{5} \cdot B$
A is 4% greater than B.	$A = B + \frac{4}{100} \cdot B$
A is 4% less than B.	$A = B - \frac{4}{100} \cdot B$

After you learn the new forms of comparison and logical conversion, you will be able to solve challenging word problems involving parts and percentages. Good luck mastering these problems!

Section 20.1 Greater by a Fraction of Its Value

Section 20.1 analyzes the *Internship* problem, where S_2 *is greater than* S_1 *by a fraction of* S_1.

Internship Problem

Nina has a salary of $750 per week. After she completes her internship, her salary will be higher by one-tenth of the current value. What will Nina's salary be after she completes her internship?

S_1 | 750 (Whole)

S_2 | ▭ $\frac{1}{10} S_1$

?

Organizer* Initial salary was $750.
At the end, the salary is higher by 1/10 of the initial value.
What is the salary at the end?

Parameters S_1 - The initial salary.
S_2 - The salary at the end.

S_2 contains the part which equals S_1. In addition, S_2 contains the part that is $\frac{1}{10}$ of S_1.

So, Stella, I can say S_2 makes one whole and $\frac{1}{10}$ part of S_1. Hence, $S_2 = (1 + \frac{1}{10}) \cdot$

Look at these alternative solutions for the *Internship* problem, starting with the Unit-Block Approach.

Internship Problem: Unit-Block Approach

$S_1 = 750\ d. = 10 \cdot b_{10}$
$b_{10} = S_1 \div 10$
$S_2 = (10 + 1) \cdot b_{10} = 11 \cdot b_{10}$

$S_2 = ?\ d.$

$b_{10} = 750\ d. \div 10 = 75\ d.$
$S_2 = 11 \cdot b_{10} = 11 \cdot 75\ d. = 825\ d.$

Answer: Nina's salary will be $825 per week.

Stella, in the Unit-Block Approach, after you found b_{10}, I would just add it to S_1.

* Since it is a change-problem, instead of a Prep, we create a Time & Change Organizer.

Sure, you can do that, but I wanted to show you the general approach. Now it is time for formal calculations. I will translate ALL data into algebraic language and simplify ALL expressions within the Algebraic Organizer.

Internship Problem: Formal-Calculation Approach

$S_1 = 750\,d.$
$S_2 = \left(1 + \frac{1}{10}\right) \cdot S_1 = 1.1 \cdot S_1$ $S_2 = 1.1 \cdot 750\,d. = 825\,d.$

_____

$S_2 = ?\,d.$

Answer: Nina's salary will be $825 per week.

I see, Stella. Both models produced the same answer. OK, I'm ready for practice.

Summary

If M is greater than K by a fraction $\frac{P}{Q}$ of K, M makes $\left(1 + \frac{P}{Q}\right)$ of K or $M = \left(1 + \frac{P}{Q}\right) \cdot K$.

(1) P is greater than N by ½. What is P if N is 5? Illustrate your solution.

(2) P is greater than N by ½ of its value. What is P if N is 5? Illustrate your solution.

72   *Solve the problem depicted on the right.*

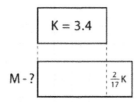

73   If the first number is 1/3 greater than the second number, and the second number is greater than the third number by 1/3 of its value, what is the sum of the numbers? It is known the third number is 30.

Section 20.2 Less by a Fraction of Its Value

Ezra, Section 20.2 analyzes the *Village K* problem where P_2 *is less than* P_1 by a fraction of P_1.

Village K Problem

This year the population of village K was calculated as 46,920. It is predicted that next year the population will be lower by 3/23 of its current value. What is the predicted population for the next year?

46,920 (Whole)

P_1 [| $\frac{3}{23}P_1$]

P_2 [?]

Organizer   Initial population is 46,920.
Predicted population is lower by 3/23 of the initial value.
What is the predicted population for the next year?

Parameters P_1 - Initial population.
P_2 - Predicted population.

P_1 consists of a part equal to P_2 and a part which makes $\frac{3}{23}$ of P_1.

Therefore, Stell, P_2 makes one whole of P_1 minus $\frac{3}{23}$ part of P_1.

So, $P_2 = (1 - \frac{3}{23}) \cdot P_1$.

Now look at two alternative solutions for this problem.

Village K Problem: Unit-Block Approach

$P_1 = 46{,}920\ p. = 23 \cdot b_{23}$
$b_{23} = P_1 \div 23$
$P_2 = (23 - 3) \cdot b_{23} = 20 \cdot b_{23}$

$b_{23} = 46{,}920\ p. \div 23 = 2{,}040\ p.$
$P_2 = 20 \cdot b_{23} = 20 \cdot 2{,}040\ p. = 40{,}800\ p.$

$P_2 = ?\ p.$

Answer: The predicted population is 40,800 people.

In the Unit-Block Approach, I started with finding a unit block, b_{23}.

I see. Now, I will present the Formal-Calculation Approach. I will begin with translation into algebraic language, which I know really well.

Village K Problem: Formal-Calculation Approach

$$P_1 = 46{,}920\ p.$$
$$P_2 = \left(1 - \frac{3}{23}\right) \cdot P_1 = \frac{20}{23} \cdot P_1$$

$$P_2 = \frac{20}{23} \cdot 46{,}920\ p. = 40{,}800\ p.$$

$$P_2 = ?\ p.$$

Answer: The predicted population is 40,800 people.

As was expected, both approaches resulted in the same answer.

Summary

If M is less than K by a fraction $\frac{P}{Q}$ of K, M makes $\left(1 - \frac{P}{Q}\right)$ of K or $M = \left(1 - \frac{P}{Q}\right) \cdot K$.

(1) P is less than N by $\frac{2}{5}$. What is P if N is 20? Illustrate your solution.

(2) P is less than N by $\frac{2}{5}$ of its value. What is P if N is 20? Illustrate your solution.

74   *Solve the problem depicted on the right-hand side.*

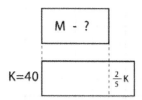

75   There are three numbers, and the first number is 20. It is less than the second number by 2/3 and less than the third number by 2/3 of its value. Find the sum of the second and third numbers.

Section 20.3 Greater by *p*%

Ezra, Section 20.3 analyzes the *Graduation* problem involving the clause *greater by p%*.

Graduation Problem

Nina has a salary of $750 per week. After she graduates, her salary will be 40% higher. What will be Nina's salary after graduation?

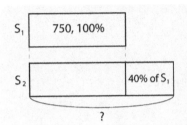

S_1 750, 100%

S_2 40% of S_1

?

Organizer Initial salary was $750.
At the end, salary is 40% higher.
What is the salary at the end?

Parameters S_1 - the initial salary
S_2 - the salary at the end

The box S_2 contains area S_1 and the part which makes 40% of S_1. Therefore,
$S_2 = (100 + 40)\% \cdot S_1$.
In the *unit-block* solution, we must find a unit block, h, and then the answer.

Graduation Problem: Unit-Block Approach

$S_1 = 750 \, d. = 100h$
$h = S_1 \div 100$
$S_2 = (100 + 40) \cdot h = 140 \cdot h$

$h = 750 \, d. \div 100 = 7.5 \, d.$

$S_2 = 140 \cdot h = 140 \cdot 7.5 \, d. = 1{,}050 \, d.$

$S_2 = ? \, d.$

Answer: After graduation, Nina's salary will be $1,050 per week.

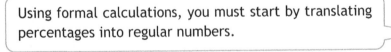

Using formal calculations, you must start by translating percentages into regular numbers.

Graduation Problem: Formal-Calculation Approach

$S_1 = 750 \, d.$
$S_2 = (100 + 40)\% \cdot S_1 = 140\% \cdot S_1 = \frac{140}{100} S_1 = 1.4 S_1$

$S_2 = 1.4 \cdot 750 \, d. = 1{,}050 \, d.$

$S_2 = ? \, d.$

Answer: After graduation, Nina's salary will be $1,050 per week.

Once again, both models resulted in the same answer.

Summary

If M is $n\%$ more than K, then M makes $(100 + n)\%$ of K. $M = (100 + n)\% \cdot K = (100 + n)/100 \cdot K$.

(1) P is 50% more than T. T is $76\frac{7}{9}$. What percentage of T does P make? Illustrate your solution.

(2) P is more than T by 20% of its value. T is 76. What percentage of T does P make? Illustrate your solution.

76   *Solve the problem depicted on the right-hand side.*

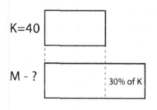

77   There are two numbers. The first number is 6% greater than the second number and it is the largest two-digit number. What is the quotient of the first and second numbers?

Section 20.4 Less by *p*%

> Ezra, section 20.4 analyzes the *Highland Boots* problem involving the clause *less by p%*.

Highland Boots Problem

The tag says the original price of Stuart Weitzman Highland Boots is $750. What would be the price after a 40% reduction?

Organizer	Initial price is $750. At the end, price is 40% lower. What is the price at the end?
Parameters	P_1 - the initial price P_2 - the price at the end

(Diagram: box labeled 750, 100%; P_1 with "40% of P_1"; P_2 with "?")

> Whoa, Stella! Those boots are awfully expensive! They better be good. In the picture, P_1 is greater than P_2 by 40%, so $P_1 = (100 + 40)\% \cdot P_2$. Correct?

> Incorrect. In this picture, P_1 represents a whole. So, 40% is $p(P_1)$. The box P_2 is less than P_1 by <u>40% of P_1</u>. So, $P_2 = (100 - 40)\% \cdot P_1$.

> But Stella, your formula has the same meaning as mine. Minus 40% is the opposite of +40%!

> This is not true. You will see it in Section 20.5. For now, let us just look at the two solutions for the problem.

Highland Boots Problem: Unit-Block Approach

$P_1 = 750\,d. = 100h$ $h = P_1 \div 100$ $P_2 = (100 - 40) \cdot h = 60 \cdot h$	$h = 750\,d. \div 100 = 7.5\,d.$ $P_2 = 60 \cdot h = 60 \cdot 7.5\,d. = 450\,d.$
$P_2 = ?.$	

Answer: After the price reduction, the Stuart Weitzman Highland Boots will cost 450 dollars.

> As you can see, the boots will cost $450. With your formula, your answer would be around $540!
> Now, the formal calculations.

Highland Boots Problem: Formal-Calculation Approach

$P_1 = 750 \, d.$

$P_2 = (100 - 40)\% \cdot P_1 = 60\% \cdot P_1 = \frac{60}{100} P_1 = 0.6 P_1$

$P_2 = ? \, d.$

$P_2 = 0.6 \cdot 750 \, d. = 450 \, d.$

Answer: After the price reduction, the Stuart Weitzman Highland Boots will cost 450 dollars.

> Stella, I think your boots are too expensive even after 40% off...OK, OK. Back to the topic. I hope after the next section I'll understand why my formula was incorrect.

Summary

If M is $n\%$ less than K, M makes $(100 - n)\%$ of K. $M = (100 - n)\% \cdot K = \frac{100-n}{100} \cdot K$.

(1) P is 30% less than T. T is $7\frac{7}{11}$. What percentage of T does P make? Illustrate your solution.

(2) P is 70% less than T. T is 7. What percentage of T does P make? Illustrate your solution.

78   *Solve the problem depicted on the right.*

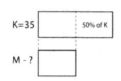

79   There are three numbers, and the first number is 15. The second number is 60% less and the third number is 60% greater than the first number. What is the quotient of the difference between the first two numbers and the difference between the first and the third numbers? Identify the unnecessary data for solving this problem.

80   *Translate each sentence into algebraic language. Then, express K in terms of M.*

(a) M is $\frac{3}{7}$ more than K.   (b) M is $\frac{3}{7}\%$ more than K.   (c) M is $1\frac{3}{7}$ times K.   (d) M is K over $1\frac{3}{7}$.

(e) M is $\frac{3}{7}\%$ less than K.   (f) M equals $\frac{3}{7}$ of K.   (g) $\frac{3}{7}$ of M is the reciprocal of K.

(h) M is additive inverse of $-K$.   (i) M makes K and $\frac{3}{7}$.   (j) $\frac{3}{7}$ of M is less than K.

81   There are four numbers, and the first number is 60.4. It is 2/3% more than the second number, which is 2/3 greater than the third number. In turn, the third number makes 2/3% of the fourth number. Find all the numbers.

82   *Translate each statement below into algebraic language. Then, apply logical conversion and find K.*

(a) M is $43\frac{3}{7}\%$ greater than K.   (b) M is 200% more than K.   (c) M makes 200% of K.

(d) M is 4% less than K.   (e) M makes 4% of K.   (f) G is greater than K by 0.4%.

(g) R is less than K by 40%.   (h) R makes 104% of K.   (i) Q is greater than K by 104%.

(j) T is less than K by $66\frac{2}{3}\%$.

83   There are five numbers. The first number is five-elevenths and makes half of the fifth number. The first number also makes three-quarters of the fourth number. The second number is 7% of the third number and is as big as 33% of 110. What is the quotient of the product of all the numbers and $2\frac{1}{7}$?

Section 20.5 Comparing Numbers Using Percentages

 Ezra, next we will compare two problems where the difference is expressed using percentages.

Greater Salary Problem

Martin's salary is 800 dollars per week. John's salary is 1,200 dollars per week. By what percentage is John's salary greater than Martin's?

$M = \$800$

$p_M(M) = 100, [\%]$

$h = M \div 100$

$J = \$1,200 = p_J(M) \cdot h$

$p_J(M) = J \div h$

$p_J(M) - p_M(M) = ?$

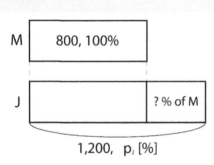

$J - M = 1,200 - 800 = 400, [\$]$

$h = 800 \div 100 = 8, [\$ \text{ per } 1\%]$

$p_J(M) - p_M(M) = (J - M) \div h =$

$= 400 \div 8 = 50, [\%].$

Answer: John's salary is greater than Martin's by 50%.

 As you can see, the calculations show $1,200 is 50% greater than $800. Now, Ezra, read the *Lower Salary* problem.

The same problem! It just has the opposite question, so the answer must be 50%! Why is your answer different? Hmm...let me analyze the picture and calculations.

Lower Salary Problem

Martin's salary is 800 dollars per week. John's salary is 1,200 dollars per week. By what percentage is Martin's salary lower than John's?

$M = \$800 = p_M(J) \cdot h$

$p_M(J) = M \div h$

$J = 1,200 = 100 \cdot h$

$h = J \div 100$

$p_J(J) = 100, [\%]$

$p_J(J) - p_M(J) = ?$

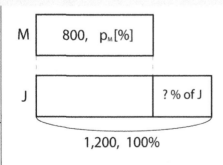

$J - M = 1,200 - 800 = 400, [\$]$

$h = 1,200 \div 100 = 12, [\$ \text{ per } 1\%]$

$p_J(J) - p_M(J) = (J - M) \div h =$

$= 400 \div 12 = 33\frac{1}{3}, [\%].$

Answer: Martin's salary is lower than John's by $33\frac{1}{3}$%.

The calculations are correct, so why is the answer $33\frac{1}{3}$% and not 50%?

The *Lower Salary* problem demonstrates 800 is $33\frac{1}{3}$% less than 1,200 while the *Greater Salary* problem shows 1,200 is 50% greater than 800. The value of a percent changes if the value of the whole is different. Since $1,200 > 800$, one percent of 1,200 is greater than one percent of 800.

I see, Stella. As your examples show, <u>the percentage difference varies depending on the value of one percent</u>.
Let me summarize: if A is greater than B by a non-zero percentage, B cannot be less than A by the same percentage.

Summary

If M is n% less than K, K cannot be n% greater than M. There is only one exception, $n = 0$.

(1)   By what percentage is 200 greater than 100? Illustrate your solution.

(2)   By what percentage is 100 less than 200? Illustrate your solution.

84   The first number is 3 more than the second. The second number is 5. By what percentage is the first number greater than the second number?

85   The first number is 3 less than the second number. The second number is 5. By what percentage is the first number less than the second number?

86   The first number is twice as big as the second. The second number is 5,789.37. By what percentage is the first number greater than the second number?

87   The first number is 3 times the second number, which is 0.04. By what percentage is the second number less than the first number?

88 N is greater than K by 100%. K is less than N by p%, and it is known that p is one of the following numbers: 0, 50, 100, 150, or 200. Find p.

89 N is less than K by 20%. K is greater than N by p%, and it is known that p is one of the following numbers: 0, 10, 15, 20, 25, 30, or 35. Find p.

90   Specify the values of M and K. *Start by translating each problem into algebraic language and making* logical conversions *when needed. Show all necessary calculations.*

     (a) M is $41\frac{1}{7}$% more than K. $M = 2$.   *(b)* M is 200 % more than K. $M = 0.3$.

     (c) K makes 200% of M. $M = 8$.   *(d)* M is 6% less than K. $M = 50$.

     (e) M makes 3% of K $M = 90$.   *(f)* M is greater than K by 100%. $M = 3$.

     (g) M makes .5% of K. $M = 24$.   *(h)* K makes 11.2% of M. $K = 14$.

     (i) M is greater than K by 10%. $M = 4\frac{5}{7}$.   *(j)* K is less than M by $60\frac{2}{3}$%. M is 300.

91   *Translate each statement into algebraic language and convert into numeric (not percent!) format. Then, insert the given numbers into each formula. <u>Do not solve the problems.</u>*

   (a) M is $k\%$ greater than L. $L = 43\frac{3}{7}$. $M = 200$.   (b) M makes $k\%$ of L. $M = 0.3$. $L = 0.3$.

   (c) M is $k\%$ less than L. $L = 10$. $M = 8$.   (d) K is 6% less than M. $M = 50$.

   (e) L makes $4\frac{18}{9}\%$ of K. $L = 15$.   (f) M is greater than G by $k\%$. $G = 14$. $M = 28$.

   (g) T is less than M by $k\%$. $T = 0.03$. $M = 2.34$.   (h) Q makes $k\%$ of M. $M = 305$. $Q = 30.5$.

   (i) M is greater than N by $k\%$. $M = 3\frac{5}{9}$. $N = 2\frac{7}{9}$.   (j) R makes $k\%$ of $23\frac{2}{3}$. $R = 25$.

92   There are two numbers. The first number is 7% less than the second number and equals 31. What is the second number?

93   There are three numbers. The first number is 10% greater than the second number and 10% less than the third number. The first number is also $1\frac{1}{3}\%$ of 3,300. What is the quotient of the second and third numbers?

94   There are three numbers. The first number is 23% greater than the second number, makes 23% of the third number, and is the reciprocal of $\frac{3}{52}$. What are the numbers?

95   What is the arithmetic mean of two numbers where the first number is the geometric mean* of 30 and $13\frac{1}{3}$, and the second number is 20% greater than 30?

96   There are five numbers, and the middle number is 100. Starting from the first number, each next number makes 150% of the previous number. What are the arithmetic and geometric means* of these numbers?

---

* See the Glossary.

Section 20.6 Logical Conversion

The chart below presents logical conversion formulas for three types of comparisons.

Logical Conversion for Various Kinds of Comparisons

A is **k greater** than B.	B is **k less** than A.
A is **k less** than B.	B is **k greater** than A.
A is **k times** B.	A is B **divided by k**.
A is B **divided by k**.	A is **k times** B.
A is **k% greater** than B.	B is $\frac{100k}{100+k}$ % **less** than A.
A is **k% less** than B.	B is $\frac{100k}{100-k}$ % **greater** than A.

Conversion for percentages is rather complicated. Ezra, I will demonstrate how logical conversion works using the *Than-Be* problem.

OK, Stella. Just please don't make Zom-be problems. I don't like zombies.

Than-Be Problem: Percent-Type Comparison

A is greater <u>than *B*</u> by 40%. By what percentage is *B* less than *A*?

$p_A(B) - p_B(B) = 40\%$	Since *A* is greater than *B* by 40%, $A = (100 + 40)\% \cdot B = \frac{7}{5}B$.
	Therefore, $B = \frac{5}{7}A$. In percent form, $p_B(A) = \frac{5}{7} = \frac{500}{7} = 71\frac{3}{7}$, [%].
────────────	Since $p_A(A) = 100\%$ and $p_B(A) = 71\frac{3}{7}\%$, we can solve the problem:
$p_A(A) - p_B(A) = ?$	$p_A(A) - p_B(A) = 100\% - 71\frac{3}{7}\% = 28\frac{4}{7}\%$.

Answer: When *A* is 40% greater than *B*, *B* is only $28\frac{4}{7}$% less than *A*.

To solve a *comparison* problem, use a Comparison Organizer. It will help you understand what number represents a reference value, i.e., the value that makes 100%. To create a *Comparison Organizer*, use a *box-oval* diagram like this one.

First, inside the box, write any information regarding the *reference*— the value that makes 100%. Then, insert into the oval all information concerning the value we compare to the reference. Finally, add the description of the comparison next to the connecting line.

Comparison Organizer

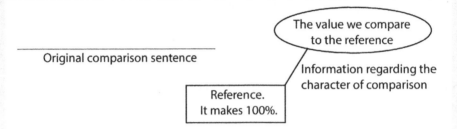

Original comparison sentence

The value we compare to the reference

Information regarding the character of comparison

Reference.
It makes 100%.

Ezra, you can use this organizer to present any kind of comparison.

OK, but now that I think about the *Than-Be* problem...doesn't the problem require two organizers?

It does, Ezra. One Comparison Organizer describes only one case of comparison.

Than-Be Problem: Comparison Organizers

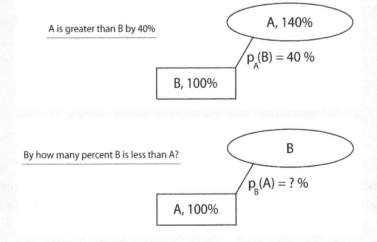

A is greater than B by 40%

A, 140%

$p_A(B) = 40\%$

B, 100%

By how many percent B is less than A?

B

$p_B(A) = ?\%$

A, 100%

You know, Ezra, you can also use a shortened Version of a Comparison Organizer.

Than-Be Problem: Shortened Comparison-Organizers

By how many percent is (B) *less* than A *?*   (A) *is greater* than B *by 40%.*

$$p_B (A)$$ $$p_A (B)$$

Nice! The organizers will help me to remember the difference between writing $p_B(A)$ and $p_A(B)$. I still make mistakes in percentage problems.

One final clue, Ezra: the reference frequently follows the word *than*.

Summary

Use Comparison Organizer to determine what is the reference for each case of comparison.

A is 10% greater than B, and C is 10% greater than A.
(1) Visualize the relationship. (2) One percent, h, of which number is greater: A, B, or C?
(3) Which difference is greater: B − A or C − B?

97   There are 4 numbers. The first number is 100 and every other number is 10 more than the previous number.
  (a) How much larger is the fourth number than the first number?
  (b) How much smaller is the first number than the fourth number?
  (c) By what percentage is the fourth number greater than the first number?
  (d) By what percentage is the first number less than the fourth number?

98   There are 2 numbers, and the second number is four times the first number. Find the difference between the numbers in a percentage format. *Illustrate your solution.*

99   If every number in the series is as large as one over three hundred and twenty-two times the previous number, and the middle number is one, what is the difference between the first number and the reciprocal of the fifth number, which is the last number of the series?

100   It is known the first number is $3\frac{5}{7}$ and is 35% less than the second number. What is the difference between the second and third numbers if the third number is 35% greater than the first number?

101   If A is 100 and makes 35% of the whole, what is B, which makes 17% of the whole?

102   There are two identical products. The price of the first product is $3.50 per pound and there's a 20% discount. The price of the second product is $4.00 per pound and there is a 25% discount. Which product is cheaper with the discount? By how much is 10 pounds of the less expensive product cheaper than 10 pounds of the more expensive product?

Chapter 21
Advanced Change-Problems

Ezra, Chapter 21 will concentrate on change-problems involving fractions and percentages.

Well then, I will be drawing a lot.

You will. Below are examples of clauses used in this chapter:

a number was increased to $\frac{1}{3}$

a number was increased by $\frac{1}{3}$ of its value

a number was increased to one and $\frac{1}{3}$ of its value

a number was increased to one hundred and $\frac{1}{3}$ of a percent

a number was decreased to $\frac{1}{3}$ of a percent

a number was increased by $\frac{1}{3}$ of a percent

a number was decreased by $\frac{1}{3}$ of a percent

a number was decreased by $\frac{1}{3}$

a number was decreased by $\frac{1}{3}$ of its value

a number was decreased to $\frac{1}{3}$ of its value

a number was increased by $\frac{1}{3}$

a number was decreased to $\frac{1}{3}$

Stella, these clauses are almost the same. Do they all mean different things?

Mm...of the entire list, only two pairs of clauses describe the same transformations. Can you find these pairs before turning the page and reading the chapter?

I will try...

In the chart above, find the two pairs of clauses that describe the same transformations.

Section 21.1 Change-Problems with "To" and "By"

Section 21.1 will illustrate the first four clauses from the introduction: *increased to, decreased to, increased by,* and *decreased by.*

Increased To Problem

N was increased to $\frac{1}{3}$. What do you know about the initial value of N?

Organizer N_1 was increased and became $N_2 = \frac{1}{3}$.

Time Line

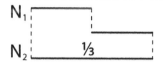

Time Plane

Answer: $N_1 < \frac{1}{3}$.

Stella, in the *Increased To* problem, Time & Change Organizers and Time Lines do not help me solve the problem.

I agree, Ezra. However, a Time-Plane Model clearly shows $N_2 < N_1$. It also shows N_2 is one-third. Therefore, $N_1 < \frac{1}{3}$. A similar situation happens in the *Decreased To* problem, too.

Decreased To Problem

N was decreased to $\frac{1}{3}$. What can you say about the initial value of N?

Organizer N_1 was decreased and became $N_2 = \frac{1}{3}$.

Time Line

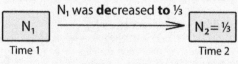

Time Plane

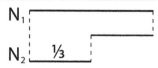

Answer: $N_1 > \frac{1}{3}$.

In the *Decreased To* problem, Stell, the last illustration shows $N_2 = 1/3$. Since $N_2 < N_1$, I figured out $N_1 > 1/3$. It was simple.

For both the *Decreased To* and *Increased To* problems, 1/3 was the final number. Now, Ezra, think what will happen if, instead of the preposition *to*, we insert the preposition *by*.

The problems will change—the relationships between the initial number, N_1, and the final number, N_2, will be different. I am ready to see your examples.

Increased By Problem

N was increased by $\frac{1}{3}$. Present the relationship between the initial and final values of *N*.

Organizer N_1 was increased by $\frac{1}{3}$ and became N_2.

Time Line
Time Plane

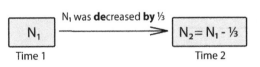

Answer: $N_2 = N_1 + \frac{1}{3}$.

The phrase "N_1 *was increased by* 1/3," Ezra, means the following: N_1 becomes N_2, which is 1/3 greater than N_1.

Then, Stella, the phrase "N_1 was decreased by 1/3" means that N_1 becomes N_2, while N_2 is 1/3 less than N_1. These are simple addition and subtraction problems!

Decreased By Problem

N was decreased by $\frac{1}{3}$. Use algebraic language to present the relationship between the initial and final values of *N*.

Organizer N_1 was decreased by $\frac{1}{3}$ and became N_2.

Time Line
Time Plane

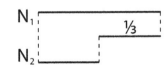

Answer: $N_2 = N_1 - \frac{1}{3}$.

This section demonstrates the importance of prepositions in change-problems.

Also, the first two examples showed that, sometimes, a *change* provides information about the values.

Therefore, for even the simplest change-problems, pay attention to detail and thoroughly analyze all available information.

Summary

N was increased (or decreased) to A means N was changed and became A. N was increased by A means N became $N + A$. N was decreased by A means N became $N - A$.

A number from the set {-1, 3, 7, 8, 12} was reduced and became 7. What was the number before the reduction? Explain your answer.

103   *Translate the data into algebraic language. Use time coordinates in the form of numerical indexes, i.e. 1, 2, 3, and 4.*

(a) A number decreased by 2, then increased by a factor of 6.

(b) A number was reduced to 2 units, then divided by 17. In the end, the number was multiplied by 51.

(c) First, a number was reduced by a value of $1\frac{3}{7}$, then increased by $\frac{2}{3}$. In the end it was doubled.

(d) A number was increased to 4, then decreased by one-quarter. In the end, it was divided by one-quarter.

104   The number was first decreased by 2, then increased 15 times and became 18. What was the value of the number initially?
Make a Time-Plane and/or a Time-Line model and solve the problem.

105   A number was reduced to 12. Then, it was divided by 17. In the end, the number was multiplied by 51. Find the initial number if it is known that, before the changes, the number was a prime and belonged to a set containing 10 numbers: $\{7, 17, -7, -14, 14, 5, 35, -35, 50.2, 37.3\}$.
Make a Time Line and solve the problem.

106   A number was doubled several times until it reached 128. If it is known the initial number is a one-digit number and the number of times the initial number doubled does not exceed 4, what was the initial number?

107   Negative three-sevenths was decreased by three-sevenths. The result's absolute value doubled. What number was obtained in the end?

108   Five hundred sixty-seven and seven-elevenths was increased by six hundred seventy-four and six-sevenths, multiplied by 203 and reduced to 6. What is the quotient of 54 and the number calculated at the end?

Section 21.2 Changing by a Fraction of a Value

In some problems, a number changes by a fraction of its value. To teach you how to solve such problems...Ezra, I desperately need your help.

Desperately? How can I help you teach myself?

Until now, I easily named the problems. But now, I cannot find a name for a problem dealing with increasing N by a fraction of its value.

Stella, it's so simple. I will happily make a name for the problem below. The name will be, mmm...the *Up-By* problem.

Up-By Problem: Increasing by a Fraction of the Value

N was increased by $\frac{1}{3}$ of its value. Use algebraic language to present the relationship between the initial and the final values of N.

Organizer

N_1 was increased and became N_2.
N_2 is $\frac{1}{3}N_1$ greater than N_1.

Time Line
Time Plane

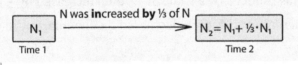

N_1
$N_2 = N_1 + \frac{1}{3}N_1.$

──────────

$N_2 = ?$

$N_2 = N_1 + \frac{1}{3}N_1 = \left(1 + \frac{1}{3}\right) \cdot N_1 = \frac{4}{3}N_1$

Answer: $N_2 = \frac{4}{3}N_1.$

When increased by a fraction of its value, the number contains the initial number and some additional fraction of it: $N_2 = N_1 + \frac{1}{3}N_1$. So, increasing the number by $\frac{1}{3}$ of its value means $\frac{4}{3}$ of the number. Is that clear?

It is. Stella, now it's time for the *Down-By* problem. To decrease a number by a fraction of its value, we will have to...subtract the portion of a number from its initial value.
Now, I present the *Down-By* problem.

Down-By Problem: Decreasing by a Fraction of the Value

N was decreased by $\frac{1}{3}$ of its value. Use algebraic language to present the relationship between the initial and the final values of N.

Organizer
N_1 was decreased and became N_2.
N_2 is $\frac{1}{3}N_1$ smaller than N_1.

Time Line
Time Plane

N_1
$N_2 = N_1 - \frac{1}{3}N_1.$

$N_2 = N_1 - \frac{1}{3}N_1 = \left(1 - \frac{1}{3}\right) \cdot N_1 = \frac{2}{3}N_1$

$N_2 = ?$

Answer: $N_2 = \frac{2}{3}N_1.$

Nice presentation, Ezra. You decreased a number by one-third of its value and obtained the answer. The answer makes two-thirds of the initial number. The general case for changing a number by a fraction of its value is below.

General Formulas: Changing a Number by a Fraction of its Value

Increasing a number by a fraction, $\frac{m}{n}$, of its value means multiplying the number by $\frac{n+m}{n}$:

$$N_2 = N_1 + \frac{m}{n} \cdot N_1 = \left(1 + \frac{m}{n}\right) \cdot N_1 = \frac{n+m}{n} \cdot N_1.$$

Decreasing a number by a fraction, $\frac{m}{n}$, of its value results in $\frac{n-m}{n}N_1$:

$$N_2 = N_1 - \frac{m}{n}N_1 = \left(1 - \frac{m}{n}\right) \cdot N_1 = \frac{n-m}{n}N_1.$$

Those are the general formulas for illustrative purposes only. You will not need them for solving practice problems.

When solving problems involving changing values by their parts, use Time & Change Organizers, Time Lines, and Time Planes and always convert mixed fractions into improper fractions. The latter will simplify your calculations.

Summary

If N is changing by a fraction of its value, use formulas $N_2 = N_1 + \text{fraction} \cdot N_1$ or $N_2 = N_1 - \text{fraction} \cdot N_1$.

 K was decreased by ½ and then increased by ½ of its value. How did K change after the trans-formations?

Draw a Time Line and a scaled Time-Plane for the problem above.

---

109   *Translate the data onto algebraic language. Use time coordinates in the form of numerical indices, i.e., 1, 2, 3, and 4.*

    (a) The number was first decreased by $\frac{2}{3}$ of its value, then it was increased by one-half of its value.

    (b) The number was reduced by ¼ and again by ¼ of its value. Finally, the number was increased by ½.

    (c) At first, the number was reduced by a value of $\frac{3}{7}$, increased by $\frac{3}{7}$ of its value, and became equal to $\frac{3}{7}$.

    (d) A number was reduced to one-quarter, increased by one-quarter of its value, and decreased by a factor of 2.

110   When a number was decreased by $\frac{1}{3}$ of its value and then increased by $\frac{1}{3}$ of its value, the resulting number was 8. What was the initial number?

111   A number was increased by a factor of 7, then decreased by 7, and finally one-seventh of it was removed. What was the number at the end if the initial number was 10?

Section 21.3 Changing to a Fraction of a Value

 We already discussed problems with simple number changes. Here, Ezra, we will look at a more advanced example: a number is *changing to a fraction of a value*.

Up-To Problem

N was increased to $1\frac{1}{3}$ of its value. Present the relationship between the initial and the final values of N.

Organizer

N_1 was increased to $1\frac{1}{3}$ of its value and became N_2.

N_2 is N_1 times $1\frac{1}{3}$.

Time Line

Time Plane

N was **increased to** 1⅓ of N

| N_1 | $\longrightarrow$ | $N_2 = 1\frac{1}{3} \cdot N_1$ |
| Time 1 | | Time 2 |

N_1

N_2 $1\frac{1}{3} \cdot N_1$

Answer: $N_2 = 1\frac{1}{3} \cdot N_1 = \frac{4}{3} N_1$.

These problems are quite simple. I added this section to cover all possible constructions for change-problems. Now see how we decrease a number to a fraction of its value.

Down-To Problem

N was decreased to $\frac{1}{3}$ of its value. Present the relationship between the initial and the final values of N.

Organizer

N_1 was decreased to $\frac{1}{3}$ of its value and became N_2.

N_2 is less than N_1 by $\frac{1}{3}$ of N_1.

Time Line

Time Plane

N was **decreased to** ⅓ of N

| N_1 | $\longrightarrow$ | $N_2 = \frac{1}{3} \cdot N_1$ |
| Time 1 | | Time 2 |

N_1

N_2 ⅓·N_1

Answer: $N_2 = \frac{1}{3} \cdot N_1$.

Stella, your examples are very similar. In both cases, the result is a product of the initial number and a given coefficient.

 Correct. Thus, I will translate your observation into algebraic language. To transform N to $\frac{m}{n}$ of its value, use multiplication: $N_2 = \frac{m}{n} \cdot N_1$.

Summary

If N was decreased (or increased) to a fraction (or mixed number) of its value, then, $N_2 = \text{fraction} \cdot N_1$ or $N_2 = \text{MixedNumber} \cdot N_1$.

The starting price was $100 and then a change occurred. Which change has no meaning?
In all meaningful cases, what is the new price?
(1) The price was decreased by 9/4.   (2) The price was decreased by 9/4 of its value.
(3) The price was increased by 9/4 of its value.   (4) The price was decreased to ¾ of its value.
(5) The price was increased to ½ of its value.   (6) The price was decreased by ¾ of its value

112   *Match the information on the right and on the left.*

1)	N was decreased to 0.7 of its initial value.	P	$N_2 = \frac{3}{10} \cdot N_1$
2)	N was increased by $5\frac{3}{8}$ of its initial value.	I	$N_2 = \frac{43}{8} \cdot N_1$
3)	N was decreased by 0.7 of its initial value.	E	$N_2 = \frac{7}{10} \cdot N_1$
4)	N was increased to $5\frac{3}{8}$.	X	$N_2 = 6.375 \cdot N_1$
5)	N was increased to $5\frac{3}{8}$ of its initial value.	N	$N_2 = 5\frac{3}{8}; N_2 < N_1$
6)	N was increased by $5\frac{3}{8}$.	L	$N_2 = 5\frac{3}{8}; N_2 > N_1$
7)	N was decreased to 0.7.	T	$N_2 = .7; N_2 < N_1$
8)	N was decreased to the value of $5\frac{3}{8}$.	S	$N_2 = \frac{8}{51} \cdot N_1$
9)	N was decreased by a factor of $6\frac{3}{8}$.	C	$N_2 = N_1 + 5.375$

1	2	3	4	5	6	5	7	8	1	9	9

113   A number was reduced to one-quarter of its initial value. Then, the number was increased by one-quarter. Finally, it was divided by one-quarter. What was the value of the number initially if the final value of the number is 8?

114   *Translate each sentence into algebraic language: (a) N was increased by $\frac{1}{2}$. (b) N was decreased by $\frac{1}{2}$.*
   (c) N was decreased by a factor of 2.   (d) N was increased by $\frac{1}{2}$ of its value.   (e) N was divided by $\frac{1}{2}$.
   (f) N is decreased to ½ of its initial value.   (g) N is increased to 6 and one-half of its original value.
   (h) N is increased by 6 and one-half of its original value.

115   A number was decreased by ½ of its value two times. Then, the number was increased by ½ of its value twice. What is the difference between the initial number and the number at the end if the latter is 18?

116   A number was increased to 3 times its value, then decreased to two-sevenths of its value. Finally, it was increased by three-quarters of its value. What was the difference between the initial value of the number and its value at the end if the initial number was 14?

117   A number was increased to $3\frac{7}{9}$ of its value, then decreased to $\frac{2}{3}$ of its initial value. The number at the end was 5. What was the initial number?

Section 21.4 Increasing to and by *p*% of a Value

 Ezra, you are already familiar with the clauses *increased by* and *increased to*. Here, we will use these clauses in percent problems.

Increased By % Problem

N was increased *by* 200% of its value. Use algebraic language to present the relationship between the initial and the final values of *N*.

Organizer

N_1 was increased and became N_2.
N_2 is 200% greater than N_1.

Time Line

Time Plane

N was **in**creased **by** 200% of N

N_1 — Time 1 → $N_2 = N_1 + 200\% \cdot N_1$ — Time 2

N_1	100%	
N_2		200% of N_1

N_1
$N_2 = N_1 + 200\% \cdot N_1.$
———————————
$N_2 = ?$

$$N_2 = N_1 + \frac{200}{100} N_1 = (1 + 2) \cdot N_1 = 3N_1$$
or $N_2 = 100\% \cdot N_1 + 200\% \cdot N_1 = 300\% \cdot N_1 = 3N_1$

Answer: $N_2 = 3N_1.$

Stella, I did not expect the number to triple! I would like to see what happens if you substitute *by* with the preposition *to*.

Increased To % Problem

N was increased *to* 200% of its value. Use algebraic language to present the relationship between the initial and final values of *N*.

Organizer

N_1 was increased and became N_2.
N_2 makes 200% of N_1.

Time Line

Time Plane

N was **increased to 200%** of N

N_1 — Time 1 → $N_2 = 200\% \cdot N_1$ — Time 2

N_1	100%
N_2	200% of N_1

N_1
$N_2 = 200\% \cdot N_1.$
———————————
$N_2 = ?$

$$N_2 = \frac{200}{100} N_1 = 2N_1$$

Answer: $N_2 = 2N_1.$

With **to**, the number is only 200% of its initial value! Huge difference.

Now, review the visual models, which present a general case for *the number N increased to $p\%$ or increased by $p\%$ of its value.*

Increased by $p\%$ versus Increased to $p\%$

N was increased <u>by</u> $p\%$ of its value.

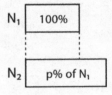

N_1	100%

| N_2 | | $p\%$ of N_1 |

$N_2 = N_1 + p\% \cdot N_1 = 100\% \cdot N_1 + p\% \cdot N_1 = (100\% + p\%) \cdot N_1$

$$N_2 = \frac{100+p}{100} \cdot N_1$$

N was increased <u>to</u> $p\%$ of its value.

N_1	100%

| N_2 | $p\%$ of N_1 |

$$N_2 = p\% \cdot N_1$$

$$N_2 = \frac{p}{100} N_1$$

Stella, your presentation shows that when we increase a number **by** $p\%$, the new number contains the initial number, N, as well as $p\%$ of N. When we increase a number, N, **to** $p\%$ of its initial value, a new number contains only $p\%$ of N.

Ezra, I am glad you recognized the difference between the prepositions **to** and **by**. One last piece of advice. For easier calculations, convert percentages to fractions within your Algebraic Organizers.

Summary

If N was increased by $p\%$, $N_2 = \frac{(100+p) \cdot N_1}{100}$. If N was increased to $p\%$, $N_2 = \frac{p \cdot N_1}{100}$.

There were two equal numbers, M and R. First, R was increased by 36% and became 784. Then M was increased to $p\%$ of its value and became 784. Find p.
Visualize your solution.

118-119   *Make visual models and then solve the problems.*

118   A number was first increased to 150% and then increased by 150%. The resulting number was 173. By what percentage is the resulting number greater than the initial number?

119   A number was first increased by 150% and then increased to 150%. By what percentage is the initial number less than the resulting number, which is equal to 0.7?

Section 21.5 Decreasing to and by *p*% of a Value

This section analyzes the difference between *decreased by* and *decreased to* in problems involving percentages.

Decreased By % Problem

N was decreased by 20% of its value. Use algebraic language to present the relationship between the initial and final values of N.

Organizer

N_1 was decreased and became N_2.
N_2 is 20% less than N_1.

Time Line
Time Plane

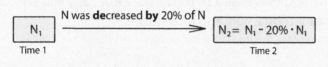

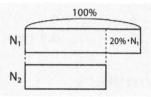

N_1
$N_2 = N_1 - 20\% \cdot N_1$
_____
$N_2 = ?$

$N_2 = N_1 - \frac{20}{100} N_1 = (1 - 0.2) \cdot N_1 = 0.8N_1$

or $N_2 = 100\% \cdot N_1 - 20\% \cdot N_1 = 80\% \cdot N_1 = 0.8N_1$

Answer: $N_2 = 0.8N_1$.

In the example below, the preposition *by* is substituted with the preposition *to*.

Decreased To % Problem

N was decreased *to* 20% of its value. Use algebraic language to present the relationship between the initial and final values of N.

Organizer

N_1 was decreased and became N_2.
N_2 makes 20% of N_1.

Time Line
Time Plane

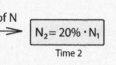

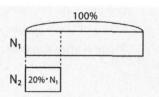

N_1
$N_2 = 20\% \cdot N_1$.
_____
$N_2 = ?$

$N_2 = \frac{20}{100} N_1 = 0.2N_1$.

Answer: $N_2 = 0.2N_1$.

Decreased by and *decreased to* clauses provided quite different results!

You will see why it happens when you compare the general formulas for the two clauses. When a number, N, is decreased **by** $p\%$, the new number becomes $p\%$ less than N: $N_2 = (100\% - p\%) \cdot N_1 = \frac{100-p}{100} \cdot N_1$.

When we decrease a number N **to** $p\%$ of N, the new number contains exactly $p\%$ of N: $N_2 = p\% \cdot N_1 = \frac{p}{100} \cdot N_1$.

Nice touch, Ezra. Now you know the difference between the clauses *decreased by* $p\%$ *of its value* and *decreased to* $p\%$ *of its value*. So, you will correctly translate these phrases into mathematical language.

Summary

If N was decreased by $p\%$, $N_2 = \frac{100-p}{100} N_1$. If N was decreased to $p\%$, $N_2 = \frac{p}{100} \cdot N_1$.

Identify the sentences that have no meaning. Explain your answers.
(1) K was reduced by 70%.   *(2) P was decreased to 70%.*
(3) K was increased to 70%.   *(4) N was decreased to 130%.*
(5) L was decreased by 130%.   *(6) M was increased by 130%.*

---

120   *Use algebraic notation, number format (no %), and improper fractions to represent the following statements:*

(a) N was increased by 500% of its initial value.   *(b) N was increased to 500% of its initial value.*
(c) N was decreased by 40% of its initial value.   *(d) N was decreased to 40% of its initial value.*
(e) N was increased by 35% of its initial value.   *(f) N was decreased to 11% of its initial value.*
(g) N was increased by 136% of its initial value.   *(h) N was increased to 136% of its initial value.*
(i) N was decreased by 32% of its initial value.   *(j) N was increased by K% of its initial value.*

121   The number was first reduced to 40% of its value, then increased by 150%, and reduced by 40%. In the end, the number was increased to 150% of its initial value. What is the final number if the initial value of the number was 120?
Make a visual model and then solve the problem.

162

Section 21.6 Combining Fractions and Percentages

Section 21.6 will review materials presented in previous sections, but the problems will have complex numbers like $\frac{1}{3}\%$ and $1\frac{1}{3}\%$.

Those are quite unpleasant numbers.

Convert these numbers into fractions and they will become pleasant. Here, I even made you examples of the conversion.

Fra % Problem

An initial number is N. What will the value be after N is *increased by* $\frac{1}{3}\%$?

Organizer

N_1 was increased and became N_2.
N_2 makes $100\% + \frac{1}{3}\%$ of N_1.

$N_1 = N$
$N_2 = \left(100\% + \frac{1}{3}\%\right) \cdot N_1$

$N_2 =?$

$$N_2 = \left(100\% + \frac{1}{3}\%\right) \cdot N = \frac{100 + \frac{1}{3}}{100} N = \frac{300 + 1}{300} N = \frac{301}{300} N$$

Answer: $N_2 = \frac{301}{300} N$.

Now, I see, Stella. After the $100\frac{1}{3}\%$ of N was converted into $\frac{301}{300} N$, the number became *normal*. OK, show me the example with decreasing value.

Mixed-Fra % Problem

An initial number is N. What will its value be after N is decreased by $1\frac{1}{3}\%$?

Organizer

N_1 was decreased and became N_2.
N_2 makes $100\% - 1\frac{1}{3}\%$ of N_1.

$N_1 = N$
$N_2 = \left(100\% - 1\frac{1}{3}\%\right) \cdot N_1$

$N_2 =?$

$$N_2 = \left(100\% - 1\frac{1}{3}\%\right) \cdot N = 98\frac{2}{3}\% \cdot N = \frac{98\frac{2}{3}}{100} N = \frac{294 + 2}{300} N = \frac{296}{300} N = \frac{74}{75} N$$

Answer: $N_2 = \frac{74}{75} N$.

> After percentages and mixed numbers are converted into regular or improper fractions, the data are ready for logical conversion—discussed in the next section.

Summary

Convert percentages and mixed numbers into fractions.

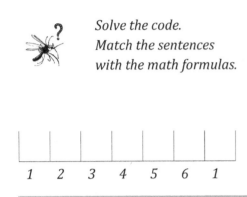

Solve the code.
Match the sentences
with the math formulas.

(1)   *Increasing a number by* $\frac{3}{2}$.   S $\frac{100+\frac{1}{3}}{100} \cdot N.$

(2)   *Increasing number by a factor of* $\frac{3}{2}$.   L $\frac{3}{200} \cdot N.$

(3)   *Having* $\frac{3}{2}$ % *of a number.*   I $\frac{100+\frac{3}{2}}{100} \cdot N.$

(4)   *Increasing a number by* $\frac{3}{2}$%.   C $\frac{3}{2} \cdot N.$

(5)   *Adding to a number* $\frac{3}{2}$ *of it.*   E $N + \frac{3}{2}.$

(6)   *Increasing a number to 100 and 1/3%.*   P $\left(1+\frac{3}{2}\right) \cdot N.$

1 2 3 4 5 6 1

---

122   *Use algebraic notation, number format (not %), and improper fractions to represent the following statements.*

(a) *N was decreased by 0.5% of its initial value.*   (b) *N was increased to 0.5% of its initial value.*

(c) *N was increased by 40% of its initial value.*   (d) *N was decreased to 4/7% of its initial value.*

(e) *N was increased by* $33\frac{1}{3}$% *of its initial value.*

(f) *N was decreased to* $11\frac{4}{7}$% *of its initial value.*

(g) *N was increased by* $137\frac{8}{11}$% *of its initial value.*

(h) *N was increased to* $137\frac{8}{11}$% *of its initial value.*

(i) *N was decreased to* $33\frac{1}{2}$% *of its initial value.*   (j) *N was decreased by K% of its initial value.*

123   *K was transformed and became M. Express M in terms of K. Then, perform logical conversions and express K in terms of M.*

(a) *K was increased by 120% of its initial value.*   (b) *K was increased to 200% of its initial value.*

(c) *K was decreased by 3% of its initial value.*   (d) *K was decreased to 4% of its initial value.*

(e) *K was increased by* $3\frac{1}{8}$% *of its initial value.*   (f) *K was decreased to 11% of its initial value.*

(g) *K was increased by* $137\frac{3}{11}$% *of its initial value.*

(h) *K was increased to* $100\frac{3}{7}$% *of its initial value.*   (i) *K was decreased to* $5\frac{1}{2}$% *of its initial value.*

(j) *K was increased by 1.3% of its initial value.*

124   A number was first reduced to 93.75% of its value and then increased by $40\frac{4}{9}$%. The final number was 3.16. What was the initial number?

125   A number was increased by 6/7 of its initial value and then decreased by 6/7%. What number was obtained at the end if the initial number was 3/52 less than 1?

Section 21.7 Reversibility of a Change

 Do you agree that, when we increase a number by 100 and then decrease it by 100, the number remains the same?

 Sure, Stella. If $N_2 = N_1 + 100$ and $N_3 = N_2 - 100$, then $N_3 = N_1$.

 And if we increase a number by 100% and then decrease it by 100%?

 After two opposite changes, the number stays the same.

 Got you! These changes are not opposite. The increase doubles it....

 Oh! After the number is decreased by 100%, the result is...zero.

 Right. Now, I will calculate the percentage by which I must decrease the number to obtain the initial number.

Balance Problem: Illustration

The number N was increased by 100%. By what percentage must we decrease the number to obtain the initial value, N?

Organizer

N_1 was increased by 100% and became N_2.
N_2 must be decreased by $p\%$ to become $N_3 = N_1$.

Visual Model

 Stella, the picture shows 100% is the same as 50%! I think 100% of N_1 is the same as 50% of N_2 because N_2 is twice N_1. Also, because 1% of N_1 is as big as 2% of N_2.

Balance Problem: Solution

$N_1 = N$
$N_2 = (100\% + 100\%) \cdot N_1$
$N_3 = N_1 = (100\% - p\%) \cdot N_2$

$p = ?\%$

$N_2 = \frac{100+100}{100} N = 2 \cdot N$
Since $N_2 = 2 \cdot N$, to make N, we need to remove half of it. One-half of N_2 means 50% of N_2.
Also, $N_3 = (100\% - 50\%) \cdot N_2 = 0.5 \cdot (2 \cdot N) = N$. So, $p\% = 50\%$.

Answer: $p\% = 50\%$.

The example shows that if a number was increased by $k\%$, it must be decreased by a different percentage to result in the initial value.

Summary

Changing by $p\%$ does not always mean changing by the same value. The size of 1% depends on a whole number.

If A was decreased by 50% to obtain B, by what percentage do we need to increase B to obtain A? (1) Choose the correct answer. (2) Visualize your solution.
(a) 50% (b) 25% (c) 75% (d) 100% (e) 125% (f) 150% (g) 175% (h) 200%

126 A number was first reduced by 50%, then increased by 50%, again reduced by 50%, and then again increased by 50%. The number at the end was 225. What was the initial number?

127 *Write the data using algebraic notation and perform logical conversion.*

    (a) N is 7% greater than K.
    (b) N is the same as $7\frac{2}{3}$ of K.
    (c) Decreasing N by $\frac{3}{7}$ of it gives K.
    (d) If we add $7\frac{2}{9}\%$ to N, we get K.
    (e) If we add one-third to N, we get K.
    (f) Decreasing N by $\frac{1}{6}$ gives K.
    (g) Decreasing N by $\frac{1}{6}$ of N gives K.
    (h) Decreasing N by $\frac{1}{6}\%$ gives K.
    (i) Decreasing N to $\frac{1}{6}\%$ gives K.
    (j) Increasing N to 200% gives us K.
    (k) Increasing N by $5\frac{2}{7}\%$ gives us K.
    (l) Increasing N by 200% gives us K.

128 A number was increased by 10 percent twice. Then, the number was decreased by 10 percent twice. What is the square root of the quotient of the final number and the initial number if the number after the first two transformations was eleven-ninths?

129 A number was increased to $7\frac{1}{7}$ and then decreased to 23% of its value. The result was decreased by 23%, equaling 17. What was the value of the initial number if its absolute value was $\frac{6}{7}$ greater than the absolute value of the number after the first transformation?

130-131 *Use the picture to complete the sentence and find the resulting number in each problem.*
130 The number 10 is decreased _____.
131 The number 11 is decreased _____.

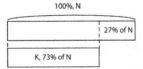
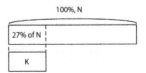

Fractions and Percentage: Extra Practice

132   There are three numbers. The second number is $3\frac{2}{11}$ and as big as 7% of the first number. What is the third number, if it is as big as 1% of the first number?

133   There are three numbers. The first number is 16% less than the second number and $5\frac{5}{6}$ times the third number, which is even and has two non-equal digits. These digits are divisible by 3. What is the sum of all three numbers if the sum is an integer?

134   Three percent of the second number makes the third number. Seven percent of the second number equals the first number, which is the same as the greatest factor of 28. Find the three numbers.

135   There are four numbers. The first number makes 300% of the second number. The second number increased by 7/8 of its initial value and becomes as big as the sum of the third and fourth numbers, which equal 75. What is the arithmetic mean of these four numbers?

136   A number increased by 100% became 3 times the difference between 15 and the additive inverse of 15. What was the initial number?

137   In March, a $40 book was discounted by 15%. Later, the price was reduced by another 20%. What was the total price reduction as a percentage?

138   In a restaurant, after receiving his check and adding an 18% tip, Alan paid $29.50. What price was written on the check?

139   As a percentage, what tip did a customer pay when she added $7.20 on her $45 check?

140   A client left a $36 tip, which was quite a high tip—40% of the check. What part of the total payment was the tip? Present your answer as *(a)* a fraction and *(b)* in percentage form rounded to the nearest tenth.

Review for Parts A through D

 The list below includes the calculation and problem-solving techniques introduced in *the* first four parts of *Soft Algebra*. The techniques and rubrics introduced in the current book are italicized.

Ezra, once again, it would be beneficial to recall the techniques before reading the list. So, start by answering the first discussion question, OK?

Simplify Informative Text and Geometry Problems

1. **Extract data to improve visibility of the important information.**
   Did I remove waste and create an outline with all the important data? Did I write the numbers as numerals?

2. **Chunk text to increase its readability.**
   Did I perform grammar- and meaning-chunking by creating small, independent sentences? Did I perform spatial chunking by writing the sentences one per row? Did I write all numbers as numerals?

3. **Make a Prep: prepare sentences for translation into algebraic language.**
   Did I keep the order of the original problem and get rid of the residual waste? Did I keep all the important information? Did I abbreviate key words and measuring units? Did I underline the question of the problem?

4. **Compose math-focused sentences to emphasize mathematical meaning.**
   Did I emphasize mathematical meaning for each data entry? Did I use the words "set" and "belongs" if needed? *Did I clearly state the measurable attributes, numerals, and the measuring units for each value? For proportion problems, did I transform sentences to include "one" instead of the word "each" or similar?*

5. **Organize data entries.**
   For non-mathematical logic problems, did I organize my data?

6. **Create a Time & Change Organizer for a change-problem.**
   Did I list all value-changing events (changes) chronologically? Did I list the values connected with each time-coordinate? Did I insert value-changing events between the time coordinates?

7. **Improve text Organizer by using an auxiliary element if needed.**
   To improve chunking, did I add a parameter-difference to a problem with the "as much as" clause?

8. **Initialize constraint-bookkeeping in problems with limited set of possible solutions.**
   Did I list all constraints, explicit and implicit? Did I consider each option looking for all answers to a problem?

9. *Use a d-t-v Approach to organize a problem with a constant rate of change.*
   In my Prep, did I specify what measurable attributes can be expressed as velocity and distance?

10. *Organize geometry problem by using auxiliary elements.*
    Did I draw symmetry axes? Did I add other lines that help me determine the structure of a problem? Did I outline repeating blocks?

11. *Chunk geometry problem by redrawing its parts separately.*
    Did I use additional lines to chunk a figure into several parts? Did I redraw independent parts elsewhere?

12. *Increase symmetry of a problem using addition and subtraction.*
    Did I add parts or took away parts to simplify my problem? Did I compensate for the changes introduced?

13. *Increase symmetry of a problem using shuffling.*
    Did I find an easier problem that my current problem can be converted to? Did I apply shuffling?

Make Algebraic Models

1. **Create a simple Algebraic Organizer.**
   Did I translate data into algebraic language? Did I organize the data? Do I have all information that was in the Prep? *Did I present measuring units in my Algebraic Organizer? Did I convert units to the same type? Did I use conventional abbreviations for my measuring units?*

2. **Improve Algebraic Organizer to include logical conversion.**
   Did I perform logical conversion, including blind logical conversion?

3. **Improve Algebraic Organizer to include mapping.**
   In the map, did I start from the question to the problem?

4. **Design talking parameters.**
   Did I define my parameters? Do my parameters remind me about the values they represent? *Did I use standard parameters (h, T, t, v, etc.), which remind me about measurable attributes?*

5. **Use overlapping parameters to describe complex data sets.**
   Did I use indices to make overlapping parameters? In half-problems, did I use N_1, N_2, and similar?

6. **Use time coordinates as indices for parameters in change-problems.**
   Did I use time coordinates for the time before changes, in-between changes, and after the changes? Did I add artificial time-coordinates when needed? Did I create parameters using given and/or artificial time-coordinates?

7. *Present the Algebraic Organizer in a form of proportion if applicable.*
   For a proportion-type problem, did I organize my data as a proportion? Did I clearly mark two types of units?

8. *Present the Algebraic Organizer using the Ratio-of-Elements Approach if applicable.*
   Does my Algebraic Organizer include a proportion organizer, which states the number of elements in a group?

9. *Present the Algebraic Organizer using the Ratio-of-Groups Approach if applicable.*
   Did I create an Algebraic Organizer that states the ratio for the numbers of groups? Did I visualize the ratio?

10. *Use the Unit-Block Approach in problems involving ratios, percentages, and parts.*
    Did I define a unit block and express all values in terms of the block? Did I examine the feasibility of the unit-block value as part of my calculations?

Use Visual Models

1. **Simple Discrete Model.**
   Did I represent data by using dots, sticks, or other figures to represent ones?

2. **Bug Model for problems with combinations.**
   Did I create a special organizer for counting combinations? Did I visualize it using discrete visual model?

3. **Time-Line Model for change-problems.**
   Did I list all values and changes using parameters with time indices? Did I mark each value in a separate box? Did I describe each change next to the lines connecting the boxes?

4. **Time-Plane Model for change-problems.**
   Did I create a visual model that reflects the spatial relations between the values at different times? Did I use a regular Time-Plane? Did I use a Simplified Time-Plane?

5. **Line-Segment Model.**
   Did I represent different numbers using line segments of different length?

Use Visual Models

6. **Area-Box Model.**

   Did I model numbers using rectangular boxes? Does the area of the box represent a value? *Did I clearly mark each box that represents a value?*

7. **Length-Box Model.**

   Did I represent different numbers using line segments of different length? *Did I clearly mark each box that represents a value? Did I present all values as boxes with the same height? Are the lengths of the rectangles proportional to the numbers they represent? Did I clearly specify what is known?*

8. **Graphs on a number line.**

   Did I use filled and hollow circles to represent existing and non-existent points? Did I use a thick line to mark the range of solutions?

9. **Graphs on a Descartes coordinate plane.**

   Did I graph a function or several functions to better understand a problem? *Did I graph functions to find an approximate solution to a problem?*

10. *Freestyle Model.*

    For a difficult-to-grasp problem, did I draw a cartoon, a map, or other pictures that help me understand the content of the problem?

11. *Visual Model for ratio problems.*

    Did I visualize the ratio when solving a ratio problem when using the Ratio-of-Groups Approach?

12. *Graphs for d-t-v problems.*

    Did I draw $v(t)$ and $d(t)$ graphs? On the graphs, did I specify measurable attributes and measuring units?

13. *Comparison Organizer.*

    Did I create a comparison organizer to identify a reference value? Did the reference follow the word than?

Use Creative Models

1. **Design a Down-Scaling Model—reduce the amplitudes of numbers.**

   Did I create an analogous problem with smaller numbers, which add sense to the problem?

2. **Design an Up-Scaling Model—increase the amplitudes of numbers.**

   Did I create an analogous problem with larger numbers, to add sense to the problem?

3. **Design an Approximation Model.**

   Did I create an analogous problem with fewer details?

4. **Design a Singleton Model.**

   Did I create an analogous problem, which represents an instance of an original problem?

Increase Your Brain Productivity

1. **Look at the presentation and solution of a problem through "alien eye".**

   Did I slow down? Did I create a checklist of the strategies I used? Did I make a Prep? Did I rewrite my calculations step-by-step? Did I concentrate on the main goal of the problem? Did I check my algebraic notation?

Skillfully Perform Calculations

1. **Use number properties for the calculations.**
   Did I apply number properties to simplify my calculations? *Did I check my calculations by analyzing the number properties I apply?*

2. **Use substitution to make sense of formulas.**
   Did I use small integers instead of parameters? Did I leave the symmetry of the initial problem unchanged?

3. **Draw an arrow and use factoring in complex problems with an exponent**
   For an exponent with an unclear base, did I draw an arrow that points to the base? Did I factor the exponent?

4. **Break and combine radicals.**
   Did I break complex radicals to simplify my calculations? Did I combine radicals with same indices?

5. *Use measuring units to check the correctness of complex calculations.*
   Did I write measuring units in a fraction format if the calculations involve derived units? Did I use derived measuring units to check the validity of my calculations if applicable?

Ezra, use the lists of forty-six techniques above to see whether you have applied all relevant techniques when solving "unsolvable" problems.

Summary

Remember your problem-solving techniques.

(1) List the problem-solving techniques you know without looking at the list of the techniques.

    (a) List thirteen techniques for simplifying text or geometry problem and ten for designing Algebraic Models.

    (b) Recall the technique for increasing brain productivity.

    (c) List thirteen types of visual models.

    (d) Name four types of creative models.

(2) Read the section and add the techniques you had missed.

(3) Which of the problem-solving techniques might you use for the following careers? A nurse, computer game designer, a teacher, an engineer, a scientist, a businessman, an actor.

Half-Problems and Graphs

D1   If the second number is the average of the first and the third numbers, and the third number is 6 more than the first number, what is the product of these numbers? The first number is the GCF of 3 and 5.

D2   There are three numbers. The first and third numbers are the same. The second number is the same as the sum of the other two numbers and greater than 25 and less than 29. What is the sum of these three numbers if all are even?

D3   Create an x-y chart and draw the graph $y = 8 - 0.5x^2 + 0.5x$. Is this a function?

D4   The first number makes 5.6% of the second number. The third number makes 16.1% of the second number. What is the second number if the difference between the first and the third numbers is 42?

D5   There are five consecutive numbers. The first four numbers are single-digit numbers. The fifth number is a two-digit number. What is the product of the first and fifth numbers?

D6   There are five numbers. The second number, the same as the third number, is the greatest common factor of 16 and 28, and is twice the fourth number. The first number is greater than -5 and is divisible by 1, 2, 3, and 6, but not divisible by any other number. The fifth number is a product of two non-equivalent, two-digit prime factors greater than 88. What is the sum of the first four numbers?

D7   There are three numbers. The sum of the first and second numbers equals the second number. The third number is an additive inverse of the least common multiple of 725 and 675. What is the first number?

D8   The first number was twice reduced by $7\frac{1}{3}$% and the second number was twice increased by $7\frac{1}{3}$%. What is the geometric mean* of the final numbers if the initial value for the former number was 2,025 and the square root of the initial value of the latter number was $\frac{1}{139}$?

D9   If the second number is the GCF of 15 and 10, and the third number is the LCM of 10 and 15 and the same as the first number, what is the difference between the first and second numbers?

D10   The quotient of a number and twelve is $\sqrt{56}$ larger than $\sqrt{1,400}$. What is the precise value of the number?

D11   Find the first number if the second number is the cubic root of the first number and has a value of $\sqrt[6]{15,625}$.

D12   There are two numbers. The second number is twice as big as the first number. The first number is the reciprocal of $25\frac{1}{3}$. What is the sum of these two numbers?

D13   Create x-y charts and draw the graphs $x = 3$ and $y = 3.5$ using a single coordinate plane.
(a) What are the coordinates of a point which belongs to both graphs?
(b) Which of the graphs is not a function?

---

* See the Glossary.

D14   There are three numbers. The first number was increased to $108\frac{7}{9}\%$, the second number was increased by $108\frac{7}{9}\%$, and the third number was increased by a factor of 108 and $\frac{7}{9}$. What is the quotient of the lowest and the greatest numbers received at the end if initially all numbers had the value of $108\frac{5}{9}$?

D15   There are three numbers. The second number is negative twelve. The first number is 4 less than the third number. The second number is 7 more than the third number. *(a)* What is the largest number? *(b)* What is the number with the greatest absolute value?

D16   There were two numbers. When the first number was reduced by $19\frac{4}{7}\%$ and the other was reduced to $8\frac{3}{70}$, they became equal. What was the initial value of the first number?

D17   The difference between two numbers is 11. The smallest number is 6. What is the sum of these two numbers?

D18   There are four numbers. The sum of the first three numbers is 11. One of them is "–7," and the other two differ by 1. The fourth number is the average of the first three numbers. What is the value of the fourth number?

Regular Word Problems

D19-22   *In these problems, there are several made-up words.*

D19   On Oguru, lingordians have no work breaks. They produce seven 25-pound kunstgoffers every 6 hours and trade them for $12 per pound. After 10 hours, the bell rings, the product sent to customers, and a new cycle of production begins. How much money will the lingordians make between two consecutive bells? *Discuss two main solutions.*

D20   While Oguru revolves 5 times around a star called Bosuy, it rotates 250 times around itself. How many days are in an Oguru year?

D21   A lingordian from Oguru, Guurr, dortates 3 times when she has a velocity of 231 kirks per hour. Dortations are always proportional to speed. How many times does Guur dortate at the speed of 693 kirks per hour?

D22   On a planet Oguru, every lingordian is born with two, one-centimeter tails, green and yellow. The green tail grows proportionally with the age of a lingordian. The yellow tail grows proportionally with the educational level of a lingordian. If a lingordian from Oguru, Tanaru, had a 3 cm green tail when he was 7 years old, what will be the length of his green tail at age 35?
Yesterday, Tanaru turned 26 years of age. His yellow tail is 1 cm. What can you say about Tanaru's education? *Explain your answer.*

D23   The Office for National Statistics (see www.ons.gov.uk) presents reports regarding numbers of UK citizens traveling abroad. The excerpts from the reports are presented below.

	1961/2	1970	1980	1990	2000	2010
Number of visits	3,319	8,482	17,507	31,150	56,837	55,562
To North America	84	256	1,382	2,325	5,060	3,653
To Europe	3,055	7,536	14,676	26,268	45,763	42,565
By air	1,727	4,894	10,748	21,368	41,392	43,239
By sea	1,592	3,588	6,759	9,782	9,646	8,056
By tunnel	-	-	-	-	5,799	4,267

(i)   What is the increase in the number of travels from the UK abroad from 1961/62 to 2010?

(ii)   What is the decrease in the number of travels from the UK to North America from 2000 to 2010? *Calculate your answers to the nearest integer percent. Use N_1 and N_2 notations.*

(iii) Why is the total number of travels to North America and Europe not the same as the "Number of visits"?

(iv)   Based on the table, estimate when the tunnel connecting England and France was built.

D24   From a 5-meter purple ribbon, Cassie cut 50 centimeters. The next day, Karen cut off 1/3 of what was left since she needed the ribbon for her Science project. So, when Lucien came, he shared the rest of the ribbon equally with Milda and Nelida. Since Milda had already some yellow ribbon and needed only a small chunk of purple, she shared her part of the purple ribbon equally with Cassie and Nelida. What part of the initial purple ribbon did Cassie have at the end? *Express your answer in a percentage and round it to the nearest tenth.*

D25   Last Thanksgiving, John wore the costume of a tiger, Cecilia was a princess, and their mother was disguised as a pirate. John's father was working late and did not come home until half past eight. John was trick-or-treating with his family starting at 5 p. m. When the family returned home, Cecilia had 20 candies and three new pencils. John had 4 less candies than his sister, but two more pencils than his brother, Tim. Tim had 5 pencils and 9 more candies than Cecilia. John's mother was walking with her children, but she did not receive treats since she did not carry a bag. After the family returned, they decided to wait until their father came home to share all treats evenly between all members of the family. How will they divide their treats?

D26   In a furniture store in Chicago, Illinois, a Blanton's chair price was reduced by 30% and then by an additional 20%. After paying $100, Corry received change of $79 and 28 cents. His friend in San Antonio bought a very similar chair at the same initial price with a discount of 40%. Who paid more for the chair? How much more? What percentage more? Who paid less? What percentage less?

D27   Zoggy is one fast rabbit and can achieve a speed of 66 km/hour. Zoggy cannot run this fast for a long time. Running from a wolf, Zoggy traveled at this speed for 2 minutes. What distance did Zoggy cover?

D28   For a Dynamic Arts exhibition, three figures—red, purple, and yellow—must meet in the middle of a screen exactly at midnight. The red circle moves from the left lower corner of the screen toward the upper right corner with a speed of 2 cm per second. The distance between the corners is 2 feet. The purple triangle moves in the opposite direction, from the upper right corner toward the lower left corner with a speed of 60 feet per hour. The yellow circle must move from left to the right side of the screen on a half-height level, while the width of the screen is 10 units—inches or feet. The yellow circle crosses the screen in exactly 1 minute. When must the figures begin their motion and what is the width of the screen?

D29   On April 2nd, a manager at Glorious Restaurant increased the restaurant prices by 30%. He intended to benefit the restaurant, but after the price increase, the restaurant lost most of its customers. In July, the manager was fired, and Bob became its new manager. Bob decided to run a 3-month sale by reducing the prices to 80% of the prices before the price increase. What will be the sale price for a Grand Kebab if the previous manager was trying to sell it for $39? By what percentage must Bob reduce restaurant prices to come to the targeted value? *Find the exact answer. Then, provide practical advice for Bob.*

D30   Three dragons were devouring a 70 cubic meter pile of golden sand. The first dragon can eat the sand in 7 days. The second dragon can eat the sand in 5 days. The third dragon can eat the sand in 10 days. How fast can these dragons eat the golden sand when eating together? *Calculate your answer to the nearest second and present it using customary units. Accompany your solution by a visual model showing how the volume of the eaten sand depends upon time.*

D31   Uma and Brad ran a full marathon. Uma ran with an average velocity of $v = 8.39\frac{mi}{hr}$. Brad had a steady speed of $9\ mi/hr$ for the first 1.5 hours. Then, he stopped for 3 minutes to take a small stone from his shoe. After this, he ran with his initial speed. For the last two miles, Brad reduced his speed to $8\ mi/hr$. Who came first, Uma or Brad? What was their time difference to the nearest minute? *Hint: Use the Internet to find the distance for a full marathon.*

D32   The population of Illinois is 12,880,000 people (when solving a problem, use 13,000,000) and the area is about 57,900 square miles (you can use 58,000) with Chicago's area as 227 square miles (use 230). If the density of population in Illinois were the same everywhere, what would be the population of Chicago? *Does this provide a good estimation for the population of Chicago? Explain.*

D33   What is the percent of potassium salt in a solution made of 2 liters of water—which weighs 2 kilograms—and 20 grams of potassium salt? *Calculate to the nearest hundredth of a percent.*

D34   *Trip to Mordechai's House:* It was a sunny "no cellphone" day. John Polansky awakened and decided to go visit his friend, Mordechai Krotovets. They were very good friends. At 9 a.m. John started to Mordechai's house in an excellent mood. In one minute, John covered 50 m. He planned to walk to the Krotovets' house at that same speed. In the middle of his trip, however, John met Claudia and stepped aside to talk with her. They sat in a small park beside the road and talked for 30 minutes about their school and their last trip to Miami. After talking with Claudia, John resumed his walk with his initial speed.

Overall, John's trip to the house of his friend, Mordechai, took 2 hours and 30 minutes. Unfortunately, John found that Mordechai went to his house at 9 a.m., too. After John learned this, he immediately started back. When Mordechai did not find John at John's house, he also immediately went back to meet his friend on the return. Like John, Mordechai walked with a constant speed, although a bit slower than John.

a) What is the distance between the two friends' houses?

b) At what time did the friends finally meet? *Use d(t) graphs to find the answer.*

D35   The ratio of boys and girls in Cornslow village is 7:6 while the ratio of women and men is 11 to 9. Cornslow village has 1,157 citizens; 286 of them are women. How many girls live in Cornslow?

D36   Estimate the time loss (as a percent) for a child who regularly plays electronic games which keep him/her in an artificial, virtual world. We do not consider educational games here, which mimic the real world and help students progress with their education.

If a child spends four hours a day playing non-educational games, and plays six hours a day on weekends, holidays, and school breaks, how much time of his/her active life is lost? *Use the calendar of one of the schools in your area to estimate the number of "schooldays" and "non-schooldays." Remember, an average child sleeps at least eight hours per day—these are non-active hours, which should not be taken into account.*

D37   Estimate the amount of apple juice (*fluid volume*) you can obtain from 1 bushel of apples assuming the efficiency of juice making machine is 75%. *Use: A dry gallon is greater than fluid gallon by 1/6th.*

D38   In the old days, 75 percent of people mauled by leopards died from infection caused by rotting meat between the leopards' toes.[*] The incidence of infection from leopard wounds is usually higher than tigers. With the advent of penicillin, deaths were cut to less than 10 percent of the people mauled.

Going by the very questionable statistics available, leopards cause a minimum of four hundred casualties annually. One-quarter of the casualties are due to man-eating leopards and the remainder to the work of wounded or cornered leopards. There must be between eight and ten thousand people alive in the world today who bear the scars of a fight with a leopard.

  a)   If 100 people were mauled by leopards, how many of them survived in the old days?

  b)   In modern times, if 100 people were mauled by leopards, how many of them would survive?

  c)   How many people are victims of non-man-eating leopard skirmishes annually?

  d)   Is this statement correct? 8,000 > "people with leopard scars" > 10,000.

  e)   On average, how many people are killed by man-eating leopards annually?

D39   Two liters of 5% saline solution was poured into a bottle, which already had 500 mL of water. Find the resulting concentration of the diluted solution. *Use the following: 1mL of water weighs 1 gram.*

---

[*] Numbers are based on data from *Man is the Prey*, by James Clarke. Published by Stein and Day Publishers, 1969.

Part E

visual algebra and word problems

x-VISION

Is this Part about x-ray, Stella?

No x-rays and no y-rays, Ezra. Just x-s, visual models, equations, and word problems with x-s and y-s.
At this point, the primary goal is fostering your x-vision.

In Part E, Ezra, you will apply number properties in a formal manner and solve equations according to algebraic rules rather than intuitively. Particularly, you will visualize mathematical expressions and use algebraic equations with one or several unknowns to solve word problems.

Finally, I'll use x, y, and z!
But... can I solve these problems without equations?

Some of them. You will start with designing equations for problems you can solve arithmetically. After you learn the algebraic methods, you will utilize equations to solve much more challenging problems.

You mean, at some point, I will face problems, which I can't solve without Algebra?

Yes, you will. For these problems, you will need to rely on formal mathematics only. For simplicity, you will start from half-problems. Then, after the training, you will solve problems involving parts and percent, velocity and distance, time and change, and so on. For some problems, you will need to combine all your knowledge of problem solving and algebra with creativity. In addition, you will need to search data on the Internet.

So, I'll solve think-puzzles using algebra and the Internet, Stella?

You can call these problems the way you wish. These multi-faceted problems will conclude Part E and the *Soft Algebra* course as well.

Prerequisites

Students must follow the problem-solving principles:*

- Simplify (simplify problems when possible),
- Clarify (present problems in a clear form),
- Govern (analyze the strategies you apply when solving problems).

---

*Find more about the problem-solving principles in *Soft Algebra PLUS*.

Chapter 22
Formal Mathematics and Number Properties

 Ezra, until now, you performed your calculations in a *casual* (informal) manner. You followed your logic and common sense. But now, you will calculate differently...

What? You don't want to say, now I must calculate without using my brains?!

 Ezra, I only say; the algebraic approach requires you to calculate in a *formal* way. Chapter 22 will teach you how to use parameters and complete *identical transformations* based solely on number properties.

Identical transformations? You mean, I will transform something, but it will stay the same? So, I must do nothing. Correct?

 Identical transformation (or *identity transformation*) changes the look of a mathematical expression but leaves its value unchanged. For example, $x + x = 2x$ is an identity transformation. The transformation does not change the expression's value for any value of x.

So, $x + x$ is identical to $2x$? No surprise here.

 This transformation involves two number properties. Chapter 22 will discuss the rules you must obey when performing this and other algebraic transformations.

---

 (1) What does it mean to perform identical transformations?
(2) Why do we need formal mathematics?

Section 22.1 In-depth Properties for Addition

In this section, Ezra, you will learn how to simplify mathematical expressions using number properties for addition.

Addition Number Properties

Commutative property.	$a + b = b + a$	
Associative property.	$a + (b + c) = (a + b) + c$	
Identity property.	$a + 0 = a$	

The number properties are *axioms*—the rules based on common sense. The *commutative property* axiom states, the order we add two numbers is unimportant.

Axi-what?

A-x-i-o-m. The rule. The *associative property* axiom states, grouping additives does not change the results of addition.

The **identity property** axiom says, a number does not change if we add zero: $a + 0 = a$. Below, I applied a combination of commutative and associative property axioms to rearrange additives.

Combining Commutative and Associative Properties for Addition

$$a + b + c + d + e + f = f + c + a + b + d + e = (c + f) + (a + e) + (d + b)$$

Basically, Stella, you say I can rearrange additives any way I want by combining commutative and associative properties. But what if I have subtraction?

Then, you must first change subtraction into addition.

You mean, instead of $a - b$, I must write $a + b$?

180

Ezra, your transformation must always result in an identity, but $a - b \neq a + b$. However, you can make an identical transformation like $a - b = a + (-b)$. To simplify math expressions involving subtraction, apply these three steps:

1. Transform subtraction into addition.
2. Use number properties for addition.
3. Change addition of negatives to subtraction.

Identical transformations below exemplify the procedure:

Using Number Properties for Addition in Subtraction Problems

$-a + b + c - d + a - 8 + d + 6 = (-a) + b + c + (-d) + a + (-8) + d + 6 =$
$[(-a) + a] + b + c + [(-d) + d] + [(-8) + 6] = 0 + b + c + 0 + (-2) = b + c + (-2) = b + c - 2$

Stella, to simplify the expression, $-a + b + c - d + a - 8 + d + 6$, for *Step 1*, you changed subtraction to addition. Then, for *Step 2*, you applied associative and commutative properties for addition.

Sure, Ezra. Also, for *Step 2*, with zeroes, I used identity property axiom. I made two transformations with *Step 2*.

Finally, for *Step 3*, you changed addition of negative two to the subtraction. Thanks, Stella. I think I am ready to practice with identical transformations.

Summary

After change subtraction to addition, use number properties of addition to simplify problems.

Which of the following events commute?
(1) Release a fish-line and catch a fish.
(2) When making tea, add sugar and insert a tea bag.

1   *Visualize the math identities. Specify what number properties are applied.*
    a) $x + 5 = 5 + x$ *b)* $7 + y + (6 + x) = y + x + (6 + 7)$

2   *Simplify the expression, $5 + x + 2$, using a combination of commutative and associative properties for addition. Visualize your solution.*

3   *Simplify. In each step, explain what property you used.*
    a) $-x + y + 18 - d - 8 + x - y$
    b) $257x + 675 + (815 + (-675)) + (-257x) + (99 + (-816))$
    c) $-a + 378 + 495 + 622 + (705 + (-500)) + 4b - 4$
    d) $\left(1\frac{1}{2} - \frac{1}{3}\right) + \left(1\frac{1}{3} - \frac{1}{4}\right) + \left(1\frac{1}{4} - \frac{1}{5}\right) + \left(1\frac{1}{5} - \frac{1}{6}\right) + \left(1\frac{1}{6} - \frac{1}{7}\right) + \cdots + \left(1\frac{1}{23} - \frac{1}{24}\right).$

Section 22.2 In-depth Properties for Multiplication

Ezra, can you illustrate a ***commutative property for multiplication***? The axiom says the order of multiplication for two numbers makes no difference.

Sure, I can. I will use the picture of two rectangles: the area of a rectangle doesn't vary with the order in which the sides are multiplied. But I don't know how to visualize an associative property.

The *associative property* axiom shows, different ways of grouping factors do not change the result of multiplication. So, I can illustrate associative property using the picture of a rectangular prism. Look at the visual models below.

Multiplication Number Properties

Commutative property. $a \cdot b = b \cdot a$

Associative property. $a \cdot (b \cdot c) = (a \cdot b) \cdot c$

Identity property. $a \cdot 1 = a$

The volume of a prism can be calculated as the area of its base $(b \cdot c)$ multiplied by its height, a. So, the prism on the picture has the volume, $V = a \cdot (b \cdot c)$.

The equation, $V = (a \cdot b) \cdot c$, considers $(a \cdot b)$ the area of the base and c the height. The volume of a rectangular prism does not depend on the choice of a *base*. I think, you do not need a picture for the identity property… The *multiplicative identity* axiom postulates, a number does not change when multiplied by one.

Sure, Stella. I need no help with identity property. Moreover, I can design an example for number properties of multiplication without your help, too.

Combining Commutative and Associative Properties for Multiplication

$$a \cdot b \cdot c \cdot d \cdot e \cdot f = f \cdot c \cdot a \cdot b \cdot d \cdot e = (c \cdot f) \cdot (a \cdot e) \cdot (d \cdot b)$$

Like with addition, a combination of number properties for multiplication allows many rearrangements. However, Stella, what to do when I have a division problem? Should I transform division into multiplication?

Ezra, your idea will work. Here are the steps for division problems:
1. Transform division into multiplication.
2. Use number properties for multiplication.
3. Change fractions to division when feasible.
Identical transformations below exemplify the procedure:

Properties for Multiplication in Division Problems

$$\frac{2a}{b} \cdot (b \div 4) = 2 \cdot a \cdot \frac{1}{b} \cdot \left(b \cdot \frac{1}{4}\right) = \left(2 \cdot \frac{1}{4}\right) \cdot a \cdot \left(\frac{1}{b} \cdot b\right) = \frac{1}{2} \cdot a \cdot 1 = \frac{1}{2} \cdot a = \frac{a}{2}$$

For *Step* 1, in the expression, you transformed a fraction and the division into multiplication. For *Step* 2, you used the associative and commutative properties by ignoring the parentheses and grouped all factors of similar kinds.

After I calculated what is inside of each group, the expression became quite simple: $\frac{1}{2} \cdot a \cdot 1$. Then, I applied the identity property to eliminate 1.

I see. At the end, you presented the expression as a fraction. Although, I think, $0.5a$ would look much better.

Present the simplified answer as $\frac{a}{2}$ or $0.5a$. Both answers look feasible. The key here is to provide readability. In this case, both answers are perfectly readable.

Summary

To simplify math expression, change division to multiplication and use number properties for multiplication.

(1) Describe number properties for multiplication. Present examples.

(2) Which of the number properties for multiplication work in division problems?

4   *Visualize identities: (a)* $7 \cdot 4 = 4 \cdot 7$;   *(b)* $a \cdot 5 \cdot 2 = 5 \cdot 2 \cdot a$.

5   *Simplify expressions using commutative, associative, or/and identity properties.*

a) $7 \cdot 4 \cdot 77 \cdot 25 \cdot 16 \cdot 25 \cdot \left(913 \cdot \frac{1}{77}\right) \cdot \left(\frac{67}{9130} \cdot \frac{250}{7}\right)$

b) $45\,a \cdot 27\,b \cdot \frac{c}{ab} \cdot \left(\frac{5n}{81} \cdot \frac{8}{3c}\right)$

c) $\left(1\frac{1}{2} \cdot \frac{1}{3}\right) \div \left(\frac{1}{3} \cdot \frac{1}{4}\right) \cdot \left(\frac{1}{4} \cdot \frac{1}{5}\right) \div \left(\frac{1}{5} \cdot \frac{1}{6}\right) \cdot \left(\frac{1}{6} \cdot \frac{1}{7}\right) \div \ldots \div \left(\frac{1}{23} \cdot \frac{1}{24}\right)$

Section 22.3 Exponent Properties

Ezra, before presenting new material, I will present a chart, which reviews the material you already learned.

Exponents: Important Definitions

b^x b to the *x-th* power. b is a base. x is index, power, or exponent.

Negative power: $b^{-z} = \frac{1}{b^z}$

Radicals: $\sqrt[y]{b} = b^{\frac{1}{y}}$ b is a radicand. y is an index. $\sqrt{}$ is a radical sign.

Fractional exponent? I didn't learn this!

Ezra, fractional exponents are simply roots written differently. All the times you were messing with roots, you used fractional exponents. When you formally apply the properties for exponents, it is better to use the fractional format than radicals. So, you must change your habits.

OK. To write, $\sqrt[3]{64}$ or $64^{\frac{1}{3}}$ is not a big difference for me!

Below, I will list the six properties for exponents: property for addition, property for subtraction, property for multiplication, property for division, exponent *distribution*, and identity property.

The addition property for exponents is a logical extension of an addition property for whole exponents, which I derive below.

Addition and Subtraction Properties for Exponents

$a^x \cdot a^y = a^{x+y}$

$2^3 \cdot 2^4 = 2^{3+4}$

For any whole indices, x and y,

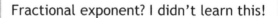

$$a^x \cdot a^y = (a \cdot \underbrace{a \cdot a \cdot \ldots \cdot a \cdot a \cdot a}_{x\text{-times}}) \cdot (a \cdot \underbrace{a \cdot a \cdot \ldots \cdot a \cdot a \cdot a}_{y\text{-times}}) = a^{x+y}$$

For division,

$\dfrac{a^x}{a^z} = a^{x-z}$

As follows from the addition property for exponents,

$$\frac{a^x}{a^z} = a^x \cdot a^{-z} = a^{x+(-z)} = a^{x-z}.$$

Stella, I see the addition property for exponents is based on commutative and associative properties of multiplication. As for the subtraction..., it's an extension of the addition property for exponents.

Now, I will derive the multiplication property for exponents with whole indices. The multiplication property for <u>any</u> indices is an extension of this derivation.

Multiplication and Division Properties for Exponents

$(a^x)^y = a^{xy}$

$(2^3)^4 = 2^{3 \cdot 4}$

For any whole indices, x and y,

$$(a^x)^y = \underbrace{(a \cdot a \cdot \ldots \cdot a \cdot a)}_{x\text{-times}} \cdot \underbrace{(a \cdot a \cdot \ldots \cdot a \cdot a)}_{x\text{-times}} \cdot \ldots \cdot \underbrace{(a \cdot a \cdot \ldots \cdot a \cdot a)}_{x\text{-times}} = a^{x \cdot y}$$

y-groups

For radicals, $\sqrt[y]{a^x} = a^{x \div y}$.

It follows from the multiplication properties for exponents,

$$\sqrt[y]{a^x} = (a^x)^{\frac{1}{y}} = a^{x \cdot \frac{1}{y}} = a^{x \div y}.$$

Now, I will discuss distributive property. Like other properties, distribution can be understood with the example of whole indices and extended toward the general case.

Exponent Distribution

$(a \cdot b)^z = a^z \cdot b^z$

$(2 \cdot 5)^3 = 2^3 \cdot 5^3$

If z is a whole number,

$$(a \cdot b)^z = \underbrace{(ab \cdot ab \cdot \ldots \cdot ab \cdot ab)}_{z\text{-times}} = \underbrace{(a \cdot a \cdot \ldots \cdot a \cdot a)}_{z\text{-times}} \ldots \cdot \underbrace{(b \cdot b \cdot \ldots \cdot b \cdot b)}_{z\text{-times}} = a^z \cdot b^z$$

$\sqrt[z]{a \cdot b} = \sqrt[z]{a} \cdot \sqrt[z]{b}$

$$\sqrt[z]{a \cdot b} = (a \cdot b)^{\frac{1}{z}} = a^{\frac{1}{z}} \cdot b^{\frac{1}{z}} = \sqrt[z]{a} \cdot \sqrt[z]{b}$$

Finally, the identity property.... The *identity property for exponents* states, zero power applied to any expression results in one.

Exponent Identity Property

$a^0 = 1$ $a^x \cdot a^0 = a^{x+0} = a^x = a^x \cdot 1$

As we completed discussing the number properties for exponents, we will apply these and other properties to simplify math expressions.
In my first example, I will simplify the expression by transforming fractions to products. Then, I will combine factors with identical bases.

Combining Properties for Exponents

1) Simplify.

$$\frac{\frac{a}{b}\cdot\frac{c^6}{a}}{\left(\frac{c^2}{b^2}\right)^3}=\left(\frac{a}{b}\cdot\frac{c^6}{a}\right)\cdot\frac{1}{\left(\frac{c^2}{b^2}\right)^3}=\left(a\cdot\frac{1}{a}\cdot c^6\cdot\frac{1}{b}\right)\cdot\frac{1}{(c^2\cdot b^{-2})^3}=c^6\cdot b^{-1}\cdot c^{-2\cdot3}\cdot b^{2\cdot3}=c^{6-6}\cdot b^{6-1}=c^0\cdot b^5=b^5.$$

2) Remove a radical from the denominator.

$$\frac{2}{\sqrt[3]{a}}=\frac{2}{a^{\frac{1}{3}}}=2\cdot a^{-\frac{1}{3}}=2\cdot a^{-\frac{1}{3}+1-1}=2\cdot a^{\frac{2}{3}-1}=2\cdot a^{\frac{2}{3}}\cdot a^{-1}=\frac{2\sqrt[3]{a^2}}{a}.$$

In your second example, you could multiply numerator and denominator by $\left(\sqrt[3]{a}\right)^2$ and finish the problem. However, formal mathematics took you six steps instead of two. Can I stay with my charming radicals, huh, Stella?

To develop fluency with exponents, you must show each formal step. Do not worry, you will combine steps as you achieve proficiency.

Summary

Use properties for exponents: $a^x\cdot a^y=a^{x+y}$, $(a^x)^y=a^{x\cdot y}$, $(a\cdot b)^z=a^z\cdot b^z$, $\sqrt[z]{a\cdot b}=\sqrt[z]{a}\cdot\sqrt[z]{b}$, and $a^0=1$.

(1) Properties for exponents are based on number properties. However, we cannot say exponent properties can be derived from number properties. Explain why.

(2) What exponent property allows "break" or "combine" radicals?

6   *Simplify. Present your results in the <u>non-radical</u> format. Specify what properties of the exponent you used.* In this problem, x and y are positive. Also, $a\neq 0$ and $b\neq 0$.

(a) $\sqrt{(x^b y^a)^3}\,x^{-0.5b}.$ (b) $\sqrt[3]{\frac{c^8}{d^{-6}}}\div\frac{5}{c^{-\frac{2}{3}}}.$ (c) $\frac{8^{-3}a}{9^{-2}\left(b^{\frac{-2}{5}}\right)^2}\div\left(\sqrt[5]{a}\cdot\sqrt[5]{(ab)^4}\right).$

7   *Simplify using properties for exponents. Present your results in <u>a radical format</u>.* In this problem, a and x are positive.

(a) $\sqrt[3]{2x}\div\sqrt{\frac{\frac{2}{x}}{\frac{x}{2}}}\cdot(-x)^{\frac{2}{3}}.$ (b) $\frac{\sqrt{8\cdot\sqrt[2]{3a}}}{\sqrt[6]{36a^3}}\div(2a)^{-\frac{5}{2}}.$

Section 22.4 Distributive Property in Depth

Stella, I know how to illustrate the *distributive property*!

Distributive Property and its Visual Models

$$a \cdot (b + c) = ab + ac$$

a	ab	ac
	b	c

$$3 \cdot (20 + 8) = 3 \cdot 20 + 3 \cdot 8$$

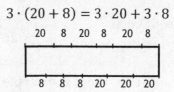

Ezra, the distributive property axiom has numerous applications in Algebra. The property allows us to transform multiplication into addition, change addition into multiplication, *play* with the negative sign, and *collect like terms*.

Collect terms? How do I know what to collect and where to put them? Term is not a mushroom or Pokémon!

You will place all terms (additives) with x in one group, y-terms in other group, xy-terms in another group, x^2-terms in some other group, and so on. *Numeric terms* will also form a group. You will find an example of *collecting terms* below.

How Can Students Use the Distributive Property?

Turn multiplication into addition.

$$4(a + b) = 4a + 4b$$

Factorize.

$$3x + 6y = 3(x + 2y)$$

Remove a minus sign before a parenthesis.

$$-(4 - b) = -1(4 - b) = -4 + b$$

Collect like terms.

$$5x + 2xy + x + 3xy = (5 + 1)x + (2 + 3)xy = 6x + 5xy$$

Distribute in division problems.

$$(a + b) \div c = (a + b) \cdot \frac{1}{c} = a \cdot \frac{1}{c} + b \cdot \frac{1}{c} = \frac{a}{c} + \frac{b}{c}$$

$$95 \div 5 = (50 + 45) \cdot \frac{1}{5} = 50 \cdot \frac{1}{5} + 45 \cdot \frac{1}{5} = \frac{50}{5} + \frac{45}{5}$$

Multiply mixed numbers.

$$4\frac{4}{7} \cdot 1\frac{7}{8} = 4 \cdot 1 + 4 \cdot \frac{7}{8} + \frac{4}{7} \cdot 1 + \frac{4}{7} \cdot \frac{7}{8} = 4 + \frac{7}{2} + \frac{4}{7} + \frac{1}{2} = 8\frac{4}{7}$$

How Can Students Use the Distributive Property? More Examples

Change signs in an expression. $b - c = -1 \cdot (-1)(b - c) = -1 \cdot (-b + c) = -(-b + c) = -(c - b)$

Multiply polynomials (expressions with two or more terms). $(a + b)(c + d) = a(c + d) + b(c + d) = ac + ad + bc + bd$

Change a fraction into addition. $\frac{3a+6b}{7} = \frac{1}{7} \cdot (3a + 6b) = \frac{1}{7} \cdot 3a + \frac{1}{7} \cdot 6b = \frac{3a}{7} + \frac{6b}{7}$

Simplify an expression. $20 - 7 \cdot (3 + x) = 20 + (-7) \cdot (3 + x) = 20 + (-7) \cdot 3 + (-7) \cdot x =$
$= 20 - 21 - 7x = -1 - 7x$

Stella, the last example is so tricky! Firstly, you got rid of subtraction by "giving" minus to the seven. Then, you applied the distributive property. I need a lot of practice to solve such problems with fluency. Can I start now?

Summary

Distributive property, $a \cdot (b + c) = ab + ac$, has a variety of applications in Algebra.

(1) Use the distributive property to factor the expression: $x + 3x$.

(2) Show how you can use the distributive property to simplify the expression below.
   $-(a - b) + (b - a)$.

8   *Visualize identities: (a) $3 \cdot (4 + x) = 3 \cdot 4 + 3x$; (b) $4 \cdot (y + x) = 4y + 4x$.*

9   *Visualize the <u>given</u> math expression. Then, rearrange the variables and the numbers, placing variables in one group and numbers in another. Visualize the <u>resulting</u> math expressions. What number properties did you use to simplify these expressions?*
   a) $3(x + 13)$; b) $2x + 1 + 4x + 8$; c) $(x + 2) + 4(x + 1)$; d) $(x + 6) \cdot 3 + 2(x + 2)$.

10   *Use distributive property to multiply factors in these expressions.*
   a) $7(x - 5)$;   b) $-y(x - 3y)$;   c) $-6(x + 5)$;   d) $(2 + x) \cdot (3 + y)$;
   e) $0.25 \cdot (2^2 - x + y)$;   f) $(x - y) \cdot (x + 4)$;   g) $-(-3x + 2y - z)$;   h) $(-6) \cdot (-5x + y)$.

11   *Factor using distributive property. Then, simplify if possible.*
   a) $4x + 7x$;   b) $-3z + 3x$;   c) $25xy - 5y$;
   d) $-yx + 8y^2 + yz$;   e) $(a + b) \cdot 3 + (a + b) \cdot z$;   f) $6x + 8y$;
   g) $-7w - 8w$;   h) $-5x + 5x$;   i) $4x - x$.

12   *Simplify the following expressions. In the expressions, $x + y \neq 0$ and $a \neq 0$.*
   a) $8(x - y^2) - y(x - 8y) + xy$.   b) $-3z + 5x - 5z - x$.
   c) $-6x + 8z - 2z + 6$.   d) $25xy - 5y - 6xy + y$.
   e) $-yx + 8y^2 + yx + 8y(2 - y)$.   f) $8x + 2xy - x$.
   g) $-6x + 8y - 2(x - y)$.   h) $x \cdot (y - 2z) \cdot y + (-xy^2)$.
   i) $\frac{7a+a^3}{a}$.   j) $\frac{7(x+y)}{(x+y)} + 8(2 + x)$.

Section 22.5 Mistakes in Identity Transformations

Ezra, many mistakes occur when students completely rely on Algebra rules and forget common sense—in this case, students simply mix different rules. Sometimes, students make mistakes when their intuitive answer differs from the correct answer. Below, I will present several types of common mistakes:

Mistakes Made in Algebraic Transformations

	Incorrect	Correct
Negative base mistakes.	$-a^2 = (-a) \cdot (-a) = (-a)^2$	$-a^2 = -a \cdot a$
Incorrectly combine or break exponents when dealing with radicals.	$\sqrt{\sqrt[2]{2} + \sqrt[2]{3}} = \sqrt{\sqrt[2]{2}} + \sqrt{\sqrt[2]{3}}$ $\sqrt[2]{2} \cdot \sqrt[3]{3} = \sqrt[5]{2 \cdot 3}$ or $\sqrt[2]{2} \cdot \sqrt[3]{3} = \sqrt[6]{2 \cdot 3}$	No properties, which allow to simplify this expression: $\sqrt{\sqrt[2]{2} + \sqrt[2]{3}}$. $\sqrt[2]{2} \cdot \sqrt[3]{3} = 2^{\frac{1}{2}} \cdot 3^{\frac{1}{3}} = 2^{3 \cdot \frac{1}{6}} \cdot 3^{2 \cdot \frac{1}{6}} =$ $= (2^3)^{\frac{1}{6}} \cdot (3^2)^{\frac{1}{6}} = (2^3 \cdot 3^2)^{\frac{1}{6}} = \sqrt[6]{2^3 \cdot 3^2}$
Confuse multiplication and addition properties for exponents.	$a^2 \cdot a^3 = a^{2 \cdot 3}$ $(a^2)^3 = a^{2+3}$	$a^2 \cdot a^3 = a^{2+3}$ $(a^2)^3 = a^{2 \cdot 3}$
Confuse power with addition.	$x + x = x^2$	$x + x = 1x + 1x = x(1 + 1) = 2x$
Mix signs.	$4 - a + b - a - b = 4$	$4 - a + b - a - b = 4 - 2a$
Reduce fractions and obtain 2 instead of 1/2.	$\dfrac{a}{2a} = 2$	$\dfrac{a}{2a} = \dfrac{1}{2}$
Distribute products.	$a \cdot (b \cdot c) = (a \cdot b) \cdot (a \cdot c) = a^2 bc$	$a \cdot (b \cdot c) = a \cdot b \cdot c$
Forget ones.	$x + 3zx + xy = x(3z + y)$	$x + 3x + xy = x(1 + 3z + y)$

Ezra, in the last example, I will present a fraction-over-fraction or, as I like to call it, a *multistory building* problem. I mean, the problems, where the numerator and the denominator are fractions.

I understand you only fractionally... There are too many fractions. Can you show me an example?

Sure. I will present the *Multistory Building* problem. Ezra, when solving the problem, you must recognize, the "fraction line" means division. Then, you must transform "division by a fraction" into multiplication.

Multistory Building Problem: Fraction-Over-Fraction Mistakes

	Incorrect	**Correct**
Forget the fraction is division.	$\dfrac{\frac{14c}{7b}}{\frac{8c}{2d}} = \dfrac{\frac{2c}{b}}{\frac{4c}{d}}$ *Not finished!*	$\dfrac{\frac{14c}{7b}}{\frac{8c}{2d}} = \dfrac{\frac{2c}{b}}{\frac{4c}{d}} = \dfrac{2c}{b} \div \dfrac{4c}{d} = \dfrac{2c}{b} \cdot \dfrac{d}{4c} = \dfrac{2cd}{4bc} = \dfrac{d}{2b}$

Stella, thanks for the example. Now I will always get rid of multistory buildings. I prefer a rural life.

Summary

Use number properties and exponent properties. Say *no* to multistory buildings in algebraic expressions.

---

(1) What type of mistakes can someone make when simplifying the following expressions?

(a) $a - b - a$;   *(b)* $-4z - 8z + 4a^2$, *where* $a = -3$.

(2) List the mistakes you have made when performing identical transformations.

---

13 *Simplify expressions using the best approach. Explain what properties you used.*

a) $5x + 87 + 7x + 2y + 45 + x - 87 - 3y + y$;   b) $15 \cdot (b + 3) \cdot 25 \cdot (\sqrt{4} \cdot 4) - 10{,}000$;

c) $1 \div \left(1\frac{1}{2} + \frac{1}{3}\right) + 2 \div \left(1\frac{1}{2} + \frac{1}{3}\right) + \cdots + 9 \div \left(1\frac{1}{2} + \frac{1}{3}\right) + 10 \div \left(1\frac{1}{2} + \frac{1}{3}\right)$;

d) $-x^4 \div (-x)^2 + 3 \cdot (x \cdot 4) + x - x^2$;   e) $\dfrac{\sqrt[2]{\sqrt[2]{16} - \sqrt[3]{a}}}{4 - \sqrt[3]{a^6}} \div \dfrac{1}{\sqrt[2]{4 - \sqrt[3]{a}}}$.

14 *a) Use number properties and properties for exponents to simplify the expressions below.*

b) Perform substitution ($x = -37.9$ and $y = -125$) and calculate resulting values.

1) $-(-x + y) - (-y + 2x)$;   2) $\dfrac{-yx^y}{x^{-y}} \div \dfrac{\sqrt[2y]{x}^{\frac{1}{2y}}}{4}$;   3) $(257xy)^0 - x^{\sqrt[5]{1}}$;

4) $-x - x - x - x - x - x - x - x - x - x$;   5) $\dfrac{0.011}{0.0011}x - \dfrac{0.08}{0.0004}x + \dfrac{0.060}{0.0003}x$;

6) $\left(4(x - y) - 4(x + y)\right)^2 = (4x - 4y - 4x - 4y)^2$;   7) $-9(-x - 2y) - 10x - 34y$;

8) $\left(\sqrt[3]{y} + \sqrt[3]{27{,}000} + \sqrt[2]{-x}\right) \cdot \left(x + y \cdot \sqrt[3]{64}\right) \div \left(30 + \sqrt[3]{y} + \sqrt[2]{-x}\right)$.

15 *Simplify. The variables, a, b, and c are positive.*

(a) $\dfrac{\frac{2}{b}}{3bc} \div \dfrac{c}{b}$;   (b) $\dfrac{\frac{a}{3} + \frac{a}{5}}{\frac{ab}{25}}$;   (c) $\dfrac{\sqrt{b^4} - \sqrt[2]{28b} + \sqrt[2]{7} \cdot (2\sqrt{b} + \sqrt{7b^2})}{\frac{1}{2b}}$;   (d) $-|a + b| - a + b$;

(e) $\dfrac{\frac{\frac{1}{abc}}{c}}{\frac{ab}{\frac{1}{b}}} = \dfrac{\frac{1}{abc}}{\frac{c}{ab}} \cdot b$;   (f) $\dfrac{\frac{2}{ab} \div \frac{4}{bc}}{\frac{a}{2c}} \div \dfrac{b}{c^{-3}}$;   (g) $\dfrac{\frac{\sqrt[3]{16c}}{\sqrt{11}}}{\frac{\sqrt[3]{c} \div \sqrt[2]{11}}{2^{\frac{2}{3}}}}$.

16   *Simplify and explore. In all problems, $x > 0$ and $y < 0$.*

<u>Hint</u>: Do not forget, if a radical has an even index, the root is <u>always</u> positive. To solve some of these problems you might need to use the absolute value sign.

(a) $7(y - 2b) - 77x - (-14b + x) + 39(2x - y)$;

(b) $\left[2\frac{6}{7}x - \frac{40}{44}y - \frac{36}{33}(x + y) - \left(\frac{6}{7}x - 2y\right)\right] \div \frac{5}{22}$;

(c) $\frac{\sqrt[3]{x^6}}{\sqrt[4]{x^2}} + \frac{2x}{3}\sqrt[3]{27x^3} - \sqrt[2]{x^3} - 2\sqrt[2]{0.25x^4} - \sqrt[6]{x^9}$;

(d) $\frac{\frac{1}{x} + \frac{3}{2x} + \frac{1}{4x} - \frac{1}{5x}}{0.85}$;

(e) $\frac{-|4x+2| - 4(1-x) - y\left(\sqrt{(x+1)^2} - \sqrt[4]{x^4} - \sqrt[8]{1^4}\right)}{-0.2}$;

(f) $\sqrt{y^2} + y + \sqrt{x^2} + x$;

(g) $\frac{-|4y-2| - 4(1-y) - x\left(\sqrt{(y-1)^2} - \sqrt[4]{y^4} - \sqrt[8]{(-1)^4}\right)}{-0.2}$;

(h) $|5y - 4| - \left(4\sqrt{y^2} + 4\right)$;

(i) $\sqrt[2]{(9xy)^2} - 9x \cdot (17 - y) - 17x$;

(j) $\frac{\sqrt{x^2}}{x} + \frac{\sqrt{y^2}}{y} + \frac{|x|}{x} + \frac{|y|}{y} + \frac{|x-1|}{x-1} + \frac{|y-1|}{y-1}$.

Chapter 23
Formal Mathematics and Equalities

Ezra, you already solved equations like $x + 2 = 5$.
For finding the answer, you use logical conversion:

if x increased by 2 is 5,
then 5 decreased by 2 is x.
Therefore, $x = 5 - 2 = 3$.

Stella, I also used substitution: I can substitute x with a number which solves the equation.

Chapter 23 will teach you formal rules for solving equations, but first, we must discuss a couple of important points.
Traditionally in mathematics, to make an equation with one unknown, we use x. For equations with two or three unknowns, we use x, y or x, y and z. For more unknowns, there is no custom for creating variables. So, now you are ready to create equations, but first, we must define what does *solving equations* mean.

Solving Equations—What does this mean?

Solving equation means finding the value of x, which transforms the equation into a true statement.

In the equation, $5 = x + 2$,

when $x = 3$, we obtain <u>a true statement</u>: $5 = 3 + 2$.
when $x = 1$, we obtain <u>a false statement</u>: $5 = 1 + 2$.

The value of x, which transforms an equation into a true statement, is *the root of the equation*.

Stella, now I know what solving equations means formally! So, I am ready to start Chapter 23.

(1) Is it possible to use 'a' as an unknown when creating and solving an equation?
(2) What does it mean to solve an equation?
(3) Why x, y, and z are more popular than other letters for using as unknowns in equations?

Section 23.1 Visualizing Equations

Ezra, to develop a deep understanding of the equations, you must know how to visualize the simple equations and their solutions.

The first rule for visualizing equations is a convention for easier communication between teachers and students:

    A. Represent two sides of an equation using two parallel lines:
        the upper line segment represents the left side of an equation.
        the lower side represents the right side of the equation.

A. Upper and bottom sides of a rectangle represent left and right sides of an equation

Translation: $5 = x + 2$.

Steps B and *C* reflect the precision of the visual model:

    B. Show each variable separately. The visual representation must reflect the order of the variables and the numbers in the equation.
    C. Use longer line segments for greater numbers when possible.

So, basically, I'll use the pictures as a language for *Soft Algebra* teachers and students.

You may say so, Ezra. Below, I present three pictures that visualize an equation, and, according to *rule B*, only one picture is correct.

B. All variables are shown separately, and the order of numbers and symbols is preserved

Visualize: $3(x + 5) + 2 = 6x$.

Incorrect Presentation

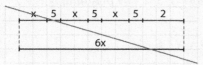

Six *x*-es are glued together.

Incorrect Presentation

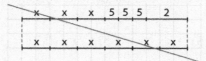

Terms are in incorrect order.

Correct Presentation

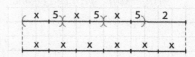

For the first picture, all is precise: x, 5, x, 5, x, 5, and 2. The order is correct.

Ezra, look at the bottom line. All six *x*-es are combined. The second picture has the wrong order. Finally, the third picture is correct and has parentheses. The parentheses reflect grouping in an equation.

One more question. The third picture shows line segment, 2, is longer than line segment, 5. I think, it is incorrect by *rule C*.

In the third picture, 2 is longer than 5 for the following reason—when drawing visual representations for an equation, we do not know the exact value for *x*. Drawing greater numbers using longer line segments, in accordance with *rule C*, is troublesome. Therefore, we consider *rule C* to be a *wish* rather than a *requirement* and follow it only when it makes sense.

Summary

Visualizing: upper line => left side of an equation, the order is unchanged. Try: larger value => longer line.

 Below is the visual representation of an equation, $x + 3 + 2x + 2 = 7 + 2(x + 1)$.
The representation must follow the rules es-
tablished in this section. One of the pictures
has four mistakes. Identify the mistakes.

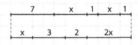

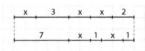

17 *Visualize the given equations. From the list of possible answers, -11, 0, 1, 2, 1.5, 2, 3, 4, 11, substitute values, which will transform the equations into true statements.*

    a) $2(x + 3) = 12$ *b)* $3x + 7 = 19$ *c)* $9 = 2(2x + 1) + 1$

    d) $19 + x = 13 + 2x + 3x$ *e)* $x + 13 = 2(x + 1)$

18 *Write the math expression that corresponds to the given visual representations. Which of the expressions is an identity?*

    a)

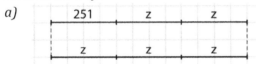

    b)

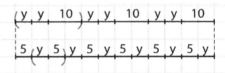

19 *Match the equations with their roots. The roots are: -5, -4, 3, 10.*

    <u>*Hint*</u>: *start with the easiest equations and the easiest roots. Particularly, start by plugging 3 and 10 into Equation (b)...*

    a) $\frac{2}{7}(x - 3.5) - x = \frac{4}{7}(0.5x + 7);$ *b)* $7x - 0.2x = 3(9 - x) + 71;$

    c) $0.01x - 2x = -0.99x + 4;$ *d)* $5(x - 2x) = \frac{4}{5}(-10x + 15) - 3$

Section 23.2 Subtraction Property for an Equality

Stella, why do we need properties for equalities?

Ezra, to solve equations, you must apply equality properties.
I will start from the subtraction property. Now, look at the illustration for the equation, $5 = x + 2$, and its solution.

The $5 = x + 2$ Equation and Subtraction Property for an Equality

Solve equation, $5 = x + 2$, and visualize its solution.

$$5 = x + 2$$

$$5 - 2 = x + 2 - 2$$

$$3 = x$$
$$x = 3$$

Stella, to find x, you <u>cut 2</u> from the rectangle that represents the equation. Yes?

You are correct, Ezra. From a mathematical point of view, *cut away 2* means *subtract 2 from each side of the equation*.

Taking away two from both sides lead to the answer, $3 = x$.

In the last step, I switched x and 3. I did it because the standard way to represent x requires writing x on the left-hand side: $x = 3$.

Stella... All you did was based on intuition and common sense. Where is the subtraction property?

The equation was solved using a *subtraction property for an equality*.

The subtraction property for an equality axiom states, taking away the same value from each side of the equation does not change the roots of the equation.

The subtraction property for an equality is a formal rule based on common sense. In the following sections, we will discuss the rest of the properties.

Summary

When solving equations, you may subtract the same value from each side of an equation.

 To solve some equations, you subtract a number from each side of the equation. To solve other equations, you subtract a term with an unknown from each side of the equation. Explain when you perform each of these actions.

20-22 *Solve the equations below using visual and algebraic approaches.*

20   (a) $x + 3 = 7$;   (b) $2 + x = 8$.

21   (a) $3x = 2x + 6$;   (b) $4x + 2 = 3x + 7$.

22   *As a first step, combine all variables and numbers on each side.*
        (a) $2 + 4x + 3 + x = 2x + 7 + 2x$;   (b) $2(3x + 1) = 4(x + 2) + x$.

23-25 *Solve these equations using the formal algebraic approach:*

23   (a) $4x + 7 = 5x$;   (b) $x + 23 = 28$.

24   (a) $3x + 87 = 4x + 7$;   (b) $5(x + 7) = 6x$.

25   (a) $3x - 87 = 4x$;   (b) $5.2(x + .3) = 4.2x + 20$.

Section 23.3 Division Property for an Equality

Divide and conquer!

Stella, let me guess. Division property for an equality will state, we can divide both sides of an equation by the same number.

Close, but not precise. You must also mention that we cannot divide by zero.

I will discuss the division property for an equality using two examples. First, the equation, $3x = 7$, will help introduce the property. Then, the second example will present typical mistakes students make. But the introductory example first.

Division Property for an Equality

Solve equation, $3x = 7$, and visualize its solution.

$$3x = 7$$

$$\frac{3x}{3} = \frac{7}{3}$$

$$x = \frac{7}{3} = 2\frac{1}{3}$$

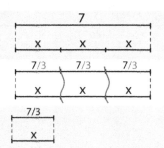

To find x, Stella, you cut the rectangle representing the equation into three parts.

In the algebraic format, *subdividing into 3 parts* means *divide the expressions on each side of the equation by three*. The equation, $3x = 7$, was solved using the division property for an equality axiom.

The *division property for an equality* axiom states, dividing each side of an equation by the same <u>non-zero value</u> does not change the roots of the equation.

Now, the second example, the equation, $x^2 = 3x$.
Ezra, in the incorrect solution to the equation, sloppy division by x leads to losing one of the roots of the equation.

Division Property for an Equality: Dividing by a Variable

Solve the equation $x^2 = 3x$.

Incorrect Solution	**Correct Solution.**
$x^2 = 3x$	$x^2 = 3x$
$\dfrac{x^2}{x} = \dfrac{3x}{x}$	a) If $x \neq 0$, then $\dfrac{x^2}{x} = \dfrac{3x}{x} = 3$. Therefore, $x = 3$.
$x = 3$	b) If $x = 0$, then $0^2 = 3 \cdot 0$. Therefore, $x = 0$.
Incorrect Answer: $x = 3$.	**Correct Answer:** $x_1 = 3$ and $x_2 = 0$.

I see, Stella. This example demonstrates, dividing each side of the equation by a variable can lead to losing *root zero* for the equation.

 You are correct...almost. If you divide sloppily an expression by $(x - 2)$, you can miss the root, $x = 2$. As you can see, it is not always zero that you can miss.

Therefore, you and other students must use the division property for an equality with caution.

 Teachers and mathematicians should use it with caution, too, Stella.

Summary

You can divide each side of an equation by the same number. Do not divide by zero! Do not miss the roots.

 Use the division property to solve the following equation:
$$y \cdot y = 50 \cdot y \cdot y \cdot y.$$

26-28 *Solve the equations below using visual and algebraic approaches.*

26   *(a) $9 = 2x$; (b) $7x = 42$.*

27   *(a) $6x = 4x + 6$; (b) $20x = 2$.*

28   *$3(x + 2) + 4 = 23$.*

29   *Solve the equations by substitution. One of the problems has 3 answers.*
     (a) $x \div 2 = 6$;   *(b) $x \cdot 36 = x \cdot x \cdot x$.*

30   *Solve equations using the formal algebraic approach. First, apply the subtraction property for an equality and then the division property. (a) $13x + 7 = 4x + 77$; (b) $45x + 29 = 72x + 26$.*

31   *Solve equations using the formal algebraic approach. First, group numbers and variables. Then, apply subtraction and division properties for an equality.*
     (a) $14x = 7(x - 8) + 8$;   *(b) $5.2(x + .3) = 2.2x + 180$.*

Section 23.4 Equations in Geometry Problems

In this section, Ezra, you will apply the properties for an equality to solve word problems, which you can easily visualize.

You mean, super easy problems, Stella?

I understand, Ezra, there is a drawback in such an approach. The problems are so easy that sometimes, you will know the answer before making an equation.

You mean, super easy problems, Stella?

Don't worry. I will push myself to make the equations. You already explained why I must do this.

OK. Then, we will start by following the procedure below:

<u>Step 1</u>: In an *Algebraic Organizer*, express all values in terms of x.
In geometric problems, use S_1, S_2, S_3, ... for the sides of a polygon.
Use W and L for the sides in a rectangle and a for the sides in a square.
Use α (*alpha*), β (*beta*), and γ (*gamma*) as measures for angles with vertices A, B, and C.

I understood your parameters—they're normal, but I didn't get the part with x.

After you introduce your *normal* parameters, express them in terms of x...
The *Algebraic Organizer* and a visual model below illustrate the point.

Rectangle-3 Problem. First Three Steps for Solving Word Problems Using Formal Equations

A rectangle's length is 3 cm longer that its width. Find all sides if the perimeter of the rectangle is 30 cm.

$W = x\ cm$
$L = (x + 3)\ cm$
$L + W + L + W = 30\ cm$
$x + (x + 3) + x + (x + 3) = 30$

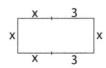

$x + (x + 3) + x + (x + 3) = 30$
$4x + 6 = 30$
$4x + 6 - 6 = 30 - 6$
$4x = 24$, so $x = \dfrac{24}{4} = 6$.
$W = 6\ cm$ and $L = (6 + 3)\ cm = 9\ cm$

$L - ?\ cm;\quad W - ?\ cm.$

Answer: $L = 9\ cm$ and $W = 6\ cm.$

Stella, you used W and L to mark the length for the sides of the rectangle. Then, you wrote, $W = x\ cm$. I think, this means you expressed W in terms of x.

It does. In addition, I expressed L in terms of x, $L = (x + 3)\ cm$. Finally, I expressed the perimeter in terms of x, too.
Now, I will present *Step* 2 for formatting algebraic "visual" problems.

Step 2:   Make a drawing that illustrates the problem in terms of x.

In the illustration to the *Rectangle-3* problem, the lengths of the sides are shown in terms of x. This allows estimating the relative length for line segments and provides additional insight toward solving the problem. For now, I will ask you to illustrate all the problems. Later, you will use illustrations only when needed.

Step 3:   Perform calculations and find the answer.

Step 4:   Reality check: ensure the result makes sense.

Stella, the last expression in the *Algebraic Organizer* is an equation. So, in the calculations for the *Rectangle-3* problem, you simply solved the equation. It's clear, but I have a question regarding measuring units.
In the *Algebraic Organizer* and in the calculations, the lengths of the sides, L and W, are expressed in cm. However, x does not have any units. Why?

In this problem, x represents the quantity of centimeters that makes the length W. Such approach reduces the amount of writing units in algebraic calculations and allows to concentrate on computations. Less units in calculations means less cluttering and therefore, less mistakes. Now, I think you are ready to discuss the reality check. Are you?

Step 4. Reality Check

The rectangle with $L = 9\ cm$ and $W = 6\ cm$ can be drawn. So, the answer makes sense.

In geometric problems, a reality check involves checking all lengths are positive. As you know, the length could never be a negative six inches! Or centimeters. Additional *geometric* constraints will be discussed in the next section.

So, for now, I must remember not to make negative rectangles and triangles. Any final advice?

When making an Algebraic Organizer, it is preferable to mark the least value with x. Usually, this reduces the number of mistakes in calculations.

You mean, with pluses and multiplication, I will make less mistakes than with minuses and division... I agree.

Summary

Algebraic Organizer: all values in terms of x. Illustration with x-es. Check the answers against the constraints.

In the following fragment, which sides of a pentagon will you denote with x? Why? In a pentagon, two sides are twice the other two. And the fifth side is 5 inches shorter than the fourth side. Draw the pentagon.

32-40 *Use equations to solve practice word-problems for Section 23.4. Visualize each problem.*

32   The equilateral triangle has a perimeter 65 cm. All three sides are same. What are the lengths of the triangle's sides?

33   In the rectangle with perimeter 52 cm, all four sides are the same. *(a)* What are the lengths of rectangle's sides? *(b)* How can you call this rectangle?

34   In a trapezoid (figure with four sides; two of them are parallel) with perimeter 86 cm, three of the sides have the same length. Each is 12 cm shorter than the longest side of the trapezoid. What is the length of each side?

35   *Solve equations using the formal algebraic approach. First, group numbers and variables, and then apply subtraction and division properties of equality.*

   a) $1 = 3(x - 8) + 25$ b) $5.25 \cdot (8.3x - 2) + 5 = 5\frac{1}{4}(-2 + 8.3x) + x$
   c) $3x = 4(x - 0.5) - x + 5$ d) $3x = 4(x - 0.5) + x + 5$

36   In the triangle, the first side is the shortest. The second side is 3 cm longer than the first side. The third side is 5 cm longer than the first side. How long is the longest side of this triangle if its perimeter is 80 cm.

37   The perimeter of the rectangle is 78 inches. The length of the rectangle is 12 inches longer than its width. What is the width of the rectangle?

38   The perimeter of an equilateral triangle is 32 cm. What are the lengths of its sides?

39   In the triangle with perimeter 55 cm, two sides are the same, and the third side is 14 cm long. What are the lengths of the triangle's sides?

40   In the rectangle with perimeter 55 cm, the width is 12.5 cm longer than the length. *(a)* What are the lengths of the rectangle's sides? *(b)* What is the area of this rectangle?

Section 23.5 Implicit Givens in Geometry Problems

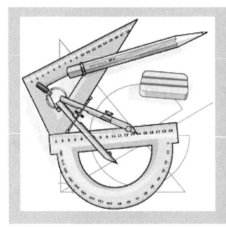

Ezra, Section 23.5 will list some facts from geometry. These facts are usually not included in geometry problems, but they are frequently implied. Some of these facts create additional equations. Other facts form constraints.

Can we start with discussing triangles?

Implicit Givens in Geometry. Three Facts Regarding Triangles

A.   The sum of the angles in a triangle is 180 degrees. | *In any triangle, $\alpha^* + \beta + \gamma = 180^0$.*

B.   A right triangle has a 90-degree angle. | *In a right triangle, $\gamma = 90^0$.*

C.   Right triangles *obey* the Pythagorean theorem: the square of the hypotenuse equals to the sum of the squares of the legs (two other sides). | *In a right triangle, $a^2 + b^2 = c^2$, where $c^\dagger$ is the hypothenuse.*

The first fact allows creating the equation, $\alpha + \beta + \gamma = 180^0$, which can be used for computing angles in triangles. Also, from the chart follows, for any right triangle, $\alpha + \beta + \gamma = 180^0$, $\gamma = 90^0$, and $a^2 + b^2 = c^2$.

Stella, you forgot to add constraints about the lengths and angles. Please, add them now.

Implicit Constraints in Geometry. Two Facts About Geometric Figures

D.   Length is always positive. The angles in closed geometric figures (closed shapes) are always positive, too. | *Length > 0*
Angle in a closed figure > 0

E.   For every closed figure, the length of each side is smaller than the sum of the other sides. | In a triangle, $a < b + c$, $b < c + a$, and $c < a + b$.
In a quadrilateral, $a < b + c + d$, $b < c + d + a$, $c < a + b + d$, and $d < a + b + c$.

---

[*] In geometry, the Greek letters alpha α, beta β, gamma γ, phi φ, and some other are used to mark the angles' measures.
[†] a, b, c, and d are lower case Latin letters that mark the lengths of line segments and the sides of geometric figures.

The sides and the angles are positive not only in triangles, but in other closed figures, too.

But, your second entry (E) says, some "positive" sides make no sense!

Sure. For example, we cannot draw a triangle with the sides 10, 20, and 30 units because, the longest side, 30 units, is _too_ long. Shrinking the longest side to, let say 25 units, would result in a *possible triangle*.
Overall, when dealing with triangles, quadrilaterals (figures with four sides), pentagons, and other multi-side figures (polygons), consider the following:

In a closed figure, each side is shorter than the sum of the other sides.

OK, Stella, I will always examine whether a triangle or other closed figure can be drawn using the lengths I obtained in my answer.

Here, we discussed only a few geometry facts rarely stated explicitly. These facts were presented to demonstrate the following:
when solving challenging word problems and creating *Algebraic Organizer*, students must account for all hidden facts.

You mean, there can be other facts you didn't cover here?

Of course, Ezra. After solving equations, always think about possible constraints of reality and take them into account.

Summary

Geometry problems frequently imply additional givens and constraints.

What information is implied in the following sentences?
(1) A right triangle has two equal angles.
(2) A square has the area of 20 square units.
(3) A radius was drawn for the circle with a diameter of 12 cm.
(4) The sides in the triangle are 10 cm, 23 cm, and K cm.

41   Each set below describes a triangle. Which of the data sets makes no sense? Why?

   1) $a = 2\ cm, b = 2\ cm$, and $c = 2\ in$.

   2) $\alpha = 75^0, \beta = 7^0$, and $\gamma = 102^0$.

   3) In a right triangle, $a = 3\ cm, b = 4\ cm$, and $c = 5\ cm$.

   4) $a = 55\ in, b = 45\ in$, and $c = 9\ in$.

   5) $\alpha = 45^0, \beta = 55^0$, and $\gamma = 80^0$.

   6) $a = 55\ in, b = 65\ in$, and $c = 19\ in$.

   7) In a right triangle, $a = 2\ cm, b = 2\ cm$, and $c = 2\sqrt{2}\ cm$.

   8) In a right triangle, $a = 10\ cm, b = 8\ cm$, and $c = 6\ cm$

   9) In a right triangle, $a = \sqrt{2}\ cm, b = \sqrt{3}\ cm, c = \sqrt{5}\ cm, \alpha = 60^0, \beta = 60^0$, and $\gamma = 60^0$.

42-49 *Use equations to solve practice problems from Section **23.5**. Visualize each problem.*

42   In a triangle, one of the angles is twice as large as one of the other angles. It is also 43 degrees less than the greatest of the angles. What is the measurement of the medium size angle?

43   In a triangle with perimeter 60 cm, the first side is the shortest. The second side is three times as long as the first side. The third side is 11 cm longer than the second side. What are the lengths of triangle's sides?

44   In the triangle, the longest side is two times the shortest side, and the shortest side is 5 cm shorter than the middle side. The perimeter for the triangle is 47 cm. What are the lengths of the sides of this triangle?

45   The perimeter of the pentagon is 76″. The second side is 2″ longer than the first side. The third side is double the first side, and the fourth side is four times the second side. The fifth side is GCF of 60 and 70, measured in inches. What are the lengths of the sides of the pentagon?

46   In a triangle, the first angle is three times as large as the second angle, which is 50 degrees greater than the third angle. What is the measurement of the greatest angle?

47   In a right triangle, one of the angles is smaller than the medium angle by 40 degrees. What is the measure of the medium-sized angle?

48   In a right triangle, the first side is the shortest. The second side is as long as the first side multiplied by the square root of three. The third side is 10 cm long. What is the shortest side of the triangle?

49   In a triangle, the first side is the shortest. The second side is 2 cm longer than the first side. The third side is twice the first side. What is the longest side of this triangle if its perimeter is 44 cm?

Section 23.6 Addition and Multiplication Properties

Here, Ezra, I will discuss the addition and multiplication properties for equalities using the equations, $\frac{1}{4}x = 7$ and $x - 2 = 5$, as examples.

Stella, why do we need more properties? I can solve the first equation using the division property for an equality. By dividing the equation by one-fourth. I can also solve the second equation by subtracting negative 2 from the equation.

Ezra, it is easier to multiply the first equation by 4 and add 2 to the second equation.

Multiplication Properties for an Equality

Solve the equation, $\frac{1}{4}x = 7$. Visualize your solution.

$$\frac{1}{4}x = 7$$

$$\frac{1}{4}x \cdot 4 = 7 \cdot 4$$

$$x = 28$$

I was curious, how will you illustrate your solution... You simply *redrew the rectangle, $\frac{1}{4}x = 7$, four times.*

In mathematics, this means *multiply each part of the equation by* 4. The *multiplication property for an equality* states, multiplying each side of the equation by a non-zero value does not change the roots.

And, if I multiply an equation by zero?

It will lead to an incorrect solution—multiplying by zero creates extra roots. Finally, the addition property for an equality.

Addition Properties for an Equality

Solve the equation, $x - 2 = 5$. Visualize your solution.

$$x - 2 = 5$$

$$x - 2 + 2 = 5 + 2$$

$$x = 7$$

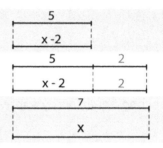

To obtain x, you *added* 2 *to each side of the rectangle.*

Applied above, the *addition property for an equality* states, adding to each side of an equation the same value does not change the roots.
At this point, we concluded a detailed discussion of each property. In the next section, we will combine these properties to begin solving challenging equations.

Summary

You may add to each side of an equation the same value or multiply each side by the same non-zero value.

What equality properties can help you solve the equations below?

(1) $x + 7 = 15$ (2) $-x \cdot 7 = 1$ (3) $x - 6 = 9$ (4) $5 + x = x + x$

(5) $x \cdot 7 = 15$ (6) $x - 7 = 10$ (7) $x + 6 = 9$ (8) $5 \cdot x = x \cdot x$

---

50   *Solve the equations below. Use the addition and then the multiplication property for an equality. List the properties you applied on the right.*

a) $10 = \frac{x}{7} - 1.1$ b) $\frac{x}{30} - 3\frac{1}{3} = 1$

Section 23.7 General Procedure for Solving Equations

 Ezra, here, I will discuss the formal procedure for solving linear equations. *Linear equations* contain terms with an unknown in the first power ($2x$, $25x$) or zero power ($4, 2, 13$). For example, $4x + 1 = x$ is a linear equation.

 You mean, $x^2 = 4$ is not a linear equation?

 It is not. The equation has x to the second power. But $5 = 3$ is a linear equation. It has only x to the zero power. Look, $5 = 5x^0$ and $3 = 3x^0$. To solve multistep linear equations, utilize these steps:

The steps for solving linear equations.
1. Simplify the equation.
2. Move all unknowns to one side of the equation and all numeric terms to the other side.
3. Isolate the unknowns by removing a coefficient (a number multiplied by x).
4. Examine the correctness of the solution.

 What does the phrase, "simplify equation," mean?

 Frequently, it means opening parentheses and *collecting like terms*. Look at the example below.

A. Simplifying an Equation

$3(2x + 1) + 2x = 4(x + 2)$ *Apply the distributive property to open parentheses.*
$3 \cdot 2x + 3 \cdot 1 + 2x = 4x + 4 \cdot 2$ *Apply the distributive property to collect like term.*
$8x + 3 = 4x + 8$

 Stella, *Step* 2 requires moving the terms with an unknown to one side of the equation and numeric terms to the other side.
We must subtract $4x$ from each side of the equation. It will place the x-terms on the left-hand side of the equation. Then, we must subtract 3 from the equation. This will place the numeric terms on the right-hand side.

B. Moving Unknowns to One Side and Numeric Terms to the Other Side of the Equation

$$8x + 3 - 4x = 4x + 8 - 4x$$ *Use the subtraction property for an equality.*
$$4x + 3 = 8$$

$$4x + 3 - 3 = 8 - 3$$ *Use the subtraction property for an equality.*
$$4x = 5$$

> Now, it is time to *isolate the unknown* by removing a coefficient. In our problem, *Step* 3 means dividing each side of the equation by 4.

C. Isolate the unknown by removing a coefficient

$$\frac{4x}{4} = \frac{5}{4}$$ *Apply the division property for equalities.*
$$x = 1.25$$

> As *Step* 4, to examine the correctness of the solution, we must substitute the value for *x* into the initial equation.

D. Examine the correctness of the solution

$$3 \cdot (2 \cdot 1.25 + 1) + 2 \cdot 1.25 = 4 \cdot (1.25 + 2)$$ $$3 \cdot (2.5 + 1) + 2.5 = 3 \cdot 3.5 + 2.5 = 10.5 + 2.5 = 13$$
$$4 \cdot (3.25) = 13$$

> Stella, I substituted *x* with 1.25 and examined both sides. Since I received identity, $13 = 13$, the root, $x = 1.25$, is correct. The procedure is easy!

> It is easy, except the step of simplification. This step is different for different equations. For example, sometimes, simplifying includes multiplication or division. See below.

Two Examples of Simplifying an Equation

Simplify the equation: $0.023x + 0.004 = 0.05$.

$$0.023x + 0.004 = 0.05$$
$$(0.023x + 0.004) \cdot 1{,}000 = 0.05 \cdot 1{,}000$$
$$23x + 4 = 50$$

Simplify the equation: $72x + 12 = 144$.

$$72x + 12 = 144$$
$$(72x + 12) \div 12 = 144 \div 12$$
$$6x + 1 = 12$$

Simplified Equation: $23x + 4 = 50$.

Simplified Equation: $6x + 1 = 12$.

> Stella, on the left-hand side, simplifying meant multiplication by 1,000. Meanwhile, for the right-hand equation, simplification meant dividing by twelve. Is *simplifying* always unpredictable?

> This is the point. Always look for ways to make equations simpler. Ezra, start with following the proposed four-step procedure and, as time passes, develop your own style and preferences. Just..., keep it simple.

Summary

When solving linear equations, first, simplify. Then, move x-s to one side and numerals to the other side. At the end, remove coefficients and check your answer using substitution.

According to the general procedure for solving equations, what would be the first step when solving the following equations? Show the first step for each calculation.

(1) $.02x = -0.03 + 0.05x$ *(2)* $\sqrt[2]{2} + 13x = -260$ *(3)* $2(x - 7) = x - 3(9 - x)$

51   *Circle linear equations. In other equations, underline terms, which demonstrate the equations are not linear. Show how one of the non-linear equations can be transformed into a linear equation.*

   a) $9x - 4 = 9$;   *b)* $3 + x^3 = x$;   *c)* $x = 9 + x \cdot x$;

   d) $\frac{8}{x} = 2x$;   *e)* $\frac{4x}{5^2} = x + 4$;   *f)* $6 - \frac{2}{x} = 2$; *g)* $3 = 0$.

52   *Solve the equations below. On the right, list the properties you applied.*

   a) $9x - 5(x - 8) = x - 1.2x + 5$;   *b)* $\frac{0.1x}{30} - 3\frac{1}{30} = 0.5$.

53   *Solve the equations below. Show your steps.*

   a) $\frac{2 + 3x}{-3} = \frac{-2(x - 6)}{6}$

   b) $0.2x \cdot (8.4 - 2x) + 8 = -5\frac{1}{5}(-2 + \frac{x}{13}) \cdot x$

   c) $432x - 144 = 36.36 - 720x$

   d) $\frac{-2^3 x}{6^3} = 12^{-1} \div \left(\frac{9}{x + 2}\right)$

Section 23.8 Word Problems with Visualizing

Until now, Ezra, you created equations only for word problems dealing with known perimeters or the sums of the angles in a closed figure.
These problems were designed to streamline your first steps into creating equations. Starting with this review, you will solve all kinds of word problems.

Short Second Problem

In a triangle, the first side is 3 in longer than the second side and 4 in shorter than the third side. In turn, the third side is 7 in shorter than the sum of the first two sides. What is the perimeter of the triangle?

$S_1 = (x + 3)in = S_3 - 4\ in$
$S_2 = x\ in$
$S_3 = ([(x + 3) + x] - 7)\ in = (2x - 4)in$
$S_3 = S_1 + 4\ in = (x + 3)in + 4\ in = (x + 7)\ in$
$2x - 4 = x + 7$

$S_1 + S_2 + S_3 =?\ in.$

$2x - 4 = x + 7$
$x - 4 = 7$
$x = 11$
$S_1 = 11\ in + 3\ in = 14\ in$
$S_2 = 11\ in$
$S_3 = 11\ in + 7\ in = 18\ in$
$S_1 + S_2 + S_3 = (14 + 11 + 18)in = 43\ in$

Answer: The perimeter of the triangle is 43 inches.

Stella, the sentence, *the first side is 4 inches shorter than the third side* and *the third side is 7 inches shorter than the sum of the first two sides,* resulted in an equation.

Sure, Ezra. This information helped solve the *Short Second* problem. Presenting all data in terms of x allowed you to easily create an equation and solve the problem. However, as you begin to solve a variety of word problems, you will need fluency with different types of equations. Therefore, I present below the summary of equality properties.
The *general rule for transforming equations* means applying the same procedure to both sides of the equations.

Summary of Equality Properties

Subtraction, addition, multiplication, and division properties of equalities.	*Taking away or adding the same value from (to) each side of the equation as well as multiplying (dividing) each side of an equation by a <u>non-zero value</u> does not change the roots.*
General rule for transforming equations – applying the same procedure to both sides.	*The roots of the equation will remain the same if the same procedure is applied to both sides of the equation while all constraints are taken into account.*

Stella, we already discussed how to apply to an equation four arithmetic operations, $+$, $-$, $\times$, and $\div$. Are there other procedures which we can apply?

Sure. Exponent, for example. You can apply power 2 to each side of an equation. Sometimes, it is useful to take a square root from each side of an equation. But be careful. Incorrectly applied properties for an equality can generate extra roots or eliminate correct solutions.

Therefore, when you apply your own procedures for solving equations, always analyze the possibilities for finding extra roots or losing some of the solutions.

He-he... I will try to gig up all the roots I need but not the extra plants. Can I start now?

Summary

You may apply the same action, for example, exponent, to both sides of an equation.

 (1) What can you do to both sides of the equation to find x? (2) Which of the equations has 2 roots?
(a) $x + 4 = \sqrt[2]{9}$ *(b)* $-x = 6$ *(c)* $x^2 = 9$ *(d)* $\sqrt[2]{100} = \sqrt[2]{x}$.
(3) What is the difference between applying the second power to both sides of an equation and the properties of equalities you have already learned?

54-57 *Create visual representations, equations, and solve the problems.*

54 In a pentagon with a perimeter of 61 inches, two sides have the same length. The third side is 7 inches shorter than the sum of the first two sides, 1 inch longer than the fourth side, and 3 inches shorter than the fifth side. What are the lengths of the equal sides of the pentagon?

55 There is a triangle with one side 5 inches longer than the other two. It is also known that that side equals the sum of the lengths of the other two sides. Find the length of the sides of the triangle.

56 In the rectangle, the length is GCF of 48 and 36, in inches. The area of this rectangle is 6 inches².
   (a) What is the width of this rectangle?
   (b) What is its perimeter?

57 In a trapezoid (figure, with four sides; two of them parallel) with a perimeter of 69 cm, two opposite sides have the same length. The lengths of the other two sides differ by 4 cm. The shortest side is 9 cm shorter than the longest sides. What is the length of each side?

58 Complete the chart. Visualize the math identities. If there is a picture, finish writing the identity. Specify the number property you applied.
   a) $3(x + 5) = 3x + 3 \cdot 5$;   *b)* $x + 8 = 8 + x$;   *c)* $2 \cdot 3 = 3$;   *d)* $2 \cdot (1 + x) = 2 + 2x$.

59-65 *Create visual representations, equations, and solve the problems.*

59   In the rectangle, the length is GCF of 56 and 54, in inches. *(a)* What is the width of this rectangle if its perimeter is 6½"? *(b)* What is the area of this rectangle?

60   In the rectangle, the length is three times as long as the width. The perimeter of this rectangle is 64 cm. What is the width of this rectangle?

61   There are two triangles. The perimeter of the first triangle is LCM of 15 and 10, in cm. What are the lengths of the sides of the second triangle if this triangle is equilateral and its perimeter is equal to the perimeter of the first triangle?

62   In the rectangle, length is 3 times the width, and the width is 2.8 inches shorter than the length. *(a)* What is the perimeter of this rectangle? *(b)* What is the area of this rectangle?

63   In the rectangle, the longest side is two times the shortest side. If you cut 7½ cm from the length, it will be equal to the width. *(a)* What are the sides of this rectangle? *(b)* What is the perimeter of this rectangle? *(c)* What is the area of this rectangle?

64   The perimeter of the square is the same as the perimeter of the equilateral triangle with side 7½ cm. What is the length of the square's side?

65   In the triangle, the second side is 2.2" longer than the first side. The sum of the first two sides is 2.4" greater than the third side, which is 7.8" long. What are the lengths of triangle's sides?

66-71 *Create visual representations, equations, and solve the problems.*

66   If the length of the rectangle is doubled and the width decreases by 3 cm, the rectangle will have dimensions $45cm \times 16cm$. What are the initial dimensions of this rectangle?

67   In the rectangle, length is 4 times as long as the width, and the width is 2.7 inches shorter than the length. What is the perimeter of the rectangle?

68   In the rectangle, the shortest side is one-fourth the length. The sum of the length and the width is 12.4 cm longer than the width itself. *(a)* What are the sides of the rectangle? *(b)* What is the perimeter of the rectangle?

69   If we cut off two-thirds of the length of the rectangle and increase the width by 2 *cm*, we will have a $3cm \times 3cm$ square. What are the initial dimensions of this rectangle?

70   In the rectangle, the difference between the length and the width is GCF of 15 and 11, measured in inches. *(a)* If the width of this rectangle is "*w*," what is the length of this rectangle? *(b)* If the length of this rectangle is 7.8 inches, what is the width of this rectangle?

71   The perimeter of the triangle is four times its shortest side. The medium side of the triangle is ¼ cm longer than the shortest side and 0.25 cm shorter than the longest side. *(a)* What are the lengths of the sides of the triangle? *(b)* What is the perimeter of the triangle?

Chapter 24
Systems of Linear Equations and Half-Problems

 Ezra, Chapter 24 will teach you sophisticated methods for solving equations. Meanwhile, you will continue solving word problems, particularly, like the problem presented below.

A Half-Problem: a *Non-Visual* Problem

What is sixteen-fifteenths of the product of three numbers where the sum of the first and second numbers equals the third number taken two times, while the first number is 3 more than the second number and makes one-third of the third number?

$N_1 = x$

$N_2 = N_1 - 3 = x - 3$

$N_3 = 3x$

$N_1 + N_2 = 2N_3$

$x + (x - 3) = 2(3x)$

$\frac{16}{15} \cdot N_1 \cdot N_2 \cdot N_3 = ?$

$x + (x - 3) = 2(3x)$

$2x - 3 = 6x$

$-3 = 4x$

$\frac{4x}{4} = \frac{-3}{4}$

$N_1 = x = -\frac{3}{4}; N_2 = -3\frac{3}{4}; N_3 = -\frac{3}{4} \cdot 3 = -\frac{9}{4}.$

$\frac{16}{15} \cdot N_1 \cdot N_2 \cdot N_3 = \frac{16}{15} \cdot \frac{-3}{4} \cdot \frac{-15}{4} \cdot \frac{-9}{4} = -\frac{3 \cdot 9}{4} = -6.75$

Answer: $\frac{16}{15} \cdot N_1 \cdot N_2 \cdot N_3 = -6.75.$

Stella, I see why you called it the *Non-Visual* problem. I don't think I can visualize this one.

 In this chapter, many of the problems will be difficult to visualize. You will solve these problems by applying number properties and properties of equality. Finally, you will cross the bridge from an intuitive to formal mathematics.

Section 24.1 Linear Equations and Substitution Method

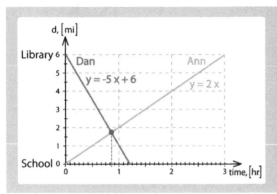

Ezra, Section 24.1 will introduce a formal way for solving a system of equations having a curly French bracket, $\{$, on the left-hand side.

Stella, why can't I use normal parenthesis?

The *curly bracket* means *together true*. The roots must transform each of the equations into a true statement.

$$\begin{cases} y + 5x = 6 & \text{TRUE} \\ y - 4x = -2x & \text{TRUE} \end{cases}$$

Below, I will show how to solve the <u>system of linear equations</u> using a substitution method.

Xy Problem. The Substitution Method

Find a solution to the system of linear equations with two unknowns using the substitution method:

$$\begin{cases} y + 5x = 6 \\ y - 4x = -2x \end{cases}$$

A. Express one of the variables in terms of another variable.

$y - 4x = -2x \quad \rightarrow \quad y = 2x$

B. Substitute the obtained value into another equation.

$y + 5x = 6 \quad \rightarrow \quad 2x + 5x = 6$

C. Solve the resulting equation to determine both unknowns.

$2x + 5x = 6$

$\dfrac{7x}{7} = \dfrac{6}{7}$

$x = \dfrac{6}{7}$

$y = 2 \cdot \dfrac{6}{7} = 1\dfrac{5}{7}$

Check validity: substitute unknowns into the equations.

$1\dfrac{5}{7} + 5 \cdot \dfrac{6}{7} = 1 + \dfrac{5}{7} + \dfrac{30}{7} = 6$

$0.25 \cdot \dfrac{12}{7} - \dfrac{6}{7} = \dfrac{3}{7} - \dfrac{6}{7} = -\dfrac{3}{7} = -\dfrac{1}{2} \cdot \dfrac{6}{7}$

Answer: $x = \dfrac{6}{7}$ and $y = 1\dfrac{5}{7}$.

As I see it, Stella, at the beginning, you expressed y in terms of x using the second equation. Then, you substituted $y = 2x$ into the first equation. The resulting equation, $2x + 5x = 6$, had only one unknown. So, you solved it and then found y. Basically, in two steps, you obtained a single linear equation. The rest was easy.

The graph on the right illustrates the solution to the *Xy* Problem after both equations are transformed to express y in terms of x.

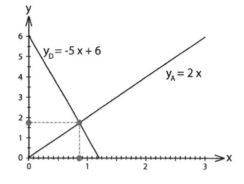

I see, Stella. The intersection of the $y(x)$ graphs presents a solution to the system. But..., it isn't precise!

It is an approximate solution, Ezra. However, we can use it to examine the validity of the results. Now, I will summarize what we completed here.

When solving a system of equations using the *substitution method*, we express one of the unknowns in terms of the other and substitute the obtained result into another equation. The substitution reduces the number of unknowns. So, you can apply substitution method in equations with several unknowns. But first, you must learn another approach—the method of linear combinations.

Summary

Substitution method: express one unknown in terms of the others and substitute it into one of the equations.

(1) Solve the system of the equations presented above expressing y from the first equation in terms of x. (2) Solve the system by expressing x from the second equation in terms of y.
(3) Did each approach work? Which approach was better and why?

72 *Solve the following systems of linear equations using the substitution method.*

a) $\begin{cases} x - 2y = 7 \\ 3x + 2y = -19 \end{cases}$

b) $\begin{cases} 14x - 5y = 7\frac{1}{3} \\ 6y - 7x = -6 \end{cases}$

c) $\begin{cases} z - 2x = 3x - 5 \\ z + x = -z - 4.5 \end{cases}$

d) $\begin{cases} 8x - 7y - 11 = 2(-4y + 3x) \\ 0.01x = 0.05y - 0.11 \end{cases}$

73 There are three numbers. Their sum is 48. The second number is the same as the first number; and the third number is 3 more than the second number. What is the first number?

74 The product of two numbers is 180 and the first number is one-fifth the second number. What is the sum of these two numbers?

75 Find three consecutive numbers whose sum is 366.

76 The difference between two numbers is 34. The second number is one-third the first number. What is the sum of the digits of the first number?

77 *Solve the following systems of equations using the substitution method.*

a) $\begin{cases} 6y - x = 7 \\ 0.3x + 0.2y = 1.8 \end{cases}$

b) $\begin{cases} x - 5 = \frac{y}{3} \\ 6y + 6x = -2 \end{cases}$

c) $\begin{cases} 3x + 2y = -85 \\ 2y + 4x = 4 \end{cases}$

d) $\begin{cases} -5x + 2y - 6 = 0 \\ 9x - 3 = 5y \end{cases}$

215

Section 24.2 Intro to Method of Linear Combinations

 The *method of linear combinations* is based on combining linear equations with the goal of eliminating one of the unknowns.

Xy Problem. Linear Combination Method

Find a solution to the system of equations using the linear combination method.

$$\begin{cases} y + 5x = 6 \\ y - 4x = -2x \end{cases}$$

A. Perform linear combination: subtract one equation from another.

$$y + 5x - (y - 4x) = 6 - (-2x)$$
$$5x + 4x = 6 + 2x$$

B. Solve the resulting equations to determine both unknowns.

$$7x = 6$$
$$\frac{7x}{7} = \frac{6}{7}$$
$$x = \frac{6}{7}$$
$$y = 2 \cdot \frac{6}{7} = 1\frac{5}{7}$$

Answer: $x = \frac{6}{7}$ and $y = 1\frac{5}{7}$.

Stella, I recognized the *Xy* Problem from the last section. But...does the *combination method* always require subtraction?

 The method involves either subtraction or addition. In the example above, I subtracted the second equation from the first to eliminate y. The resulting equation had only one unknown, x, and, therefore, was easy to solve.
The next example will demonstrate how the addition helps combining equations.

Xy-Nine Problem. Linear Combination Method

Find a solution to the system of equations using the linear combination method.

$$\begin{cases} 7y + 5x = 10 \\ 9y - 5x = -2 \end{cases}$$

A. Perform linear combination: add the equations.

$$7y + 5x + (9y - 5x) = 10 + (-2)$$
$$16x = 8$$

B. Solve the resulting equations.

$$\frac{16x}{16} = \frac{8}{16}$$
$$x = 0.5$$
$$7y + 5 \cdot 0.5 = 10$$
$$7y = 7.5$$
$$y = 1\frac{1}{14}$$

Answer: $x = 0.5$ and $y = 1\frac{1}{14}$.

In the *Xy-Nine* problem, $5x$ was eliminated in one step, by addition of two equations. In this problem, substitution would take more steps than a combination.

I see. Does the linear combination method always work in one step?

Not always. Section 24.3 will teach you how to eliminate unknowns in complex systems of equations, where elimination requires two-three steps.

Summary

Combine (add or subtract) the equations to eliminate the unknowns.

The system of equations in Example 1 (see the system of equations in Section 24.2) was solved using the subtraction property of equality.

   (1) Show how to solve this system of equations using the addition property of equality.

   (2) Which method, subtraction or addition, was better? Why?

78 *Solve the following systems of equations using the method of linear combinations.*

a) $\begin{cases} x - 2y = 7 \\ 3x + 2y = -19 \end{cases}$

b) $\begin{cases} 4x - 14y = -1 \\ x - 14y = 5 \end{cases}$

c) $\begin{cases} 0.5z - 4x = x - 5 \\ \frac{z}{2} + x + 7 = 2.5 \end{cases}$

d) $\begin{cases} 5x - 35y = 47 \\ 26x + 35y = 46 \end{cases}$

79   There are three numbers. The second number is thirty-five. The first number is four less than the third number. The sum of these numbers is 107.
(a) What is the largest number? *(b)* What is the average of these three numbers?

80   There are four numbers. The sum of the first two numbers is 48, and the sum of the last two numbers is 56. The second number is twice as big as the first. The third number is the same as the first number. What is the value of the fourth number?

81   There are five numbers. The second, fourth, and fifth numbers are the same. The product of the first and third numbers is 8. Half of the first number is 4. The sum of all five numbers is 39. What is the fifth number?

82   The sum of two even consecutive numbers is 52. What are they?

83 *Solve the following systems of equations using the method of linear combinations.*

a) $\begin{cases} -4z + 2y = 7 \\ 4z = y - 16 \end{cases}$

b) $\begin{cases} 3x + 4y = -1 \\ 4y + 3x = 5 \end{cases}$

Section 24.3 Advanced Linear Combination Method

Stella, will we start with two-step or three-step elimination?

Ezra, easier things first. Below, I will present the *Two-Step Elimination* problem.

Two-Step Elimination Problem. The Linear Combination Method

Find a solution to the system of equations using the linear combination method.

$$\begin{cases} 8y + 5x = 7 \\ 2y - 2x = 5 \end{cases}$$

A. Multiply one of the equations by a number to obtain identical (or opposite) coefficients for one of the unknowns.

$$2y - 2x = 5 \xrightarrow{\times 4} 8y - 8x = 20$$
$$\begin{cases} 8y + 5x = 7 \\ 8y - 8x = 20 \end{cases}$$

B. Perform linear combination.

$$8y + 5x - (8y - 8x) = 7 - 20$$
$$5x + 8x = -13$$

C. Solve the resulting equations.

$$13x = -13$$
$$x = -1$$
$$2y - 2 \cdot (-1) = 5$$
$$2y = 3$$
$$y = 1.5$$

Answer: $x = -1$ and $y = 1.5$.

Stella, what does the symbol "$\times 4$" above the arrow mean?

Before combining equations, I multiplied the second equation by 4. After the multiplication, I had $8y$-term in both equations!
I obtained the equivalent coefficients for y in just one step. However, the next problem will require two multiplication steps before using a linear combination. Please, read the example below and then list my multiplication steps.

Three-step Elimination Problem. The Linear Combination Method

Find a solution to the system of equations using the linear combination method.

$$\begin{cases} 3y + 5x = 7 \\ 2y + 2x = 5 \end{cases}$$

A. Multiply both equations by numbers to obtain identical (or opposite) coefficients for one of the unknowns.

$$3y + 5x = 7 \rightarrow 6y + 10x = 14$$
$$2y - 2x = 5 \rightarrow 6y + 6x = 15$$
$$\begin{cases} 6y + 10x = 14 \\ 6y + 6x = 15 \end{cases}$$

B. Perform a linear combination.

$$6y + 10x - (6y + 6x) = 14 - 15$$
$$10x - 6x = -1$$

C. Solve the resulting equations.

$$4x = -1$$
$$x = -0.25$$
$$2y + 2 \cdot \frac{-1}{4} = 5$$
$$2y = 5.5$$
$$y = 2.75$$

Answer: $x = -0.25$ and $y = 2.75$.

Stella, you multiplied the first equation by 2. Then, you multiplied the second equation by 3. You obtained the coefficient 6 for both equations because $6 = LCM(2,3)$. You see, I understand the method and ready for a

Summary

Multiply one or both equations to change coefficients and prepare the equations for a linear combination.

There is a system of equations.

(1) In the first equation, the coefficient of y is 3. In the second, it is 5. How will you change the equations to eliminate y using the linear combination method?

(2) If the coefficients are -7 and 14, what are the new coefficients?

(3) If the coefficients are 42 and 36, what are the new coefficients?

(4) If the coefficients are a and b, and the new coefficient of y is c, what can you say about the mathematical relationships between a, b, and c?

84 *Solve the following systems of equations using the method of linear combinations.*

a) $\begin{cases} 5x - 4y = 2 \\ 3x + 2y = -1 \end{cases}$

b) $\begin{cases} 6 - 5x = 7y \\ 4y + 6 = 5x \end{cases}$

c) $\begin{cases} 5y - 4x = x - 5 \\ 4(22x + 77) = 44(y - 3x) \end{cases}$

d) $\begin{cases} \frac{x}{7} - \frac{y}{3} = 2 \\ \frac{x}{4} + \frac{y}{12} = 3 \end{cases}$

85 There are three consecutive multiples of four. Eight less than the sum of the first and third numbers is 96. What is the second number?

86 From three numbers with the same absolute value, the second number is different from the other two numbers. The sum of these three numbers is 187. What is the second number?

87 The quotient of the first and second numbers is additive inverse of –7/9. If both these numbers are positive one-digit numbers, what is the first number?

88 The second number decreased by five is seven. This number is one-third the first number. What is the first number?

89 *Solve the following systems of equations.*

a) $\begin{cases} 5x = 12 + y \\ 3x + 2y = -4 \end{cases}$

b) $\begin{cases} \frac{x-3y}{5} = -2 \\ \frac{7x-4y}{x} = 5 \end{cases}$

90   If all five numbers are prime numbers and their product is 210, what are these numbers? Show these numbers in descending order.

91   There are two numbers. The first number is two times the second number. The difference between these two numbers equals the greatest common factor of 12 and 30. What are these numbers?

92   There are three numbers. Their sum is 56. The second number is the same as the first number. The third number is five times the second number. What is the difference between the third and second numbers?

93   *Solve the following systems of equations.*

a) $\begin{cases} 5x = 4 + 2y \\ -3x + 2y = -6 \end{cases}$

b) $\begin{cases} \frac{2x-3y}{7} = -2 \\ \frac{8x-4y}{4} = 176 \end{cases}$

c) $\begin{cases} 5y - 4(x + 2) = x - 5 \\ 10x - 10y = -6 \end{cases}$

d) $\begin{cases} 5x - y = 7 \\ -21x + 4y = 4 \end{cases}$

94   There are three numbers. The second number is one-third the first number. The third number is 5 more than the second number. What is the average of these numbers if the first number is 24?

95   The sum of three numbers is 110. The second number is four more than the first number. The third number is four times the second number. What is the product of digits for the second number?

96   *Solve the following systems of equation using linear combinations.*

a) $\begin{cases} 5x - 3y = 1 \\ -3x + 2y = -2 \end{cases}$

b) $\begin{cases} 4 - 6y = 5x \\ 5 + 5y = -3x \end{cases}$

c) $\begin{cases} 5y - 2z = z - 8 \\ 10z - 3y = 6 \end{cases}$

d) $\begin{cases} 4x - 3y = -7 \\ -3x + 11y = 1 \end{cases}$

97   There are four numbers. The sum of all numbers is 36. The first number is two less than the second number. The third number is twice the first number. The fourth number is twice the second number. What is the second number?

98   There are four numbers. The second number is twenty-five more than the first number. The first number is unknown. The third number is two times the first number. The fourth number is ten less than the first number. What are the numbers if their sum equals 100?

99   *Solve the following systems of equations.*

a) $\begin{cases} 5x - 3y = -1 \\ 3x + y = -9 \end{cases}$

b) $\begin{cases} \frac{2x-3y}{7} = \frac{2y-3}{2} \\ \frac{8-y}{4} = \frac{x-3}{5} \end{cases}$

c) $\begin{cases} 2(x - y) = 3(x + y) \\ x = y + 1 \end{cases}$

d) $\begin{cases} 4x - 3y = -7 \\ 3y - 4x = -7 \end{cases}$

100   There are three numbers. The first number is three times as big as the third number. The second number is twice as large as the first number. The sum of the second and third numbers is 77. Find each number.

101   There are three numbers. The third number is six more than the first number. The second number is three times the first number. The difference between the third and second numbers is 26. What is the second number? *(a)* All numbers are positive. *(b)* All numbers are negative.

Chapter 25
Word Problems with Elements of Algebra

Ezra, Chapter 25 will teach you how to present and solve ratios, proportions, and problems with percentage using algebraic methods.

Finally, I have reached algebra!

I bet you did, Ezra. You will solve a lot of...*stimulating* problems in this chapter. But first, tell me: what is the problem-solving idea behind using x and other unknowns? Why do we need x, y, and z?

Easy. We introduce the unknowns to create algebraic equations. The main idea is <u>to use the auxiliary elements, x, y, z or alike, to represent word problems as equations and then apply algebraic formulas</u>.

Great answer, my dear brother! I am speechless. You are definitely ready to start applying algebra. Just be aware, for the last set of problems, you will apply not only algebra but your problem-solving skills, persistence, and all the problem-solving techniques you know.

I am ready to start. I hope, this chapter and final review will show me how much I have progressed and...I will appreciate my achievements. And you'll not scare me by talking about challenging problems.

Section 25.1 Word Problems and Systems of Equations

Ezra, starting from this section, you will face problems that require solving equations with several unknowns. For example, in the problem below, x and y mark the number of apples of each kind while p_x and p_y mark the prices of a single apple for each type.

Ezra, read the Apples' problem. Then create four equations with four unknowns (x, y, p_x, and p_y) before reading the problem's solution.

Apples' Problem

A box of Honey Crisp and Granny Smith apples costs \$20.74 and has 28 apples in it. The price of a pair of apples, one Granny Smith and one Honey Crisp, is \$1.50. By exchanging one Honey Crisp apple by one Granny Smith apple, we would reduce the price of the box to \$20.48. How many apples of each kind are in the box? *The price per apple does not depend on the apples' quantity.*

$N_H = x$
$N_G = y$
$AApplePrice_H = p_x$
$AApplePrice_G = p_y$
$p_x + p_y = 1.50$
$xp_x + yp_y = 20.74$
$(x-1)p_x + (y+1)p_y = 20.48$
$x + y = 28$

$x = ?$

$y = ?$

$$\begin{cases} p_x + p_y = 1.50 \\ xp_x + yp_y = 20.74 \\ (x-1)p_x + (y+1)p_y = 20.48 \\ x + y = 28 \end{cases}$$

After subtracting equation $(x-1)p_x + (y+1)p_y = 20.48$ from $xp_x + yp_y = 20.74$, we obtain $p_x - p_y = 0.26$.

To solve the system of two equations below, we combine the equations.

$$\begin{cases} p_x + p_y = 1.50 \\ p_x - p_y = 0.26 \end{cases}$$

The result is, $2p_x = 1.76$, and therefore, $p_x = 0.88$ and $p_y = 0.62$.

After substituting the known prices for the apples into the main equations, we have a new system of two equations:

$$\begin{cases} x + y = 28 \\ 0.88x + 0.62y = 20.74 \end{cases}$$

Substitution leads to a single equation, $0.88x + 0.62(28 - x) = 20.74$.
$0.26x = 20.74 - 17.36 = 3.38$, so $x = 13$ and $y = 15$.

Answer: There were 13 Honey Crisp and 15 Granny Smith apples in the box.

Mr. Refiner, I got the same answer as Stella! Although...my solution was a bit longer. From the *Apples'* problem I can assume, problems with several unknowns can be quite challenging. Right?

You are correct, Ezra, the problems can be quite... motivating. Therefore, when solving algebra-level problems, you must be ready to apply the techniques you have learned in addition to solving algebraic equations.

Summary

To solve problems with several unknowns, utilize all your problem-solving knowledge and skills.

(1) What method is better for solving word problems with several unknowns, linear combinations, or substitution?

(2) Create and solve a system of two equations.

102-104 *Solve the problems below.*

102   The sum of the first two numbers is twice the sum of the other two numbers. Meanwhile, the second number is greater than the first by 14, and the fourth number is less than the second number by a factor of 2. The sum of the third and first numbers is thirty and one-third. Find these numbers.

103   In a pentagon, the sum of two sides equals the sum of other two sides and equals the fifth side. The first and the third sides combined are longer than the fifth side by 6 inches. The sum of the second and fourth sides is 4 inches longer than the fifth side. Find the length of the sides of the pentagon.

104   When students began school in September, they decided to organize a competition—who will collect more recycling paper? At the end of October, they found the amount of the paper collected by the first and second grade classes equaled double the amount of paper collected by the third-grade class. Meanwhile, one-seventh of the amount collected by the second-grade class equals the difference between the weights collected by the first and third grade classes. Finally, a triple amount of paper collected by the second-grade class is 6.6 kilograms heavier than the total amount collected by all three classes. How much recycling paper did the three classes collect in all?

Section 25.2 Proportions as Equations

Ezra, your dream finally comes true. This section will introduce an algebraic approach to the proportions. We will use problems we already solved to compare arithmetic and algebraic methods. We start with the *Six Cars* problem.

Six Cars Proportion Problem: Algebraic Approach

Six cars have 30 wheels. How many cars will have 40 wheels?

6 *c.*	30 *wh.*
x c.	40 *wh.*

$$\frac{6}{x} = \frac{30}{40}.$$
$$6 \cdot 40 = 30 \cdot x$$
$$x = \frac{6 \cdot 40}{30} = 8$$

Answer: Eight cars will have 40 wheels.

In an algebraic presentation of the problem, Stella, you used *x* instead of a question-mark.

I did. It simplifies translating data into an *equation-proportion*, $\frac{6}{x} = \frac{30}{40}$. See the chart below:

6 *c.*	30 *wh.*	Direct Translation into an Equation →	$\frac{6}{x} = \frac{30}{40}$
x c.	40 *wh.*		

You will better understand such a translation if you read the givens the following way:

6 cars relate to *x* cars the same way as 30 wheels relate to 40 wheels.

I see, <u>6 to *x* is the same as 30 to 40</u>. Or $\frac{6}{x} = \frac{30}{40}$.
Can I read the proportion along the rows? I mean, <u>6 relates to 30 as *x* relates to 40</u>.
You see, Stella, 6 and 30 are on the first line while *x* and 40 are on the second.

Sure, Ezra. You will obtain $\frac{6}{30} = \frac{x}{40}$.
This is the same equation as $\frac{6}{x} = \frac{30}{40}$, but written in a different way.

224

It is all clear, but... Why didn't you define x? You always taught me to define parameters.

The meaning of x is clear just from the proportion format presentation, especially when measuring units are shown.
Now, Ezra, it is time for the *Four Bricks Proportion* problem.

Four Bricks Proportion Problem: Algebraic Approach

Four bricks have a weight of 11kg. How much will 7 bricks weigh?

4 *br.*	11 *kg*
7 *br.*	*x kg*

$$\frac{4}{7} = \frac{11}{x}$$
$$4x = 7 \cdot 11$$
$$x = \frac{77}{4} = 19.25$$

Answer: Seven bricks will weigh 19.25 kilograms.

Stella, you presented data as a proportion and the calculations became straightforward. I just think, why did I ever learn the unit block approach if I could use algebra.

Sometimes, the algebraic approach leads to incorrect results. See, the *Dragons* problem below.

Dragons Problem: Algebraic Approach

All dragons from Dundutu have an identical number of heads. If 616 of the dragons have 1400 heads, how many heads will 407 dragons have?

616 *dr.*	1,400 *h.*
407 *dr.*	*x h.*

$$\frac{x}{1,400} = \frac{407}{616}$$
$$x = \frac{1,400 \cdot 407}{616} = 925$$

Answer: 407 dragons will have 925 heads.

Stella, this is a simple problem. What mistake could I make here?

Ezra, the presented solution is incorrect. In this problem, how many heads does one dragon have?

Since 616 dragons have 1,400 heads, one dragon has $407h. \div 616dr. = 2\frac{3}{11}\frac{h.}{dr.}$. Oho-ho. It's strange.

If dragons had $2\frac{3}{11}$ heads on average, the problem would have meaning.

However, the problem said, all dragons have the same number of heads. So, even it is a fairytale, $2\frac{3}{11}$ *heads per dragon* is not a valid option.

You are correct, and the initial answer is wrong. It must be revised.

Dragons Problem: Corrected Answer

Answer: The problem has no solution because 616 dragons cannot have 1,400 heads without having $2\frac{3}{11}$ *heads per dragon*, which has no meaning.

Stella, I still think the algebraic approach is highly convenient.

Sure. However, when using the algebraic approach, thoroughly analyze the meaning of your results. OK, Ezra?

Summary

Present proportion problems using x, translate into an equation and solve. Check the meaning.

(1) Create a proportion problem with numbers 4, 5, and 20. Solve it algebraically.

(2) What property of equality did you apply for solving the problem you made?

105-107   *Solve the problems below. Use the algebraic approach.*

105   How much would 70 boxes of goods weigh if 3 boxes of the goods weigh 47.1 kg? All boxes have the same weight.

106   How many packets will be filled for delivery with 350 kg of rice if each packet of rice must weigh exactly 3 pounds, while each empty packet weighs 0.02 pounds?

107   A factory produces and delivers to customers monthly the same amount of cheese. If it produces 358 pounds of cheese in 4 months, how much time does it need to produce and deliver 1,611 pounds of cheese.

Section 25.3 Ratios as Equations

 I see, Stella, we have moved from proportions to ratios. Will we use again our *old* problems?

We will use two problems from Chapter 15, Ezra.

Girls and Boys Problem: Algebraic Approach

There are 42 girls on a team. The ratio of girls and boys on the team is 2 : 3. How many boys are there?

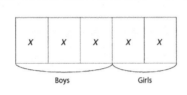

$2x$	$3x$
$42\ g.$	$B\ b.$

Boys　　　　Girls

B – the number of boys on a team.
x – the number of children in one part (unit box).

$\dfrac{2x}{3x} = \dfrac{42}{B}$ *or* $\dfrac{2x}{42} = \dfrac{3x}{B}$

$B = \dfrac{42 \cdot 3}{2} = 63.$

Answer: There are 63 boys on the team.

You picture is similar to a picture from the Ratio-of-Groups Approach. The difference is x-s. In the visual representation, the boys' box has three parts—each has x boys. The girl's box has two parts; each has x girls.

 You are correct. Just pay attention, in sophisticated problems, x's in visual representation are not separated. Look at the example below. It is written $10x$; the x's are not shown separately.

Long Proportion Problem: Algebraic Approach

The ratio of pears, apples, and strawberries on a table is 10:3:15, while there are 84 fruits altogether. How many pears, apples, and strawberries are on the table?

Parameters: x is the number of fruits in one part (unit block).

　　　　　　A –number of apples. P –number of pears. S –number of strawberries.

$P : A : S = 10 : 3 : 15$
$P + A + S = 84\ fr.$
$P = 10x$
$A = 3x$
$S = 15x$
$P =?$　$A =?$　$S =?$

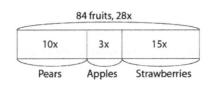

84 fruits, 28x

10x	3x	15x
Pears	Apples	Strawberries

$10x + 3x + 15x = 84$
$28x = 84$
$x = 3$
$P = 3 \cdot 10 = 30$
$A = 3 \cdot 3 = 9$
$S = 3 \cdot 15 = 45$

Answer: There are 30 pears, 9 apples, and 45 strawberries on the table.

I see, Stella. You used $10x$, $3x$, and $15x$ to represent quantities for pears, apples, and strawberries.

Also, on top of the picture, I added information regarding the total number of x's.

Stella, where did you find 28? The *Long Proportion* problem doesn't have 28 in the list of givens.

Writing $28x$ is significant for a better understanding of the problem. I took implicit information and made it explicit.
Introducing readily available information into visual representations simplifies problems involving ratios.

Summary

Present the ratio as an algebraic proportion and translate it into an equation. Use clear visual representation.

(1)   Create a ratio problem with numbers 3, 2, and 15. Solve it algebraically.

(2)   In the Section 25.3 example with boys and girls, what part of the children do the girls represent? How can the answer be seen from the picture, which illustrates the problem?

108-114   *Solve the problems below. <u>Use the algebraic approach.</u>*

108   The ratio of pears and apples on each table is 36 to 24. There are 25 fruits on an oval table. How many of them are pears?

109   The ratio of dogs and cats in a house is 6 : 8. How many dogs are there if there are 32 cats in the house?

110   The ratio of white and red roses in each vase is 6 : 18. How many white roses are in a vase with 33 red roses?

111   The recipe for a yellow cake requires 8 eggs, one glass of sugar, and one glass of flour. In case you have a dish with a capacity for 2.5 cakes, how many eggs do you need?

112   The ratio of students and teachers in all schools of Village X** is the same. In the first school, there are 720 students and 33 teachers. In the second school, there are 960 students. How many teachers are in the second school?

113   The ratio of guitar players, piano players, and clarinet players in Compotto Schools of Music is 35 : 22 : 15. Lintoppo's largest school has 3,600 students. How many students play a clarinet?

114   The ratio of decorative grass, roses, and edible plants' areas in a botanical garden is 41 : 91 : 63. The grass and edible plants combined cover 12 acres. What is the area used for the roses?

Section 25.4 Percent Picture-Problems

Ezra, difficult percent-problems usually present two challenges. First, it is not simple to make a comprehensive visual model. Second, translating the model into algebraic language can be difficult. Section 25.4 will concentrate on the second of the challenges.

You mean, in this Section, we will translate pictures into equations?

We will analyze how to <u>improve percent visual-models</u> and then translate them into algebraic language.

Simple Picture-Problem

Add implicit information to the picture and translate it into algebraic language. Then, solve the problem.

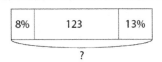

$$123 \quad - \quad 79\%$$
$$x \quad - \quad 100\%$$

$$\frac{x}{123} = \frac{100}{79}$$
$$x = 155\frac{55}{79}$$

Answer: $x = 155\frac{55}{79}$.

First, I substituted a question mark with x. Then, I wrote a number, 100%, to show what value represents a whole. Also, I added information regarding percentage in the middle compound. Together, the *visual model improvements* allowed me to create a proportion and lead to solving the problem.
Below, I will present another example, the *Change* picture problem.

Change Picture-Problem

Improve the picture and translate it into algebraic language. Solve the problem.

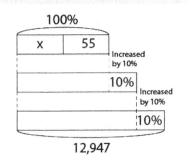

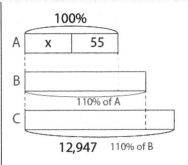

<u>*Algebraic Organizer*</u>:
$$A = x + 55$$
$$B = 1.1 \cdot (x + 55)$$
$$C = 1.1 \cdot 1.1 \cdot (x + 55) = 12,947$$

$$x = ?$$

<u>Solution</u>:　$1.1 \cdot 1.1 \cdot (x + 55) = 12.947$

$$x + 55 = \frac{12,947}{1.21} = 10,700$$
$$x = 10,700 - 55 = 10,645$$

Answer: $x = 10,645$.

First, Stella, you inserted parameters *A*, *B*, and *C*. Then, instead of the phrases "increased by 10%," you added new labels, 110% *of A* and 110% *of B*.

Sure, Ezra. Such picture-problems do not have meaning by themselves. They are valid only as a bridge toward real problems. However, any *picture problem* represents a real situation in an abridged form. To demonstrate this, I will present the *Change* problem, which will add sense to the picture-problem above.

Change Problem for Adding Sense

The first year, an electric bill for a big corporation, besides everything else, included a village voluntary tax of $55. What was the non-voluntary part of the bill during the first year if electric spending increased annually (yearly) by 10% and the total bill for the third year was 12,947 dollars?

I agree, Stella, picture problems are useful. But I'd prefer to solve real problems.... I think, soon I will be ready to solve *normal* problems with percent.

Summary

To solve picture problems, add implicit information. For any picture problem, a real problem can be created.

(1) *Improve the following picture problems:*

a)

b)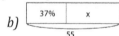

c)

d)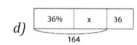

(2) *Create a word problem, which will result in the* Simple Picture *problem from this section.*

115   Redraw the picture problems in a more explicit way. Use red color to draw additional lines or add numbers. Then, solve the problems.

a)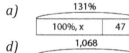

b)

c)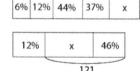

d)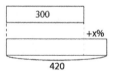

e)

f)

116   For the two pictures below, create story problems with given measurable attributes and measuring units. Draw an improved picture and solve the problems. *(a)* Use salary as a measurable attribute and dollars as units of measure. *(b)* Use volume as a measurable attribute and milliliters as units of measure. Find *y*.   (a)

(b)

117   *Make a picture-problem, which clearly describes the problem below. Solve the problem.*
A store prepared plums, apples, and pears for delivery. Plums and pears contributed to 8 and 14%, respectively, of the delivery weight. The weight of apples was 120 kg. What was the total weight of the delivery?

Section 25.5 Challenging Problems with Percent

Ezra, after you have practiced with percentage pictures for a while, will you be able to solve some challenging percentage problems?

Now, I can solve ANY percentage problems.

Do not be so shy, Ezra. Challenge can be quite different....
For the super-challenging problems, you can use a *two-picture strategy*:
   A. Create a freestyle model.
   B. Draw a detailed length-box model displaying all explicit and implicit information.
   C. Generate equations and solve the problem.
The *Mixture* problem will exemplify this strategy.

A. Freestyle Model for the *Mixture* Problem

When 20 ml of a solution from a red cup were added to 100 ml of a solution from a blue cup, the resulting solution had 12.5% sugar. When 60 ml from the red cup were combined with 30 ml from the blue cup, the concentration of sugar was 14%. Find the sugar content for the red and blue cups.

It is assumed: Z ml of sugar dissolved in P ml of water produces $(Z + P)$ ml of the solution.

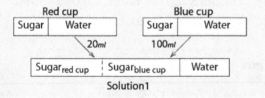
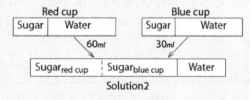

Freestyle model demonstrates how the first and second solutions were obtained using the liquid from the red and blue cups.

Stella, the problem doesn't have the word, *water*. However, your pictures do.

Ezra, problems involving mixtures frequently do not mention the main component of a solution. In these problems, usually, sugar, salt, or something similar is added to water or other liquid.

I see, now. Free style presentation helped me to make sense of the problem.

Only after you deeply understand problems, you are ready to draw a detailed visual representation. But first, you must define parameters and abbreviations:

B. Length-Box Representation for the *Mixture* Problem

$x\%$ and $y\%$ means percent content of sugar in red and blue cups.
S_R and S_B mean the volume of sugar from the red and blue cups.
W means volume of water or other liquid in the red and blue cups.

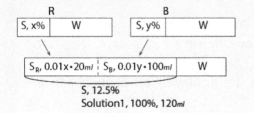 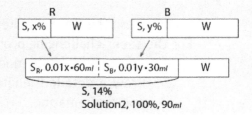

Ezra, it is great you used the word <u>volume</u> to emphasize the measurable attributes for the values in this problem.

From the picture follows, $20ml$ of $x\%$ sugar solution combined with $100ml$ of $y\%$ sugar solution creates Solution 1.
So, Solution 1 contains $0.01x \cdot 20ml + 0.01y \cdot 100ml$ of sugar.

You are correct, Ezra. Solution 2, in its turn, contains $0.01x \cdot 60ml + 0.01y \cdot 30ml$ of sugar. This information can be presented as a system of equations:

C.   Equations and Solution for the *Mixture* Problem

$0.01x \cdot 20ml + 0.01y \cdot 100ml = 12.5 \cdot 0.01 \cdot 120ml$

$0.01x \cdot 60ml + 0.01y \cdot 30ml = 14 \cdot 0.01 \cdot 90ml$

_____

$x =?, [\%]\ \ y =?, [\%]$

$\begin{cases} 20x + 100y = 12.5 \cdot 120 \\ 60x + 30y = 14 \cdot 90 \end{cases}$

$\begin{cases} 2x + 10y = 150 \\ 2x + y = 42 \end{cases}$

$9y = 108;\ y = 12$ and $x = 21 - 0.5y = 15.$

Answer: Red cup has 15% sugar. Blue cup has 12% sugar.

Stella, the *Mixture* problem was quite challenging. However, the pictures helped me understand the problem and create equations.

Generally, a two-picture strategy is highly beneficial when a percentage problem is difficult or involves changes. For easier problems, a single visual representation is sufficient. Students must estimate the level of difficulty for the problems and utilize either the *one-picture* or *two-picture* strategy.

Summary

When needed, use the two-picture strategy: free style visual presentation and detailed visual model.

   (1) The drawing represents a freestyle or another type of a visual model?
(2) Use the two-picture strategy to solve the following problem:
From a bottle of wine, one teaspoon was added to a bottle of water.

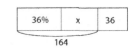

Then, from the bottle of water, one teaspoon was *returned* to the bottle of wine. Each bottle has 50 teaspoons of liquid. The final concentration of wine in each of the bottles is *98.04 and 1.96%*, respectively. *Justify the answer.*

118-127   *Solve the problems below. For challenging problems, use the two-picture strategy.*

118   A company sold 22 boxes of a new product for $408 per box with a loss of 4%. How much did the company lose on the new product?

119   Selling a container of books individually made $1,050 in revenue at 25% profit. What was the cost of the container of books?

120   Girls make 37% of the number of all students in the school. There are 286 more boys in the school than girls. How many students are in the school in total?

121   What was the initial cost of a dress if after a 50% discount and an additional 30% price reduction, the dress was sold for $22.47? The price includes 7% sales tax.

122   The raisins obtained in drying some grapes amount to 32% of the total weight of the grapes. What quantity of grapes must we take to obtain 2 kg of raisins?[1]

123   Find the weight of a drone. Its frame weighs 104 grams. The battery weighs $\frac{3}{8}$ of the whole weight of the drone. The weight of each of the 4 motors is $\frac{1}{9}$ of the weight of the drone.

124   Conchita wrote a book and spent $138,200 to print 60,000 copies in Thailand. Conchita plans to sell her book on an online store, which will advertise her book. She must pay 70% from the selling price to the online store, and $7,000 for postal expenses and customs. What must be the selling price of one book if the author wants a profit of $1 per book?

125   Saline water contains 5% (by volume) salt. How much fresh water should be added to 40 *liters* of sea water for it to contain 1% salt?

126   *Sales tax is not taken into account in this problem.*
A store sold a pair of boots and a pair of sandals for $56. The boots were sold with a 20% price reduction. The sandals were sold with a 60% price reduction. Before the sale, the price would be $29 higher. What was the price of the boots before the price reduction?

127   Two solutions were combined to make 200 ml of saline water with 13% salt. How much of each solution was added? It is known the first solution had 150 parts per thousand of salt and the second solution had 5% content of salt.

---

[1] Problems taken from N. Antonov et. al. Problems in Elementary Mathematics for Home Study, Translated from Russian by L. Levant, MIR Publishers, Moscow, 1974, p. 40.

Section 25.6 From Find-the-Number to Real Life

Ezra, this section will summarize our path toward real-life problems. *Soft Algebra* builds a pyramid of problem-solving knowledge. You already solved number problems, picture problems, textbook-type problems, and... tones of half-problems.

The chart below summarizes the structure of the *pyramid* and discusses real-life problems. The goal of *Soft Algebra* is to prepare you for life challenges.

Training Problems *versus* Real-Life Problems

Number & Picture Problems	Numbers and math operations. Pictures with some numbers.
Half-Problems	Numbers, minimal amount of text.
Textbook-Type Problems with and without Reality Constraints	Numbers and some text. Some problems contain *hidden* (implicit) information.
Long Problems with Mixed Data and Extra Information	Numbers, a lot of text including a lot of irrelevant information.
Textbook-Type Problems with Insufficient Information	Numbers and some text. Some information must be searched and added from the Internet. Students are guided to do so.
Real-Life Problems	Includes all features listed above. In addition, these are high-stake, time-sensitive problems with real-life constraints. Real-life problems frequently have insufficient information and require searching for additional information.

Solving <u>real</u> problems involves reviewing infinite amount of information. Sometimes, we are unaware that there is a problem until we fail to solve it. For example, it takes us a lifetime to learn that the *"To be or not to be..."* problem was not solved in a perfect way.

Stella, you are getting too-o-o philosophical.

Besides the regular challenges, real-life problems have the following features:
1. <u>High-stakes</u> and <u>time-sensitivity</u>.
2. <u>Real-life constraints</u>.
3. Not sufficient information or, by other words, <u>incomplete data</u>.

Real-Life Problems: Main Features

High-stakes and time-sensitivity	These problems leave no room for error. For example, doctors must find a correct diagnosis <u>today</u>. Also, drivers must avoid an accident <u>now</u>.
Real-life constraints	In these problems, reality must be taken into account. An architect considers the weather and seismic conditions of a given area and only then builds a house. Before prescribing a treatment, the doctor checks the patient's list of allergies.
Incomplete data	Some problems do not have all the data necessary for solving problems. Problem-solvers must skillfully use open sources searching for additional information.

Stella, in *Soft Algebra*, we do not have a high-stake time-sensitive environment. Nobody dies or loses a limb if I don't solve a problem.

 You are correct. However, you might pretend your life depends on solving the last problems in this book with the first attempt. If you do this, you will take the most from *Soft Algebra*—coming close to problem solving in a realistic environment.

To obtain the correct answer with the first attempt, I must check the validity of each step... Also, I must undertake steps necessary for checking the feasibility of my answers:

Checking the Feasibility of the Answers

1. Round numbers to estimate approximate answer: is it real or not?
2. Insert calculated results into the original problem.

 Approaching the final *Soft Algebra* problems as real-life problems is your choice in <u>to be or not to be a good problem-solver</u> situation.

Stella, I chose, <u>*to be*</u>!

 The current section proposes a few introductory level, real-life problems. They involve real-life constraints and might have incomplete data.

What? How can I solve problems without data?

You can use the Internet to obtain additional information. These problems will allow you to further close the gap between mathematics and real-life problem solving.

Closing the Gap Between Textbook-Type Problems and Real-Life Problems

Introductory Level Real-Life Problems include all the features of challenging word problems and, in addition...

- have real-life constraints
- might require additional information

Use Internet data to estimate real-life constraints and add needed information.

When problems talk about people, use the Internet to find humans' limitations.

What information, Stell? Phones and addresses?

In everyday life, sometimes you must find an email or postal address. Or a phone number. Solving business-related problems, you might need to know average or maximum height, life expectancy, weight range, walking or running speed, swimming speed, etc.

But if a problem talks about a black puma or a butterfly?

Then, use the Internet to find more about pumas. Or butterflies.

I think I got the point.

The problems in this section as well as in the final review will have problems of various levels of difficulty. The problem will involve many of the topics covered in *Soft Algebra*. You must determine when to use the Internet.

Stella, I think in *Soft Algebra*, I'm already used to expect unexpectable...and pivot if needed.

Ezra, concluding the course, I want to wish you and other students to become excellent problem-solvers and successfully solve challenging problems in exciting novel situations.

Summary

Always check the feasibility of your answers. Some problems in this section require using the Internet.

Provide lower and upper limits for each possible answer. Can all these problems be realistic?
(1) Tanya is 3 times as tall as Lenny. How tall is Lenny?   *(2)* How long can a turtle live?
(3) Lily carries a bucket of water. Nadine has a gallon of water in her bucket. This makes one percent of what Lily carries. How much water does Lily carry?

128-133 *Solve the problems using the best approaches and the Internet when needed. Present your work.*

128   How much water from the Dead Sea and the surface of the Black Sea must be combined to obtain the same salinity as the Red Sea? *Calculate your answer to the nearest percent.*

129   Find the product of the first and the fifth numbers if the absolute value of the first number is one-half of the third number. The third number has the same absolute value as the second number, but the opposite sign. The first number is the sum of -3 and -2. The fourth number is the average between the second and the third numbers. The fifth number is six less than the fourth number.

130   Mr. Karandash loves painting and plans to draw a picture on the wall. The area of his picture will be 9×3 ft^2. He copies a picture from a well-known piece of art. Mr. Karandash wants to paint 22% of his picture with gold paint and the remainder with several other colors.
   a) How much gold paint does he need if 100% of the picture would require 3.05 g of gold paint?
   b) Mr. Karandash has 4 g of silver paint. To color one square inch with silver, he needs 4 mg of silver paint. What part of Mr. Karandash's picture (in percent) can be covered with the silver color?
   c) Mr. Karandash has 2.16 g of green paint. Each square inch colored green requires 3 mg of green paint. What part of Mr. Karandash's picture (in percent) can be covered with green paint?
   d) What is the maximum number of square feet that can be completely covered by Mr. Karandash's gold, silver, and green paints?

131   Eleven grams of gold were extracted from 250 kg of gold ore, originating somewhere in the U.S.
   (a) What percentage of gold did the ore contain? *(b)* How much money can you receive if you sell the gold on today's market? *(c)* Was it high gold content ore or not? *Justify your response. (d)* Do you have an idea where the ore originated from?

132   In a pentagon, four sides have the same length, and the fifth side is 6 cm longer than the others. The perimeter of the pentagon is 67 cm. What is the length of the longest side?

133   Fog Factory took an order, which it planned to fulfill in 2 weeks and one day. The engineers of Drum Factory informed the media they can fulfill the same order in 1 week and 5 days. Both factories have similar technologies and work without breaks, 24/7.
   a) How fast can the order be fulfilled if the two factories were working together?
   b) Provide an example of an order that can lead to the shortest-time answer.
   c) What kind of order can lead to the longest-time answer?
   d) Provide an example of an order that results in an intermediate time.
   Round your answers to the nearest hours.

Final Review

Below, I will list 42 problem-solving techniques taught in *Soft Algebra*. To further increase your problem-solving abilities, after solving the review problems, take an enrichment class, *Soft Algebra PLUS*. However, if you are eager to faster progress in math rather than in problem solving, start Algebra.

The Complete List of Problem-Solving Techniques from *Soft Algebra*

1. Extract data

2. Chunk text

3. Make a Prep

4. Compose math-focused sentences

5. Organize data entries

6. Create a Time & Change Organizer

7. Use auxiliary elements in a text Organizer

8. Initialize constraint-bookkeeping

9. Use a *d-t-v* Approach to organize data

10. Use auxiliary elements to organize a geometry problem

11. Chunk geometry problem

12. Use addition of parts and subtraction to increase symmetry of a geometry problem

13. Use shuffling to increase symmetry of a geometry problem

14. Create a simple Algebraic Organizer

15. Use logical conversion as part of an Algebraic Organizer

16. Use mapping as part of an Algebraic Organizer

17. Design talking parameters

18. Use overlapping parameters to describe complex data sets

19. Use time coordinates as indices for parameters in change-problems

20. Present the Algebraic Organizer in a form of proportion

21. Present the Algebraic Organizer using the Ratio-of-Elements Approach

22. Present the Algebraic Organizer using the Ratio-of-Groups Approach

23. Use the Unit-Block Approach in problems involving ratios, percentages, and parts

24. Look at the presentation and solution of a problem through "alien eye"

25. Design a Simple Discrete Model

26. Design a Bug Model for problems with combinations

27. Create a Time-Line Model

28. Construct a Time-Plane Model

29. Draw a Line-Segment Model

30. Draw an Area-Box Model

31. Draw a Length-Box Model

32. Graph on a number line

33. Graph on a Descartes coordinate plane

34. Design a Freestyle Model

35. Use a Visual Model for a ratio problem

36. Construct graphs for d-t-v problems

37. Draw a Comparison Organizer

38. Design a Down-Scaling Model—reduce the amplitudes of numbers

39. Design an Up-Scaling Model—increase the amplitudes of numbers

40. Design an Approximation Model

41. Design a Singleton Model

42. Use auxiliary element in a form of x, y, z, or alike to design algebraic equations

Stell, in Part E we covered only one problem-solving technique, the technique about x, y, z, and equations. Correct?

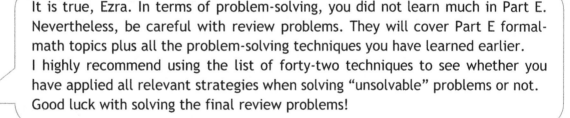

It is true, Ezra. In terms of problem-solving, you did not learn much in Part E. Nevertheless, be careful with review problems. They will cover Part E formal-math topics plus all the problem-solving techniques you have learned earlier.
I highly recommend using the list of forty-two techniques to see whether you have applied all relevant strategies when solving "unsolvable" problems or not.
Good luck with solving the final review problems!

Summary

Remember your problem-solving techniques and calculation strategies.

(1) *From the list of the techniques, choose the ten techniques that you found exceptionally useful. Start from the techniques that you prefer the most.*

(2) *List five* Soft Algebra *problems that are memorable for you.*

(3) *What problem-solving skills did you improve when studying* Soft Algebra*?*

Equations, Graphs, and Half-Problems

E1   There are five numbers. The second and fourth numbers are the same. The fifth and first numbers are the same, and the first and second numbers are the same. The third number is not greater than the second number and is not less than the fourth number. The sum of the first and third numbers is negative twelve. What is the product of the third number and seven?

E2   There are three numbers. The first number increased by $8\frac{1}{3}\%$ is as much less than the second number as the second number is less than the triple of the third. If we will decrease the first number by $16\frac{2}{3}\%$, it will be as less than the second number as the second number is less than 27, which is 237.5% greater than the third number. Find the sum the three numbers.

E3   There are four numbers. The sum of the first and second numbers is equal to the additive inverse of the sum of the third and fourth numbers. What is the sum of all four numbers?

E4   There are three positive integers. Their sum is 21. The second number is the same as the third number. The first number is one digit less than the second number. What is the first number?

E5   *Solve the equations below. Show the steps.*
    a) $x(x-4) \div x + \frac{1}{4}(8-4x) = -2;$ b) $240x - 360(2x-8) = 2{,}400x - 720;$
    c) $x \cdot (x-1) \cdot x = x \cdot (x-1) \cdot 2;$ d) $4(-1+3x) = x \cdot (6-2x) - x(-x-6).$

E6   There are four numbers, which have a product of zero. The second number is twice as large as the third. The third number is a multiple of five, has two digits, and is the least of all two-digit multiples of 5. The first number is 20 less than the third number. You have sufficient information to find the fourth number. What is the sum of these four numbers?

E7   Solve the following equations. Then, check your answers by substituting them into the equations.
    a) $\frac{8x}{x-1} + \frac{6x}{1-x} = \frac{2}{x-1};$ b) $3x - 7(8x-9) - 0.3x = 34 - 33x.$

E8   There are three numbers. The first and second numbers are the same. The third number is the product of five and seven, and 5 less than the first number. What is the product of these three numbers?

E9   There are four numbers. The sum of the first and second numbers is the same as the product of the last two numbers. The first and second numbers have the same absolute value, although they are not the same and their difference is sixteen. The fourth number is not the greatest number, although it is the product of the second number and eleven. Find the numbers.

E10   There are two numbers. The first number is less than the second number and the difference between the numbers is 84% less than their sum. What percent of the second number does the first number make? Find an exact answer.

E11   The sum of two numbers is 204. Each number has exactly two digits. What are they?

E12   There are four numbers. The second number is a negative, even, two-digit number and greater than −25. The fourth and third numbers are made from the digits of the second number and are positive. The first number is the product of the fourth and third numbers. All numbers are different. The third number has the least absolute value, and the second number has the greatest absolute value. Identify all these numbers.

E13   A point M revolves around a circle with radius one. It begins its motion at point $(1,0)$. Construct a graph to show how a quotient of y and x coordinates of M depends on the angle of rotation. We consider the angle of rotation at point $(1,0)$ to be zero. *Use a calculator to calculate the quotient.*

E14   There are five numbers. The first number is one-half the third number. The third number has the same absolute value as the second number but is not the same number. The first number is the least common multiple of 56 and 3680. The fourth number is the average between the second and third numbers. The fifth number is one-eighth of the third number taken to the seventh power. Find the product of these five numbers.

E15   There are seven numbers. It is known the fifth, sixth, and seventh numbers may form a set of consecutive integers. The sum of the first and seventh numbers is not a negative integer; however, it is not a prime or composite number either. The first number is the additive inverse of the greatest common factor of 48 and 24. The sixth number is the greatest of all seven numbers. The second number is five less than the average of the first and seventh numbers. The third number is three less than the fourth number and five more than the second number.

   (a) What are all the numbers? *(b)* How many solutions can you find?

E16   *Solve the equations below. Show the steps.*

   (a) $-2^3 \cdot x^2 = 4(x^2 - 30) + 12;$ *(b)* $7{,}325 \cdot 2^x - 326 \cdot 2^x = 10^3 \cdot 7 \div 2^{-x} - 16.$

E17   There are five numbers. The second number is as big as the first number added three times. The third number is one less than the first number. The fourth number is twice as big as the fifth number. The difference between the first and fifth numbers is 42. The fifth number is 31. *(a)* What is the sum of these five numbers? *(b)* How many answers did you find?

E18   The third and second numbers are two-digit numbers with the same pair of digits. In a mirror, the second number looks like the reflection of the third number. What is the first number if it is greater than the tens value in the third number but one less than the tens value in the second number?

E19   In mathematics, there are many interesting functions. A floor function, $Floor(x)$ or $\lfloor x \rfloor$ and a ceiling function, $Ceiling(x)$ or $\lceil x \rceil$ are two of them.

   If $y = \lfloor x \rfloor$, then for all integer x, $y = x$. However, for all fractional x, y remains an integer; $\lfloor x \rfloor$ equals the smallest preceding integer. For example, $\lfloor 3 \rfloor = 3$, $\lfloor 3.1 \rfloor = 3$, $\lfloor 3.5 \rfloor = 3$, and $\lfloor 3.99 \rfloor = 3$, but $\lfloor 4.1 \rfloor = 4$ as well as $\lfloor 4.9 \rfloor = 4$. In other words, $\lfloor x \rfloor$ is the largest integer less than or equal to x. For the ceiling function, $\lceil x \rceil$ is the smallest integer greater than or equal to x.

   (a) Find three numbers, where the first number is $\lceil 1.3 \rceil$, the second number is $\left\lfloor -1\frac{1}{3} \right\rfloor$, and the third number is $\left\lceil -1\frac{1}{3} \right\rceil$.

   (b) Draw a graph, $y = \lfloor x \rfloor$ for x-es from -6 to 6.

   (c) Draw a graph, $y = \lceil x \rceil$ for x-es from -6 to 6.

   (d) Draw a graph, $y = \lfloor x \rfloor^2 - 20$ for $x = -6$ to 6.

   For the b, c, and d parts of the problem, you might need to review Part C Exploration.

E20   There are four numbers. The sum of the first and second numbers is the same as the product of the last two numbers. The first and second numbers have the same absolute values, although they are not the same and their difference is eighteen. The fourth number is greater than all the other numbers and three times the second number.

   (a) Find the product of all four numbers. *(b)* Find all the numbers.

E21   There are three numbers. The sum of the third number and twice the second number is the same as the first number and triple $665\frac{1}{3}$. How big is the third number if all the numbers are three-digit numbers and the first two numbers are the same? How many solutions did you find?

F22   The sum of two non-equivalent positive integers is 72. Both or one of the two digits, which were used to create the first number, were used to make the second number. No other digits were used. What is the difference between these two numbers? Is your solution unique? Prove your answer.

E23   The product of two numbers is 48 and the first number is a multiple of 2, 3, and 6, and less than 20. The second number is greater than the first. What is the sum of these two numbers?

E24   In the following pattern, the last number is 199. How many numbers are there? 20, 26, 32, 38, 44, 50, 54, ...

E25   There is the list with 5 numbers. Each is $\sqrt[3]{81}$ greater than the previous number. *(a)* Find the first of these numbers if the middle number is $\sqrt[3]{1,029}$. *(b)* Provide two vocabulary words that characterize the list of the numbers.

E26   There are three numbers. The second number is 8 less than negative two. The third number is the GCF of 8 and 12. The first number is the average of the other two numbers. What is the product of the first and second numbers?

E27   Draw the following two graphs:

       (a) For $x = [-8; 0]$, $|y| = 8 + x$;   *(b)* $x^2 + y^2 = 64$
         For $x = (0; 8]$, $|y| = 8 - x$.

Regular Problems

Use the best approaches to solve the problems. Present all your work. Use the Internet when needed.

E28-29   *Solve the following two problems. These two problems contain made-up words.*

E28   When a donk borks at 48% of his capacity, he makes 960 gonji per day. When the day is windy, donks bork at their full capacity. How many gonji does a donk make when he borks on a windy day?

E29   When a donk swims, 3% of his body produces bisecols. With the 7 bisecols he produces, he can easily reach the other side of River Jokoo (width – 100m).

    (a) How many bisecols does a donk need to cross the 300 m wide River Jojokoo, if the amount of bisecols that a donk needs to cross the river is proportional to the width of the river?

    (b) Is it sufficient to use 30 bisecols to cross the 400 m wide River Jojojokoo?

    (c) When a donk is doing his push-ups, his body produces 42 bisecols. What percent of the body does not produce bisecols during push-ups?

E30   **Dany's Problem:** Glenbow Park* has a three-gallon pond called "Mozaika." Five frogs live there and demand a larger habitat. They asked you to increase the area of the bottom by 6 sq. feet leaving the depth unchanged. You want to know the depth, but no one knows it. You know a 3 square-foot pond of the same depth as Mozaika contains 6 gallons of water. How much water will the frogs have in Mozaika after remodeling?

———————————————

* The problem was contributed by Dany Kofman when he was in 3rd grade.

E31 There are three ribbons: yellow, pink, and blue. The ribbons are placed one after another to form a circle with a radius of 60 cm. The pink ribbon's length makes one-third of the yellow ribbon's length. The blue ribbon has the same length as one-half of the combined length of the pink and yellow ribbons. What is the length of the blue ribbon?

E32 A tree swallow starts flying at $t = 0$ and flies for 20 seconds. The bird's coordinates change as $x_{sw}(t) = 1.2t$ and $y_{sw}(t) = 3.6t - 0.18t^2$. Meanwhile, a dragonfly, a fly, a moth, and a bee fly nearby. The insects' coordinates change the following way:

$x_{dr}(t) = 24 - 1.2t$ and $y_{dr}(t) = 16 + 0.3t$;

$x_{fly}(t) = 32 - 2t$ and $y_{fly}(t) = 2t - 2$;

$x_{moth}(t) = 0.5t - 2$ and $y_{moth}(t) = 7.8 + 0.1t$

$x_{bee}(t) = 1.7t - 9$ and $y_{bee}(t) = 0.54t - 3.24$.

In all the functions, t is measured in seconds while x and y coordinates are measured in meters. Find what insects if any can be snaped by the swallow and when. Use graphs to better explain your solution.

E33 A company has a gold mine. In September 2009, the mine had 1,000,000 ounces of gold underground, while the price of the gold above the ground was about 1,000 dollars per ounce. The production cost of the gold in this mine is 850,000,000 dollars.

(*a*) How much can the mine make over its lifetime, if the price of gold does not change? By what percentage does the profit change, if the gold price (*b*) rises by 20% or (*c*) drops by 20%? *Consider a simplified situation–all gold mine production as well as price change occurs in one day.*

E34 There are 300 windows in a building on Sdomton Boulevard. Each window has a 30 by 70 in. frame. Ms. Kulkin must paint 42% of the windows in this house. It takes her about 30 seconds to paint a 10-in. section of the frame.

a) How many windows will she paint?

b) How many yards of frame must she paint?

c) How much time will it take for Ms. Kulkin to complete her work if every time she walks from one window to another window, it takes her 1 minute?

E35 Twelve days ago Samantha returned from Mexico, where she spent her vacation. Today, she and her new 4-woman crew are setting tables for 1,200 people who have reservations for a conference starting at 5 p.m. Reservations were made 2 months ago. If, besides a couple of big tables which hold 16 people each, and two pairs of medium tables which fit 12 people each, all other tables can fit 8 people, what is the minimum number of tables the girls must have? Besides tables for the guests, the girls must move one table to the stage for speakers to use for their notes.

E36 There is a round table within a completely symmetrical round room. Ten wizards came to the room and sat around the table on 10 identical chairs. How many ways of achieving this can you find? Seven of the wizards are identical septuplets.

E37 There is an open storage tank containing 2,000 kg of fresh water. A tourist accidently dumps 850 milliliters of Dead Sea water into the tank. Is the water in the reservoir still suitable for *(a)* drinking and *(b)* agriculture? *Calculate your answers to the nearest thousandth of a percent.*

E38   Find the areas for the figures, Gold Necklace and Warm Mitten, to the nearest one-hundredth. *For calculations, use approximation, $\pi = 3.14$. Show your steps.*

Gold Necklace

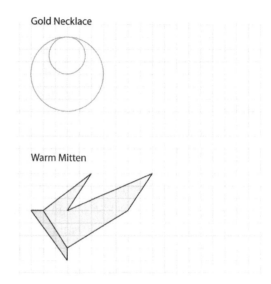

Warm Mitten

E39   What is the perimeter of the triangle if its sides are 3 in, 25 mm, and 4¼ cm long?

E40   If the area of a rectangle is increased by 44%, by how many percent will its length increase, if *(a)* the ratio between the sides remains the same? *(b)* the width will remain the same? *(c)* the length and width will be increased by the same percentage?

E41   On each side of a right triangle, a square was built the following way. One side of each square is the side of the triangle. The area of the square built on the hypotenuse makes 10% of the area of a pink star which is drawn nearby. The area of one of the other two square makes 3.6% of the star's area. What is the area of the star if the area of the triangle is 13.2 cm^2?

E42   On the Moon, one day in respect to the Sun is about 27.3 Earth days. For this problem, we will set the Moon time as following: one day on the Moon has 24 Moon hours, one Moon hour has 60 Moon minutes, and one Moon minute has 60 Moon seconds. When a dragonfly flies on a Moon-station with the speed of 380 meters per Moon second, what is the speed in kilometers per Earth hour? *Round your answer to the nearest integer.*

E43   In 1997, Shelli's annual salary was 35,000 dollars. In 1998, her salary increased by 12% and in 1999, the salary increased by an additional $3,920. For 2000, she was given a choice of four options.
        Option 1. To receive the same annual increase as for 1998 (in percent).
        Option 2. To receive the same increase of salary as for 1999 (in percent).
        Option 3. To receive the same increase of salary as in 1998 (in dollars).
        Option 4. To receive the same increase of salary as in 1999 (in dollars).
            (a) What is the highest increase possible? Express your answer in dollars.
            (b) What option is the worst? Express your answer in dollars.

E44   The ratio of students with freckles to students without freckles in a school is 1 to 72, while the ratio of boys to girls is 3 to 2. If the school has 6 girls with freckles, how many boys without freckles attend this school? The ratio of boys with freckles to girls with freckles is the same ratio as between all girls and boys.

E45   Andy* Rabbit has a whole lot of carrots. Bunny Rabbit has twelve fewer bunches of carrots. Cassie Rabbit is only beginning to collect for the winter. She has 20 fewer bunches than Bunny. Dragon Rabbit is a pro—she has 40 bunches of carrots more than Cassie and 8 more than Andy. Young Baby Rabbit just collected his first carrot bunch, and we are all immensely proud. However, Sensei Rabbit has them all beat with a total of one hundred bunches. This is 23 bunches more than Dragon Rabbit. Andy Rabbit wants to collect as many as Sensei, so how many bunches fewer does he have than Sensei Rabbit? *The solution may be easier than you think.*

---

* Problem is contributed by Oleg Ostrovskiy. March 2016.

E46 How old are my sons? If I add the ages of all my children, I will calculate 39 years. If I subtract the age of my youngest daughter from the age of my oldest son and then subtract the age of my youngest son, I will obtain a sum of the number of my sons plus eleven. If I multiply your age times the age of my oldest daughter, I will obtain zero. My second son is four years younger than my oldest son, and average age of my sons is 13 years. *All ages are expressed in integer numbers.*

E47 *I heard this story from a man who lived in the former USSR....*

When Michael became the director of a small plant, he was given a "plan" – a rigid requirement from his socialistic government. Michael was told he had one year to increase the plant's production by 5%. Also, he was ordered to decrease energy usage by 5%.

The plant produced goods requiring machinery, and the machinery needed energy. Production was based on using energy. Meanwhile, funds for technology renovation were not provided.

Michael's plant used about 1 million kilowatts (energy units) in one year. Increasing production by 5% meant the plant would need to use 5% more energy than previously—so, increasing production while decreasing energy consumption was not possible unless the technology was completely changed, which was not an option.

Fortunately, Michael had a friend in the Ministry of Energy. Michael asked the friend to help him obtain extra energy resources in an unofficial way. Michael's friend helped—and Michael could report to his bosses a 5% growth in production and a 5% economy in energy. No one found that he used unofficially obtained extra energy to achieve this.

Thus, as it was believed he used 5% less energy than the first year, the next year he again was required to reduce energy consumption by 5% while increasing production by 5%. His friend helped him again. And again. And again. For several years, this trick worked, since Michael's friend cared about Michael and his plant, and could provide "unaccounted" energy. How many years will it take for the plant use more "unofficial" energy than "official" energy?

E48 A velocity is 5 km/hr. If it increases by 20%, by how much (in percentage) will the trip time decrease? Will your answer hold for any velocity? *Prove your point.*

E49 Peter knew he needed to obtain at least a C in all subjects to participate in sports. In mathematics, this means his performance must be at least 75%. However, at the end of the semester, his grade average was D. Peter already submitted all his homework, which accounted for 300 points and had already taken the 4 quizzes, where he obtained a total (220) of 400 points because could not solve some of the problems. *(a)* What is the minimal percentage Peter must obtain on the final test to receive a C for the semester? The last test is 300 points in total and summarizes all semester materials. *Round up your answer to the nearest integer percent.* *(b)* What is the chance Peter will receive a C for the semester? *Explain your point.*

E50 Stella took a 7-day course in drone-flying and obtained average scores of 80 during the seven days. Each day it was possible to receive a maximum score of 100 points. Particularly, she received 56 points on Monday, 82 points on Tuesday, 70 points on Thursday, 97 points on Friday, and 90 points on Saturday. The scores on Wednesday and Sunday were unclear, since the paper with her scores got wet under the rain and smudged. However, Stella remembered her Wednesday score was made of the same digits as her Sunday score. Also, she remembered, the score on Wednesday was at least 10 points lower than on Sunday. What score did Stella receive on Wednesday and Sunday?

E51 Jose bought 6 bunches of bananas, 5 lbs of apples, and 4 lbs of pears. The price of 1 lb of apples was $27\frac{3}{11}$% higher than that for 1 lb of pears. If the total price of bananas and apples was $29.70 higher than the total price of bananas, and the total price of all the purchases was $27.30, what was the price of one bunch of bananas?

E52 Barehanded contests* of people against bulls remained popular in Spain until 1700, when the sword was used for the first time. Since that year, of Spain's 126 champion bullfighters, one in three has died in the arena.

Since 1900, two hundred or more bullfighters have been killed in public. Juan Belmonte was gored fifty times. Born in 1917, in 1947 Manolete had three million dollars in his bank and was gored to death that same year.

> *(a)* What was the age of the bullfighter, Manolete, when he died? How many answers did you find?
>
> *(b)* In Spain, since 1700, how many champion bull-fighters have been killed in public out of ten dozen?
>
> *(c)* Did bullfighters use a sword two hundred years ago?
>
> *(d)* Did bullfighters use a sword four hundred years ago?

E53 One factory has a 20% lower efficiency than the other. The factory with lower efficiency can finish an order for 25 items in 15 days. How fast can the order be completed by the two factories when fulfilling the order together if each item must be started and finished in one place? *Find your answer to the nearest minutes.*

E54 Three culinary school students make their dishes, one dish at a time, with speeds of 15, 20, and 25 dishes per hour. The students are forbidden to have any breaks if any of them is preparing a dish. However, every time, when all of them have completed their dishes, they must have an 8-minute break to preserve work quality. The students started preparing their dishes at 9 a.m. and will finish their work at 2 p.m. How many dishes will they prepare if they will take all the required 8-minute breaks?

E55 A group of students wants to collect money for an end of semester lunch. If each student pays $7.50, there will be a shortage of $44. If each pays $8.00, there will be $44 too much. How many students plan to participate in the end of semester lunch gathering?

E56 From an 8 by 8-inch square, a cone was made using the following procedure. First, a circle with a maximum diameter was cut. Then, the circle was cut along its radius to its center and folded in such a way the resulting cone had a double wall. Separately, from another piece of paper, a smaller circle was removed to make a bottom for the cone. Afterwards, the cone and its bottom were nicely glued together. What is the area of the outside surface of the figure received at the end? *For this problem, use the following approximation: π ≈ 3.*

---

* Numbers are based on data from *Man is the Prey*. 1969, by James Clarke. Published by Stein and Day Publishers, 1969.

E57   Five students came to the math club. A teacher had a rectangular table with 5 chairs of 5 different colors around the table. A teacher asked the students to calculate all possible options of taking their seats around the table not leaving any empty chairs. The students started experimenting. However, after changing seats for a while, they decided to make a visual model for the problem. Help the students make a visual model, which can help solve the problem and find the number of possible options.

E58   A car drove from point A to point B uphill with an average speed of 56 *mph*. On the way back, the car drove downhill so its speed was, in average, 25% higher than during the uphill trip. By how many percent, the time of the downhill trip was shorter than the time of the uphill trip?

E59   A wolf spotted a rabbit a quarter mile away and started toward the rabbit. The rabbit saw the wolf almost immediately and tried to run away. However, the road was narrow, and the rabbit had no chance to side-jump. So, the wolf caught the rabbit. How much time did it take for the wolf to catch the rabbit? It is known, the distance between the animals would triple in two and a half minutes if the rabbit would start pursuing the wolf at the similar conditions.

E60   **Spider on a Wire:** There are more than five dozen line-segments in the picture below. How many line segments are there?

Short Answers and Hints

Students may use these short answers and hints to check their solutions. If the answer is incorrect, the student needs to re-read the section and attempt to solve the problem again.

Chapter 13 Digest for Chapters 1 Through 12

Quintessential Problems

AB1   *The answer has one term. The term is presented using two identical digits and no other digits at all.*

AB2   *The sum of the digits is 11.*

AB3   *Look for repetition. Uncover patterns and you will uncover some numbers. First try to find 0 and 1. Then try to understand what the letter I is.*

AB4   *Only one of the graphs is a function. There are two points of intersection.*

Part C PHYSICS-LAND

Chapter 14 Quantitative Observations

Section 14.1 Properties of Matter

1   *Height: A, D, and E. Time: C and I.*   **2**   *N/A.*

3   *Examples of qualitative observations: Age appropriate or not. The level of vocabulary in a book: high or low. Your answers might differ from those proposed here.*

4   *Examples of quantitative observations: Volume of engine and gas usage. Your answers might differ from those proposed here.*

Section 14.2 Measurable Attributes

5   *Sentence (j) provides insufficient information. Explain why.*

6   *(c) Find the <u>length (time)</u> of a day.*

7*   *The trip to the zoo was on a date which, when the month in the numeric form (numbers 1 to 12) was added with the date (1 to 31) and the year of the trip results in a total, 2019.*

8   *Define parameters and make a Prep. The answer to this problem is more than just a number. It is impossible to answer this question with an exact number without more precise information.*

9   *Parameters must have indices—days of the week. Another option: parameters are days of the week.*

Section 14.3 Quantitative Reasoning

10   *N/A.*   **11**   *The digits for the answer add up to 9.*

12   *The digits for the answer add up to 12.*   **13**   *You need to use GCF.*

Section 14.4 International System of Units: Basics

14   *The digits for the answer add to 6.*   **15**   *The answers will vary...*

16   *(b) Question (7), question (10), and there are three more. Explain why.*

Section 14.5 International System of Units in Depth

17   *(1) $58\,cm \div 100\,\frac{cm}{m} = 0.58\,m.$*   *(3) $0.02\,dm = 0.02\,m \div 10\,\frac{dm}{m} = 0.002\,m.$*

   (5) $1,960\,g \div 1,000\,\frac{g}{kg} = 1.96\,kg.$ *(7) $120s \div 60\,\frac{s}{min} = 2\,min.$*

18-19   *N/A.*   **20**   *One entry has several answers.*   **21**   *N/A.*

22   *The problem can have two possible answers for Liana's weight. The digits for one answer add up to 23 and the digits for the other answer add up to 7.*

Section 14.6 Magic-One Approach to Unit Conversion

23   (a) $1 = \frac{1,000}{kilo}$ and $1 = \frac{kilo}{1,000}$.   (c) $1 = 1,000,000 \frac{\mu g}{g}$ and $1 = 0.000001 \frac{g}{\mu g}$.

(e) $1 = 1,000,000,000 \frac{s}{Gs}$ and $1 = \frac{1}{1,000,000,000} \frac{Gs}{s}$.   (i) $1 = \frac{2a}{b}$ and $1 = \frac{b}{2a}$.

24   (a) $6\,mg = \frac{1}{1,000} \cdot 6\,g = 0.006\,g \cdot [1,000,000 micro] = 6,000\,\mu g$.

(c) $0.004\,km = 1,000 \cdot 0.004\,m = 4\,m \cdot [10\,deci] = 40\,dm$.

(e) $1,964\,g = 1,964 g \cdot [0.001 kilo] = 1.964\,kg$.   (g) $180 s = 180 s \cdot \left[\frac{1\,min}{60\,sec}\right] = 3\,min$.

25   The digits for the weight thrown over the board, when presented in grams, add up to 11.

Section 14.7 Scientific Notation

26   N/A.   **27** (a) $1.273 \cdot 10^5 mm$. (c) $9.2 \cdot 10^{17} s$.   **28**   (a) $1.25 \cdot 10^{-1}$. (c) 1.5. (e) $4 \cdot 10^{-2}$. (g) $3.6 \cdot 10^{-1}$.

Section 14.8 Introduction to Customary Units

29-30   N/A.   **31** (a) **blackberries** and **giant tomatoes**. (e) **Liquid** quart ... **dry** quart.

32   N/A.   **33** (1) $2\,mi \cdot 1,760 \frac{yd}{mi} = 3,520\,yd$.   (3) $4oz \cdot \frac{1\,lb}{16\,oz} = \frac{1}{4} lb$.   (5) $3\,tsp \cdot \frac{1\,Tbsp}{3\,tsp} = 1\,Tbsp$.

Section 14.9 Calculations Using Customary Units

34   (a) $3\,yd\,2\,ft = 3 \times 3\,ft + 2\,ft = 11\,ft = 11 \times 12\,in = 132\,in$.   **35**   N/A.

36   (a) 12 bu 2 gal 1 qt. (c) 12 Lb 12 oz. (e) 5 gal 1 qt 1 pt 1 cp.   **37**   15,010 g or 14,990 g.

Chapter 15 Units and Unit Blocks in Word Problems

Section 15.1 Unit Abbreviations

38   N/A.   **39** Answers may vary.

Section 15.2 Derived Units: Area and Volume

40   (a) $54\,m^2 = 54 \cdot 100^2 \frac{cm^2}{m^2} = 540,000 cm^2$.   (c) $0.004\,mm^2 \div 10,000 \frac{mm^2}{dm^2} = 0.0000004\,dm^2$.

41   The length of Lola's property is $100\frac{16}{41}$ yards.

42   (b) If the Bean had a cubic shape, approximately 400,000 Beans would fit into a cubic kilometer. However, the Beans are not cubic, so the answer must be adjusted.

Section 15.3 Derived Units: Objects in Groups

43   (a) $54\,st. \div 3\,cl. = 18\frac{st.}{cl.}$.   (c) $1,964\,g \div 7\,Ku. = 280\frac{4}{7}\frac{g}{Ku.}$.   **44**   N/A.

45   It is difficult to determine a precise number because people can say "a day" when it is... The exact answer might be as low as ... hours and as high as ... hours.

46   N/A.   **47** $5.2 \frac{km}{hr}$.

Section 15.4 Proportion and the Unit-Block Approach

48   N/A.

49   The problem is non-realistic because ... We can change either of two numbers (students need to identify new, "realistic" numbers) or a word.

50   3,200 dollars.   **51**   N/A.   **52**   300 mi.   **53**   N/A.

54   Copper's density is $8.96 \frac{g}{cm^3}$. Use that for your calculations.

55   When the answer is expressed in hours and minutes (p.m.), the digits of the answer add to 17. The precise answer is unrealistic and provides only a first clue. Explain why. Estimate the final answer.

Section 15.5 The Ratio-of-Elements Approach

56   Use, $b = \frac{3\,d.}{4\,c.}$, with the meaning "1.75 dogs for each cat" and $b = \frac{4\,c.}{3\,d.}$, with the meaning "4/3 of a cat for each dog" to solve the problem by applying two alternative approaches.

57   N/A.   **58**   See example in **Section 15.5**.

Section 15.6 The Ratio-of-Groups Approach

59-60   *The illustrations:*

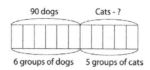

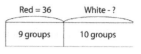

Section 15.7 Challenging Proportions and Ratios

61   *The illustration:*

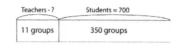

62   *The   illustration:*      **63**   *N/A.*

64   *The digits for the answer add up to 2.*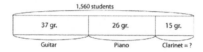

65   *The digits for the answer add up to 3.*   **66**   *N/A.*

67   *The illustration:*

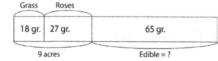

Section 15.8 Unit Conversion

68   *(c)* $55\frac{mi}{hr} = 55 \cdot \frac{1\,mi}{hr} = 55 \cdot \frac{1.6\,km}{hr} = 55 \cdot 1.6\frac{km}{hr} = 88\frac{km}{hr} = 8.8 \cdot 10\frac{km}{hr}.$

(f) $50\,s^{-1} = \frac{50}{1s} = \frac{50}{\frac{1}{3,600}hr} = 50 \cdot 3,600\frac{1}{hr} = 180,000\,hr^{-1} = 1.8 \cdot 10^5\,hr^{-1}.$

69 $v_{average} \approx 31\frac{m}{s}.$

Chapter 16 Elements of Kinematics
Section 16.1 Constant Velocity

70   *N/A.*   **71**   *The second driver lives 96 km (or 60 mi) closer to Lake on the Moon than the first driver.*

72   *Cindy spent 1 hour and 53 minutes in total on her trip.*

Section 16.2 Freestyle Model

73   *The fishermen will meet at 2:08 p.m.*

Section 16.3 Constructing *v(t)* Graphs

74   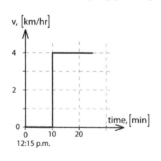   **75-76**   *N/A.*   **77**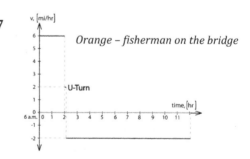

Orange – fisherman on the bridge

Section 16.4 Discussing *d(t)* Graphs

78   *Monday: Landon travelled from home toward school with a speed of $v_1 = 6\frac{km}{hr}$ for 20 minutes. Then, for 10 minutes, he travelled towards school with a higher speed, $v_2 = 24\frac{km}{hr}$, and arrived at the school at 8:30 a.m. Wednesday: Landon was home at 8 a.m. and started moving towards school with a speed, $v_1 = 18\frac{km}{hr}$. As soon as he arrived at school, he started to return home with a speed of $v_2 = 24\frac{km}{hr}$. He arrived home at 8:30.*

Section 16.5 Constructing *d(t)* Graphs

79

80   *N/A.*   **81**   *Show two different velocities on a graph.*

82

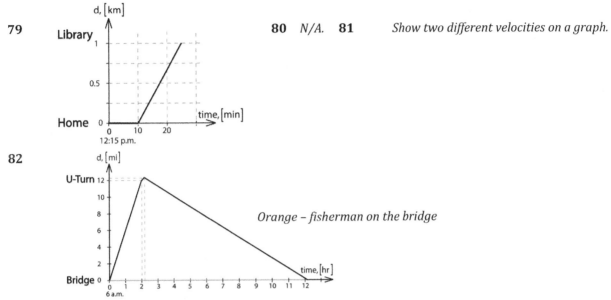

Orange – fisherman on the bridge

Section 16.6 The *d-t-v* Approach

83   *Three telephone companies proposed the following payments plans.*

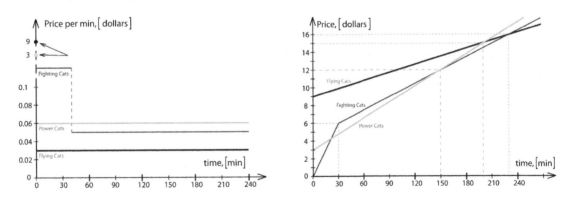

Price for 1 Hour a Month	$d_{A1} = 9d. + 0.03 \cdot 60d. = 9d. + 1.8d. = 10.8d.$
	$d_{B1} = 3d. + 0.06 \cdot 60d. = 3d. + 3.6d. = 6.6d.$ *the best deal*
	$d_{C1} = 0.2 \cdot 30d. + 0.05 \cdot 30d. = 6d. + 1.5d. = 7.5d.$

Calculations demonstrate, for 1 hours of use, it is best to purchase the phone plan from Power Cats. Present similar calculations for 2 hours of use, 3 hours of use, and 4 hours of use.

Answer: *Power Cats is the best choice for a customer who uses the telephone 1 hour per month.*

84   *The minimal resulting time is 16 hours 22 minutes and 30 seconds.*

Chapter 17 Basic Geometry and Problem Solving

Section 17.1 Perimeter

85   *(b) P = 22. Together = 190 (given).*   **86**   *The sum of the digits is 11.*

87   *P is between 25 and 30.*   **88**   *(a) P = 4,900,408. (c) P = 144.*

89   *The answer contains $\sqrt{2}$ as part of the expression.*   **90**   *−6.*   **91**   *N/A.*

92   *For the product of the answer and 8, the sum of the digits is 15.*

93   *Calculate both answers. Use the Internet to evaluate which jogging speed is more realistic than the other. Finally, choose the most realistic answer. For the product of the answer and 7, the sum of the digits is 10.*

Section 17.2 Area

94   *(b) A = 42.5.*   **95**   *(b) A = 62.5.*   **96**   *(a) P = 21.42, A = 28.26.*

97   *The parts were added and then removed. The sum of the digits is 16.*   **98**   *35.*

99   *The answer is less than 100.*   **100**   *−24.*

Section 17.3 Volume

101   *The answer is between 5 and 10 units³.*   **102**   *N/A.*

103   *When the answer is expressed in a decimal form, the sim of the digits is 12.*   **104**   *N/A.*

105   *(b) There are 4 solutions.*   **106**   *(b) The sum of the digits is 15. (c) The sum of the digits is 4.*

107   *N/A.*   **108**   *Use ratios of volumes rather than exact calculations.*   **109**   *The sum of the digits is 9.*

Section 17.4 Auxiliary Elements in Geometry

110   **111-13**   *N/A.*   **114**   *(a) A = 21.*

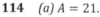

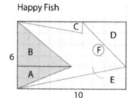

115   *A$_{AngryFish}$ = 8.72.*

116^{Prep} *In your Prep, use an auxiliary element.*   **117**   *24.*

118   *If the answer were expressed in seconds, the sum of the digits would be 9.*

Part C Exploration

C1   *(a) N/A. (b) The red-headed ant will need an extra weight.*

C2   *(a) <u>Hint</u>: Zeva must use three cubes.   (b) The red-headed ant will need an extra weight.*

C3   *N/A.*   **C4**   *(a) N/A.   (b) The blue-headed ant will need an extra weight.*

C5   *(b) For x = [−7, −3), y = (x + 5)².*   **C6**   *(b) For x = (0, 4], y = 1.5x + 0.*

C7   *N/A.*   **C8**   *(b) For x = [−3, −1.5), y = −2x − 8.*   **C9**   *The answer is a word.*

C10   *(b) For x = (−9, −5], y = (x + 7)².*   **C11**   *(b) For x = (−6, 6), y = 0.5(x + 1)² + (−8).*

C12   *The sum of the digits is 18.*

C13   *First, find what letter represents 1. Then, analyze the product, AABB × F.*

C14   *You can model the problems with toothpicks or pencils to understand and solve the problems.*
       (a) VIII / II = IV or VIII − III = V or VII − III = IV or VIII − II = VI.

C15   *(c) 950 m.*   **C16**   *(c) For t = [20min, 30min) and*
$$v = -2\frac{m}{min^2} \times t + 65\frac{m}{min}.$$

C17   *(a)   See the illustration on the right-hand side.*
       (d) For t = [0; 5s], d(t) = mt². For t = (5s; 7s], d(t) = kt.
       Students must insert fitting numbers instead of m and k.

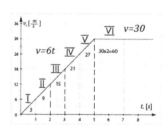

C18   *(b) the sum of the digits is 8. (c) the sum of the digits is 6. (d) one of the answers is 63 degrees.*

C19   *(b) the sum of the digits is 8. (d) the sum of the digits is 9.*   **C20**   *The sum of the digits is 9.*

Part D PARTS & WHOLES

Chapter 18 Fractions
Section 18.1 Unit-Block Approach

1   *(a) $b_3 = \frac{17}{3}$; $N_2 = 28\frac{1}{3}$.*   *(c) $b_9 = 16$.*   *(e) $b_{64} = 4$.*

2   *K is greater than M. Do not forget to finish the illustration.*

3   *(a) $b_3 = 6$; $N_2 = 18$.*   *(c) $b_9 = 9$.*   *(e) $b_{65} = 4$.*

4   *The second number is greater than the first number. Your illustration must reflect this.*

Section 18.2 Visualizing: Area-Box Model

5   *(a) $b_{12} = 2$; $A = 10$. (c) $b_{140} = \frac{9}{35}$; $A = 18$. (e) $b_{72} = \frac{5}{4}$; $A = 30$. (g) $b_{100} = \frac{1}{20}$; $A = 3.2$*

6   *(a)*

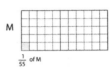

7   *$N_2 = 27.5$.*   **8**   *$N_2 = 30$.*

Section 18.3 Visualizing: Length-Box Model

9   *N/A.*   **10**   *(a)*

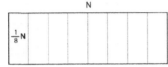   *(b)*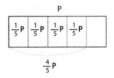

11   *N/A.*   **12**   *(a)*   *(b)*

13   *$N_2 = 29.7$.*   **14**   *The sum of all digits for the answer is 22.*   **15**   *N/A.*   **16**   *$N_2 = 0.52$.*

Section 18.4 Formal-Calculation Approach

17   *(a) $\frac{N}{24}$. (c) 8. (k) $\frac{2}{35} \cdot M$.*   **18**   *(a) 25.5. (d) 300.*   **19**   *N/A.*   **20**   *The sum of the digits is 5.*

Section 18.5 Logical Conversion and Fractions

21   *(a) $\frac{1}{20}$. (c) $\frac{180}{7}$. (j) $K + 2$.*   **22**   *(a) $N = 120$. (c) $\frac{75}{152}$. (e) $\frac{10}{161}$. (g) 300.*   **23**   *The sum of the digits is 9.*

24   *The sum of the digits is 5.*   **25**   *The sum of the digits is 13.*   **26**   *200.*   **27**   *The sum of the digits is 4.*

28   *The sum of the digits is 9.*   **29**   *The sum, $N_1 + N_2$, is greater than 6785 and less than 6790.*

30   *$\sqrt{N_1} = 0.09$.*   **31**   *The sum of the digits is 16.*   **32**   *$N_1 = 10.5$.*

Chapter 19 Percents

Section 19.1 Unit-Block Approach to Percents

33   *(a) See the illustration on the right-hand side.*

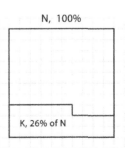

34   *$Q = 4$.*   **35**   *(a) $N_2 = 8.5$; (c) $N_2 = 7.2$.*   **36**   *$K = 1.62$*

37   *(a) $N_2 = 1{,}800$. (c) $N_2 = 175$. (e) $N_2 = 480$.*   **38**   *(a) $N_2 = 120$. (b) N/A.*

39   *$K = 200$.*   **40**   *N/A.*   **41**   *The sum of the digits is 3.*

42   *N/A.*   **43**   *0.25.*

Section 19.2 Formal-Calculation Approach to Percents

44   *The answers are not in order:* $\frac{7}{100}, \frac{113}{300}, \frac{151}{110}, \frac{K}{100}, \frac{71}{200}, \frac{1}{20}, 2, \frac{5}{4}, \frac{7}{1,300}, \frac{81}{700}.$

45   *The answers are not in order: 0.0275, 0.78, 0.4p, .006, 0.1M 34, 1.96, 0.195.*   **46**   *120 and 200.*

47   *False, False, ...*   **48** $N_2 = 2/3.$ **49**   *Meaningful word.*   **50** $N_1 = 20.$

51   *(a)* $Ai(-33\frac{6}{3}) = 35, R(-33\frac{6}{3}) = -\frac{1}{35}.$ *(c)* $Ai(-1\frac{56}{7}) = 9 \ R(-1\frac{56}{7}) = -\frac{1}{9}.$

   (e) $Ai(23\frac{45}{15}) = -26 \ R(23\frac{45}{15}) = \frac{1}{26}.$

52   *(a)* $M = 260.$ *(b)* $M = 100.$ *(c)* $M = 1,100.$ *(d)* $M = 60.$ *(e)* $M = \frac{2,000}{p}.$ *(f)* $Q = 100.$

53 $52 < |N_2 - N_3| < 120.$ **54**   *The sum of the digits is 3.*   **55** $N_2 = 0.4.$

56   *(a)* $\frac{1}{4,000}.$ *(c)* $\frac{259}{2,000}.$ *(e)* $\frac{817}{100}.$ *(g)* $\frac{39}{220}.$ *(i)* $\frac{1}{200}.$ **57** $N_2 = 0.001.$ **58**   *33.4.*   **59**   *N/A.*

60   *The answer is between 3 and 4.*

Section 19.3 Find the Percentage

61   *(a)* $N_3 = 80;$ *(c)* $N_3 = 2,500.$ **62**   *One of the answers is* $p_{N_2}(N_1) = 21\frac{9}{11}\%.$

63   *(a)* $p = 41\frac{2}{3}\%.$ *(c)* $p = 50\%.$ *(e)* $p = 33\frac{1}{3}\%.$ *(g)* $p = 64\%.$

64   *(a) 250%.*   *(b) 70%.*   *(c) 95%.*   *(d)* $57\frac{1}{7}\%.$ **65**   *The answer is less than* $-100.$ **66-67**   *N/A.*

68 $\frac{350}{131} = 2\frac{88}{131}.$ **69**   *N/A.*   **70**   *The answer is less than 1.*   **71**   *The sum of the answers is 376.*

Chapter 20 Comparison

Section 20.1 Greater by a Fraction of Its Value

72   *N/A.*   **73** $110\frac{1}{3}.$

Section 20.2 Less by a Fraction of Its Value

74   *N/A.*   **75** $80\frac{2}{3}.$

Section 20.3 Greater by p%

76   *N/A.*   **77** $N_1/N_2 = 1.06$ *is a number greater than one.*

Section 20.4 Less by p%

78-9   *N/A.*   **80**   *(a)* $K = M - \frac{3}{7}.$ *(b)* $\frac{700}{703} \cdot M.$ *(c)* $\frac{7}{10} \cdot M.$ *(d)* $\frac{10}{7} \cdot M.$ *(e)* $\frac{700}{697} \cdot M.$ *(f)* $\frac{7}{3} \cdot M.$ *(g)* $\frac{7}{3} \cdot \frac{1}{M}.$

81   *The fourth number is greater than 8,700.*

82   *(a)* $K = \frac{175}{251} \cdot M.$ *(c)* $K = \frac{1}{2} \cdot M.$ *(e)* $K = 25 \cdot M.$ *(g)* $K = \frac{5}{3} \cdot R.$ *(i)* $K = \frac{25}{51} \cdot Q.$

83   *The answer is an integer between 2,000 and 3,000.*

Section 20.5 Comparing Numbers Using Percentages

84 $p_{N_1}(N_2) - p_{N_2}(N_2) = 60\%.$ **85** $p_{N_2}(N_2) - p_{N_1}(N_2) = 60\%.$ **86-87** *N/A.*   **88**   *50%.*

89   *N/A.*   **90**   *(a)* $K = 1\frac{103}{247}.$ *(c) 16.*   *(e) 3000.*   *(g) 4800.*   *(i)* $4\frac{2}{7}.$

91   *(a)* $200 = \frac{k+100}{100} \cdot 43\frac{3}{7}.$ *(c)* $8 = \frac{100-k}{100} \cdot 10.$ *(e)* $15 = \frac{3}{50} \cdot K.$ **92**   *The answer is less than* $33\frac{2}{3}.$

93   *The answer is not one.*   **94**   *The sum of the first and third numbers is* $92\frac{16}{23}.$ **95**   *N/A.*

96   *The first answer is:* $\frac{N_1+N_2+N_3+N_4+N_5}{5} = 117\frac{2}{9}.$ *The second answer: N/A.*

Section 20.6 Logical Conversion

97   *(a)* $N_4 - N_1 = 30.$ *(d)* $p_{N_4}(N_4) - p_{N_1}(N_4) = 23\frac{1}{13}\%.$

98   *The difference between the numbers presenting the answers is 125.*   **99-101**   *N/A.*

102   *2. Present the answer in the form of a complete sentence (not in algebraic form).*

Chapter 21 Advanced Change-Problems

Section 21.1 Change-Problems with 'To" and "By"

103 (a) N_1; $N_2 = N_1 - 2$; $N_3 = 6 \cdot N_2$.

104 The sum of the digits is 5 if the number is presented in decimal format.

105 The sum of the digits is 8 if the number is presented in decimal format.

106 N/A.

107 The sum of the digits is 10 if the number is presented as an improper fraction.

108 The sum of the digits is 9.

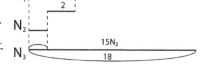

Section 21.2 Changing by a Fraction of a Value

109 N/A. **110** The sum of the digits is 10 if the number is presented as a fraction.

111 The sum of the digits is 9.

Section 21.3 Changing to a Fraction of a Value

112 Meaningful word. **113-114** N/A.

115 The latter means the second of the listed. The sum of the digits is 5. If you cannot solve the problem, make a Time-Plane Model.

116 N/A. **117** The sum of the digits is 12 if the number is presented as a decimal.

Section 21.4 Increased By and Increased To

118 The sum of the digits is 14. **119** The answer is a mixed number with the sum of the digits 14.

N_1	N was increased **by** 150% of N	$N_2 = (100+150)\% \cdot N_1$	N was increased **to** 150% of N	$N_3 = 150\% \cdot N_2 = 0.7$
Time 1		Time 2		Time 3

Section 21.5 Decreased By and Decreased To

120 (g) $\frac{59}{25} \cdot N$. (i) $\frac{17}{25} \cdot N$. **121** The sum of the digits is 9.

Section 21.6 Combining Fractions and Percentages

122 (a) $\frac{199}{200} \cdot N$. (c) $\frac{7}{5} \cdot N$. (e) $\frac{4}{3} \cdot N$. (g) $\frac{523}{220} \cdot N$. **123** (a) $K = \frac{5}{11} \cdot M$. (d) $K = 25 \cdot M$. (h) $K = \frac{700}{703} \cdot M$.

124 2.4. **125** The sum of the digits is 16 if the number is presented in decimal form.

Section 21.7 Reversibility of a Change

126 The sum of the digits is 4. **127** (a) $K = \frac{100}{107} \cdot N$. (c) $N = \frac{7}{4} \cdot K$. **128** The answer is an integer.

129 The answer is less than 7. **130** The sum of the digits is 10 if the number is written as a decimal.

131 The sum of the digits is 18 if the number is written as a decimal.

Fractions and Percentages: Extra Practice

132 The sum of the numerator and denominator is 16. **133** The sum of the digits is 19.

134 The sum of the three numbers is 440.

135 When the answer is written in a decimal format, the sum of its digits is 25.

136 The sum of the digits is 9.

137 35% is an incorrect answer. **138-139** N/A. **140** Sum of the digits is 16.

Review for Parts A through D

Half-Problems and Graphs

D1 28. **D2** 56. **D3** The graph is smooth. **D4** The sum of the digits is 4. **D5** 60.

D6 The sum of the digits is 7. **D7** N/A.

D8 When the number is presented as a decimal, the sum of the digits is 9. **D9** $|N_1 - N_2| = 25$.

D10 The answer is greater than 100.

D11 8 is the sum of the digits of the answer written in the simplest form. **D12** $\frac{9}{76}$. **D13** N/A.

D14 0.01. **D15-16** N/A. **D17** 23. **D18** N/A.

Regular Problems

D19   *The sum of the two possible "boundary" answers is 6,800 dollars.*

D20   *Oguru's year is about 1.5 of Earth's months.*   **D21**   *N/A.*

D22   *The answer to the first question is not 10 cm or 15 cm.*

D23   *(i) From 1961/2 to 2010, the number of UK citizens visiting abroad increased by ... %. The missing number is between 1 and 2. (ii) Number is between 20% and 30%. (iii) N/A. (iv) N/A.*

D24   *The sum of the digits is 14.*

D25   *The sum of the digits for the total number of items per person is 7.*

D26   *Corry paid less than his friend for the chair by 6 and a fractional part of a percent. Corry's friend paid more than Corry by 7 and a fractional part of a percent.*

D27   *When the answer is presented as a decimal, the sum of its digits is 4. Units are kilometers.*

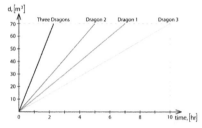

D28   *The red circle must start its motion at 11:59:45 p.m.*

D29   *The sum of the digits used for an exact answer is 21.*

D30   *The speed for the three dragons' eating is a total of the eating speeds for each dragon. It will take the three dragons 2 days 6 hours ... minutes and .... seconds to eat 70 cubic meters of golden sand.*

D31   *The marathon distance is 26 miles 385 yards or $26\frac{7}{32}$ mi using $1,760\frac{yds}{mi}$ conversion factor. "Difference between the times"$\approx$ 8 min. Show your calculations for the runners' times.*

D32   *N/A.*   **D33**   *Less than one percent. Present an exact answer.*

D34   *To help solve the problem, plot (on one graph) d(t) for Mordechai's travel with and without the meeting. On another graph, plot both Mordechai's and John's motion. It is recommended that you make two graphs rather than one. The distance between their houses can be determined precisely. The meeting time, however, can only be determined within a range.*

D35   *The sum of the digits for the answer is 15.*

D36   *Your estimate should be between 25% and 40%. You must provide a more precise answer.*

D37   *From 2 bushels of apples, we can obtain more than 5 gallons of juice. Present an exact answer.*

D38   *N/A.*   **D39**   *When the answer is tripled, the sum of the digits is 3.*

Part E x-VISION

Chapter 22 Formal Mathematics and Number Properties

Section 22.1 In-Depth Number Properties for Addition

1   *(a) Commutative property of addition. (b) A combination of commutative and associative properties of addition.*

2   *N/A.*

3   *(a) Going from subtraction to negatives. Associative and commutative properties of addition. Identity property of addition. (b) Associative and commutative properties of addition. Identity property.*

Section 22.2 In-Depth Number Properties for Multiplication

4   *(b)*

5   *(a) 67,000,000. (b) 200n. (c) 36.*

Section 22.3 Exponent Properties

6   *(a)* $x^b \cdot y^{1.5a}$.   *(b)* $0.2 \cdot c^2 \cdot d^2$.   *(c)* $\frac{81}{512}$.   **7**   *(a)* $0.5\sqrt[3]{2} \cdot x$.   *(b)* $\frac{8}{3}\sqrt[3]{4} \cdot \sqrt[12]{3^{11}} \cdot a^2 \sqrt[4]{a}$.

Section 22.4 Distributive Property in Depth

8   *(b)*

9   *(c)*

10   *(a)* $7x - 35$.   *(c)* $-6x - 30$.   *(e)* $1 - 0.25x + 0.25y$.   *(g)* $3x - 2y + z$.

11   *(a)* $11x$.   *(c)* $5y \cdot (5x - 1)$.   *(e)* $(a + b) \cdot (3 + z)$.   *(g)* $-15w$.   *(i)* $3x$.

12   *(b)* $-8z + 4x$.   *d)* $19xy - 4y$.   *(f)* $7x + 2x$.   *(h)* $-2xyz$.   *(j)* $8x + 23$.

Section 22.5 Mistakes in Identity Transformations

13   *(a)* $13x + 45$. *Commutative & associative properties. Distributive property.* *(b) N/A.*
     (c) 30. After division was converted into multiplication, distributive prop. was applied.
     (d) $-2x^2 + 13x$. *... e) N/A.*

14   *(a) 37.9.*   *(c) 38.9.*   *(e) −379.*   *(g) 2,037.9.*   **15**   *(a)* $\frac{2}{3bc^2}$. *(c)* $16b^3$. *(e)* $\frac{b}{c^2}$. *(g) 4.*

16   *One of the problems has the answer in a form of a two-piece piecewise function. The rest of the answers can be found in the following list:* $-y$, $-170x$, x^2, $4x$, 30, $-40y + 30$, $\frac{3}{x}$, $-32x$, *and* $2x$.

Chapter 23 Formal Mathematics and Equalities

Section 23.1 Visualizing Equations

17   *(a) 3. (c) 1.5.*   **18**   *N/A.*   **19**   *(a)* $x = -5$.

Section 23.2 Subtraction Property for an Equality

20   *(a) 4.*   *(b) 6.*   **21**   *(a) 6. (b) 5.*   **22** *(a) 2. (b) 6.*   **23** *(a) 7. (b) 5.*   **24**   *(a) 80. (b) 35.*

25   *(a) -87. (b) 18.44.*

Section 23.3 Division Property for an Equality

26   *(a) 4.5. (b) 6.*   **27** *(a) 3. (b) 0.1.*   **28** $4\frac{1}{3}$ **29**   *(a) 12. (b) 0; 6, and -6.*   **30**   *(a)* $7\frac{7}{9}$. *(b)* $\frac{1}{9}$.

31   *(a)* $-6\frac{6}{7}$. *(b) 59.48.*

Section 23.4 Equations in Geometry Problems

32 $S_1 = S_2 = S_3 = 21\frac{2}{3}$ *cm.*   **33** $L = W = 13$ *cm. This rectangle we call also ....*

34 $S_1 = S_2 = S_3 = ...$ *cm and* $S_4 = ...$ *cm.* $(S_4 \approx 30 \ cm)$ **35**   *(a) 0. (b) 5.*

36 $S_3 = 29$ *cm.*   **37** $W = 13.5$ *in.*   **38-40**   *N/A.*

Section 23.5 Implicit Givens in Geometry Problems

41   *(1) Impossible. (2) Impossible. (3) Possible. (4) Impossible.*   **42** α *is between 50 and 55 degrees.*

43   *N/A.*   **44** $S_1 = 10.5$; $S_2 = 15.5$ *cm*; $S_3 = 21$ *cm.*   **45-46**   *N/A.*

47 $\beta = 65^0$.   **48**   *The first answer:* $S_1 = 5$ *cm. Calculate both answers.*   **49**   *The longest side,* $S_3 = 21$ *cm.*

Section 23.6 Addition and Multiplication Properties

50   *(a) 77.7. (b) 130.*

Section 23.7 General Procedure for Solving Equations

51   *There are 3 linear equations. In addition, the equation (f) can be transformed into a linear equation.*

52   *(a)* $= -8\frac{1}{3}$. *(b) 1,060.*   **53** *(a)* -4. *(c)* $\frac{501}{3,200}$.

Section 23.8 Word Problems with Visualizing

54 $S_1 = S_2 = 10$ *in.*   **55-56**   *N/A.*   **57**   *The shortest side is shorter than 13.75 cm.*

58

59-63 *N/A.* **64** $F_1 = F_2 = F_3 = F_4 = 5.625\ cm.$ **65-71** *N/A.*

Chapter 24 Systems of Linear Equations and Half-Problems

Section 24.1 Linear Equations and Substitution Method

72 *(a) $x = -3$ and $y = -5$. (c) $x = 0.5$ and $z = -2.5$.* **73** *For N_1, the sum of the digits is 6.*

74 *There are two answers. Find both. For one of the answers, the digits add to 9.*

75-6 *N/A.* **77** *Here is a list of all answers, not in any order:* -176, $-9\frac{6}{7}$, $-5\frac{1}{7}$, -4, 1.95, $3\frac{2}{3}$, 4.7, and 89.

Section 24.2 Intro to Method of Linear Combinations

78 *(b) $x = -2$ and $y = -0.5$; (d) $x = 3$ and $y = -\frac{32}{35}$.*

79 *(a) The largest number is N_3. The sum of its digits is 11. (b) The answer is between 30 and 40.*

80-1 *N/A.* **82** *Show why the problem has no solution.* **83** *One of the problems has no solution.*

Section 24.3 Advanced Linear Combination Method

84 *Here is a list of all answers, not in any order:* -3, 1.2, -2, -0.5, 0, 12.25, and -0.75.

85-8 *The following list contains all the answers to the problems: -190, -187, 7, 28, 36, 46, 52, 187.*

89-93 *The following list contains all the answers to the problems: No solution (explain, why), an infinite number of x-y pairs obeying a certain rule (specify the rule), -200, -167, -135.5, -32, -12, -4.5, $-4\frac{4}{13}$, -6, -1, $1\frac{7}{13}$, 6, 32, 10, 12, 20, 95, 135.5, and 200.*

94-8 *The following list contains all the answers to the problems:* -17, -7, -4, -4, $-2\frac{4}{35}$, $-1\frac{23}{43}$, $-5\frac{2}{7}$, $-1\frac{21}{41}$, $-\frac{17}{35}$, 0, $\frac{6}{43}$, $\frac{6}{41}$, $7\frac{1}{7}$, 7, 9, 15, 17, 24, 34, 42 and 52.

99-101 *The following list contains all the answers to the problems: No solution, $x = \emptyset$; $y = \emptyset$. (Explain, why), -30, -20, -4, -3, -2, $-1\frac{1}{6}$, $-\frac{1}{6}$, $\frac{5}{6}$, 9.35, 11, 33, 2.92, 45, 48, and 66.*

Chapter 25 Word Problems with Elements of Algebra

Section 25.1 Word Problems with Systems of Equations

102-3 *N/A.* **104** *The sum of the digits is 18 when the answer is written as a decimal.*

Section 25.2 Proportions as Equations

105 *The answer is between 1,000 and 1,200 kg.* **106** *The answer is between 255 and 260 packets.*
107 *N/A.*

Section 25.3 Ratios as Equations

108-14 *The following list contains all the answers to the problems: 2.5, 11, 10.5, 15, 20, 24, 36, 44, 600, and 750.*

Section 25.4 Percent Picture-Problems

115 *(a) $x = 151\frac{19}{31}$. (c) $x = 3$.*
(e) $x = 57.75$.

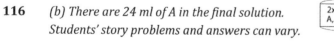

116 *(b) There are 24 ml of A in the final solution.*
Students' story problems and answers can vary.   **117** *N/A.*

Section 25.5 Challenging Problems with Percentages

118-123 *The following list contains all the answers to the problems: 4, 6.25, 7.5, 60, 90, 374, 576, 840, 960, and 1,100.*

124 *The answer is between 11 and 12 dollars.* **125** *160 liters.* **126** *N/A.*

127 *There were 160 ml of the first solution.*

Section 25.6 From Find-the-Number to Real Life

128   *7% and 93%. Students must use the Internet.*   **129**   *N/A.*   **130**   *(d) 10.*

131   *The problem has a unique solution. Students must use the Internet.*   **132**   *The sum of the digits is 11.*

133   *(a) The lower border in the range is below 7 days. The upper border is above 10 days. (b-d) For itemized and packaged orders, the time depends on the number of items.*

Review for Parts A through E

Equations, Graphs, and Half-Problems

E1 -42.   **E2**   *The sum of the digits is 16 when the answer is written as a decimal.*   **E3-4**   *N/A.*

E5   *One equation has only one solution. One equation has infinite number of solutions with a limitation. One equation has two solutions.*

E6   *20.*   **E7**   *Do not forget to examine the answers.*   **E8-9**   *N/A.*

E10   *The answer is a mixed number between 70 and 80%. The sum of the digits is 23.*

E11   *N/A.*

E12   *The sum of the answers is -10.*

E13   *The graph is undefined at several points.*

E14   *N/A.*

E15   *The sum of all four answers is 204.*

E16   *The sum of the answers is between 2 and 6.*

E17   *(b) This problem has 2 answers.*   **E18**   *N/A.*

E19 $(a) \lceil 1.3 \rceil = 2, \left| -1\frac{1}{3} \right| = -2,$ *and ... . (c) See the graph on the right.*

$y = Floor(x)$

E20   *Consider both options.*   **E21**   *There are several solutions.*   **E22**   *The sum of the answers is 130.*

E23   *The sum of the digits is 5.*   **E24**   *N/A.*

E25   *(a) The answer is between 1 and 2. (b) One of the words is "consecutive."*

E26   *30.*   **E27**   *Both figures are the closed shapes.*

Regular Problems

E28   *2,000 gonji.*   **E29**   *(a) 21 bisecols.*   **E30**   *The sum of the answer's digits is 6.*

E31   *Sum of the digits is 14 when π is abbreviated to the nearest hundredth.*

E32   *The swallow can snap two of the insects. Hint: you must check which insects have the same x and y coordinates at the same time as the bird.*

E33   *A situation of stopping production must be considered.*

E34   *(c) 23 hours and ... minutes (students must calculate the number of minutes).*

E35   *The sum of the answer's digits is 11.*

E36   *There are more than 70 ways to place the wizards around the table.*

E37   *The problem has a unique solution. Students must use the Internet.*

E38   *A$_{GoldNecklace}$ is a two-digit number plus 0.20. A$_{WarmMitten}$ is a whole number.*   **E39**   *N/A.*

E40   *The length will increase by (a) 20%.*   **E41**   *The sum of the answer's digits is 10.*

E42   *The answer is between 32 and 62.*   **E43**   *The worst option provides an increase by $3,920.*

E44   *The sum of the digits is 18.*   **E45**   *The sum of the digits is 4.*   **E46**   *N/A.*

E47   *The answer is more than 5 but less than 11.*

E48   *The answer is between 15 and 17%. The answer does not hold for all possible v.*

E49   *(a) 77%. (b) N/A.*   **E50-2**   *N/A.*

E53   *The answer is between 6 days and 17 hours and 6 days and 18 hours.*

E54   *The sum of the digits is 9.*   **E55**   *The sum of the digits is 14.*

E56   *The outside surface of the cone is between 30 and 40 square inches. Provide a precise answer.*

E57   *The number is between 90 and 161. Students must draw an illustration to explain their work.*

E58   *N/A.*

E59   *The digits of the answer expressed in the lowest terms add up to 7.*

E60   *Thoroughly chunk the problem and then reorganize the data. The answer is between 60 and 80.*

Glossary

Soft Algebra developed specific terminology needed for discussing problem solving, highlighted in grey. *Dark grey* shows that an entry is connected with a topic of problem solving.

Adding parts Technique of using *auxiliary elements* to simplify a general look of a geometry problem. 17.4

Addition property of an equality See properties of an equality. 23.6

Algebraic Organizer Outline that represents data in a well-organized, concise form while using algebraic language and separating questions from givens by drawing a line. 13.1, 13.5

Alien eye A problem-solving technique to take conscious control of the problem-solving process. The technique recommends (*a*) slow down and add steps, and (*b*) create a checklist of the problem-solving strategies and mark the strategies you have applied. 10.4, 13.5

Alpha (α) A Greek letter used to signify angles. 23. 5

Analogous problems as models These models carry the main features of original problems but are easier than the original problem. Analogous problems are designed to foster an understanding of the original problems. 6.3

Approximation model Creative model based on ignoring some details. Example: avatars in computer-generated movies. 6.2-3

Area See also, *area of a circle*.

Area of a circle Area of a circle is calculated as $A = \pi r^2$, where r is the radius of the circle. 17.2

Area-Box Model The model represents a number using a rectangle. The area of the box represents a given value. A part of the box can be shaded to represent another number. *This model is frequently referred as a Box Model.* 11.2, 18.2

Artificial time-coordinates If a *change-problem* has only implicit *time-coordinates*, it is feasible to introduce time coordinates artificially. 13.8

Attributes See *measurable attributes*. 14.1-2

Auxiliary elements Additional elements, lines, figures, or symbols added to help solve a problem. 5.3,   17.4, Ch25 intro

Beta (β) Greek letter used to mark angles. 23. 5

Blind logical conversion Logical conversion applied without a specific goal. 13.5

Box-Oval diagram Used to create a *Comparison Organizer*. 20.6

Box Model This model represents a number using a rectangle. If the area of the box represents a given value, *Soft Algebra* calls the model an *Area-Box Model*. If the length of the rectangles represents a given value, the model is called a *Length-Box Model*. 11.2, 18.2-3, 25.4, Ch 19

Glossary

Bug Model Discrete *visual model* used to visualize all possible combinations.　　13.6

Caliper Device used to measure distance between two points, often points which are diffi- 17.3
cult to reach with a ruler.

Change-problems Problems that involve values that change throughout the course of the 13.8, Ch 21
problem. For example: a number is tripled, decreased by 17, and so on.

Chunking A problem-solving technique that breaks the text of a problem into smaller 13.1
parts, or chunks. To make the chunks visually independent, each chunk (sentence) is
written starting on a new row. All chunks are independent in meaning.

Circumference Perimeter of a circle $P = 2\pi r$.　　17.1

Comparison There are multiple ways of comparing values.　　Ch. 20

Comparison Organizer Helps identify what number makes a whole and can serve as a 20.6
reference. Uses a *box-oval* diagram.

Complex index system Index system involved when there is a complex, usually multidi- Ch. 20
mensional set of data.

Comprehensive abbreviations Measuring units in number sentences are abbreviated ac- 14.4-5,　14.8,
cording to the rules that simplify unit recognition. See also *unit abbreviation*.　　15.1

Constraint It restricts a system from achieving its potential regarding its goal. In mathe- 6.1, 6.4, 23.5
matics, a constraint is a condition that a solution to a problem must satisfy. The set of
solutions that satisfy all constraints is called the feasible set.

Constraints bookkeeping Problem-solving technique: explicitly listing all constraints that 6.1, 6.4
restrict the set of feasible problem's solution. See *implicit constraints*.

Continuous visual representation or model Non-digital systems use a continuous range 13.6-7
of values to represent information. Results in "continuous" visual representation.

Conventional abbreviations for units Most customary measuring units and SI units must 14.4-5,　14.8,
be abbreviated according to well-established conventions.　　15.1

Conversion of units See *unit conversion*.　　15.8

Creative models Models that are not based on some rules. Making such models requires 6.2-3
thinking outside the box—creative reasoning.

Curvimeter Curvimeter and opisometer are mechanical devices used to measure the 17.1
length of a curve.

Customary units For example: miles, feet, pounds, or cups.　　14.8-9

d-t-v Algebraic Organizer An Algebraic Organizer that presents a problem in terms of 16.2, 16.6
time, distance, and velocity. See also *distance-time-velocity*.

d-t-v Approach See *Distance-Time-Velocity Approach*.

⸺rived units See *units of measure*.　　15.2-3

Difference *Soft Algebra* uses the following meaning of the word "difference": 13.2
The result of subtraction taken with a positive sign. The difference between N and K can be written as $|K - N|$ or $|N - K|$.

Displacement method Measures volume with help of a measuring cylinder. 17.3

Distance Measurable property of matter or measurable attribute. For example: 3 in, 2 mm, 16.1-5
5 m, or 600 km.

Distance-Time-Velocity Approach or *d-t-v Approach* A technique to solve problems in- 16.6
volving distance (d), time (t), and velocity (v).

Down-Scaling Model A creative model based on down-scaling real structures. Examples:
planetary model and rocket model. Also, sampling in statistics. 6.2-3

Extracting data A problem-solving technique that removes unimportant information. 13.1

Formal-Calculation Approach Calculations based on rules. Such calculations do not al- 18.4, 19.2
ways ensure deep understanding of a topic.

Freestyle Model The technique of using freestyle drawing to better understand what is oc- 16.2
curring in the problem.

Function Relationship where each input (x) results in exactly one output (y). 13.7

Gamma (γ) Greek letter used to mark angles. 23.5

Geometric mean Geometric mean of k numbers is a k-power root of the product of these
numbers. Geometric mean of A, B, and C is $\sqrt[3]{A \cdot B \cdot C}$. Geom. mean of A and B is $\sqrt[2]{A \cdot B}$.

Goal awareness Problem-solving skill of concentrating on the main goal while working on details. 13.5

Graph A graph presents various intervals on a number line. Graphs on the Descartes coor- 13.7, 16.3-6
dinate plane allow visualizing of various x-y relations. Graphs $v(t)$ and $d(t)$ help solve
distance-time-velocity problems.

Half-problem A mixture of a number-problem and a word-problem. We can also call them 13.1
find-the-number problems.

Index (indexes or indices) *(a)* Serves to guide, point out, or otherwise facilitate reference.
Frequently used to create comprehensive parameters. *Indexing* means to furnish with
an index or to enter in an index. *(b)* Index in a radical.

International system of units (SI) For example: *meter, kilometer, gram, second, and nano-* 14.4-6
second.

Irrational numbers Cannot be presented as a fraction of two integers, e.g. π and $\sqrt{5}$. 7.6

Kinematics Relates to motion of one or several objects. Ch16 Intro

Lazy format of writing units See *standard format of writing measuring units.* 13.1

Length The number of units of length (e.g. meters, miles) that fit into a given line segment.

Length-Box Model Visual model where a value is represented as a length of a rectangle. 18.3

Logical conversion A logical transformation of a single data entry. (1) *Ole is older than* 13.5, 18.5,
Pete. Conversion: *Pete is younger than Ole.* (2) $K = P + 5$. Conversion: $P = K - 5$. 20.6

262

Magic one Can be used for unit conversion: $1 = \frac{1km}{1000m}, \frac{1000m}{1km}$, or $\frac{1mi}{0.000621371m}$. See *multipli-*   14.6
cation by magic one.

Magic One Approach The approach to unit conversion that uses a magic one. See *magic*   14.6
one and *multiplication by magic one.*

Map Model The model that uses a *mapping* strategy.   13.5

Mapping A problem-solving technique that involves looking at a problem from the end—   13.5
from the question to the problem.

Math-focused language (text) Used to simplify translation to algebraic language. Uses   14.2-3
sentences that clarify characteristics of values, emphasize mathematical operations,
and denote logical relations between elements. "A car traveled a 40-mile distance" is a
math-focused form of the sentence, "A car traveled 40 miles."

Matter Physics calls everything that can be seen or touched "matter".   14.1

Measurable attribute Quantitative observations of properties of matter result in measu-   14.1-2
rements of time, mass, temperature—these are measurable attributes.

Measuring Comparing a value with a unit of measure.   14.1

Mining A process of simplifying problems' text. In *Soft Algebra*, mining is comprised of sev-   13.1
eral problem-solving techniques.

Modeling Finding important features of an initial problem and designing a simplified copy   6.2, 11.1,
which carries these features.   23.1

Multiplication by magic one The approach to unit conversion based on a property of *one*:   14.6
$0.5m = 0.5m \cdot \frac{100cm}{1m} = 50cm$ and $2m = 2m \cdot \frac{139.4in}{1m} = 278.8in.$

Negative power(exponent) For example, $3^{-2} = \frac{1}{3^2} = \frac{1}{9}.$ 14.7

No solution No solution fits all *constraints* of the problem. Algebraic notation, $N = \{\emptyset\}$, i.e.   6.6
the set of solutions is an empty set.

Number of percents, p Soft Algebra translates *N makes 5% of M* as $p_N(M) = 5\%$. *percent,*   19.3
percentage.

Number properties Identity property of addition and multiplication. Distributive property.   13.2, 22.1-4
Commutative and associative properties of addition and multiplication.

Organizing information Presenting information in clear, logical order while using the   13.1
problem-solving techniques taught in *Soft Algebra.*

Outline of a problem Soft Algebra introduces several outlines. The most applicable of them
are Chunked Text Outline, Prep, Text Organizer, and Algebraic Organizer (Algebraic
Model).

erlapping parameters Complex parameters combine two or more key words and use
subscripts. R_1 could mean *the number of red pins in the first group.*

Parameter A letter in a math sentence that presents a value. To avoid writing too much, first letter of a key word is used to create a parameter. All parameters must be defined for the general reader. Complex parameters may have subscripts or indices.

Parameter-Difference To chunk a sentence with the structure *as much as*, we introduce an additional parameter to mark the repeating difference.   13.3

Percent, percentage Percent equals one-hundredth of a whole. 1% of a number N is $0.01N$. Seven percent of a number N is $7/100 \cdot N$. $p\%$ of a number N is $p/100 \cdot N$. See also "number of percent, p."   Ch19, 20.3-6

Perimeter Length of a figure's border line.   17.1

Phi (φ) Greek letter used to mark angles.   23.5

Pi Written π - constant used in geometry. $\pi \approx 3.14$.   17.1

Prefixes for SI Prefixes like *kilo-*, *milli-*, *centi-* and similar.   14.5

Prep Chunked Text Outline obtained after data extraction, chunking, and detailing. A Prep has only important data, which are well chunked; key words are abbreviated. A Prep increases readability and prepares problem for translating into algebraic language.   13.1

Properties of matter For example: heavy (5 kg), elastic, solid, long (3 cm long).   14.1-2

Proportion Number relationship expressed as a ratio, $a:b = c:d$. Can also appear in other forms, such as a *proportion organizer*, $\begin{matrix} a & b \\ c & d \end{matrix}$ or a proportion equality, $\frac{a}{b} = \frac{c}{d}$ 15.3-7

Proportion Organizer or proportion type chart Presents proportional data as a 2 by 2 chart. Each column presents values with the same units. The value in the upper left corner is proportional to the value in the upper right corner the same way as the value in the lower left corner is proportional to the value in the lower right corner.   15.3

Proportion problems Involve proportional values.   15.3-7

Qualitative observations About qualities: *surface is sticky, bug grows a new leg.*   14.1

Quantitative observations About quantities: *mass is 5 kg, time is 5 minutes, and the distance is 1 meter.*   14.1

Quantitative reasoning Understanding and presenting the relationships between values in the form of equations.   14.3

Quantity The total number (amount). The extent, size, or sum of countable or measurable discrete events, objects, or phenomenon expressed as a numerical value.   14.1

Quotient The result of division or a division problem. Quotient of N and K is $N \div K$ or a result of this division.   14.3

Ratio For example, $14 : 21 = 20 : 30$. Some word problems involve ratios.   15.5-7

Ratios-of-Elements Approach A technique for solving ratio problems.   15.5

Ratios-of-Groups Approach A technique for solving ratio problems.   15.6-7

Reference When comparing values using percentage, important to always remember the reference value—considered to have 100%.   20.6

Glossary

Unit block Smallest part that can be used to build the values mentioned in a problem. In *Soft Algebra*, $b_7 = 8$ means a unit block (b) makes 1/7 of a number and equals 8. A percent, h, is a unit-block in percentage problems.
15.4, 15.5, 18.1-3, 19.1

Unit-Block Approach Problem-solving technique based on solving problems starting with determining the value of a unit block.
15.4-5, 18.1-3, 19.1

Unit conversion Changing units while simultaneously altering the numbers to produce an equivalent value.
14.6, 9, 15.2, 8

Units of measure Each value, as a rule, is characterized by a number and measuring unit. E.g. 3 *cm*, 6 *cats per mouse*, 4 *seconds*, and so on. Derived units are cm^3 and mph $\left(\frac{mi}{hr}\right)$.
2.7, 14.1-9, 15.1-3

Up-Scaled Model A creative model that is based on increasing the size of the original system. Example: atomic model.
6.2-3

Velocity Like speed, but accounts for direction of movement.
16.1-6

Visual model Visual representation of a problem. Besides graphs (see *graphs*), includes many other types of models.
13.6-8,16.2, 18.2-3, 20.6

Volume The number of unit cubes that fit inside a three-dimensional figure. See also Section 17.3 for formulas of a volume of a sphere, cylinder, and cone.
17.3

Made in the USA
Middletown, DE
17 January 2023

22318454R00157